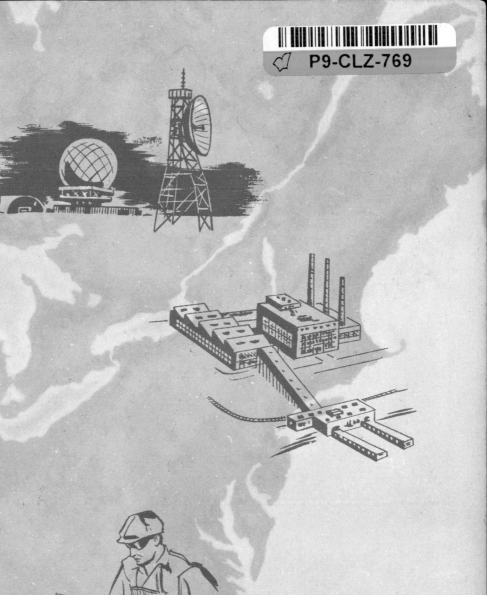

Marvels of
AMERICAN
INDUSTRY

by Donald E. Cooke

C. S. Hammond and Company

Maplewood, New Jersey

Foreword

The story of America may be told through its industries. There is no more important nor exciting aspect of our history, for it is in the dynamic growth of American industry, under free, competitive enterprise, that we see the true greatness of the United States. The record of U. S. industry is proof that capitalism in an unfettered democratic society fosters human well-being.

In this second half of the twentieth century — dawn of the Space Age — the United States is confronted by a dangerous and powerful enemy. We find ourselves in a contest for our very existence. The enemy is international Communism. Never in our history have we faced so serious a threat, not only to "our lives, our fortunes, and our sacred honor" but to the way of life which we have cherished for generations. Communism fights its cold war in subtle ways. It is an elusive and vicious enemy, planting seeds of hatred of American Capitalism in the minds of people of all nations — *including our own United States.*

It is often said that the Communists seek to destroy Democracy, or that the neutral nations are trying to choose between Democracy and Communism. Yet in all the speeches and writings of the Communists themselves it is hard to find even a casual reference to democratic forms of government. Their fanatical crusade, their avowed objective, is remarkable for its singleness of purpose. To them, the issue is clear: their aim is to destroy *Capitalism.* Never has their battle cry varied. All Communists have sung the same song, "Down with Capitalism."

The fortress which Russia and her Communist leaders must storm and destroy is American Industry. How powerful is that fortress? How well can it withstand the subversion of Socialist thinking or of Communist propaganda? Can those who guard the fortress go on the offensive and stamp out their enemies?

Facts presented in this book speak for themselves. A study of U. S. industry cannot fail to revive or affirm any American's faith in the strength and the moral purpose of his nation. American industry will impress him with its vastness; it will inspire him with its promise.

The important fact of our industrial complex is that it was financed, built, and operated by free individuals on their own initiative. Under our system of free enterprise we Americans have developed a "people's capitalism." Millions of small investors own shares of the great corporations. They, and other millions of individual bank depositors, have furnished capital to build giant steel mills, oil refineries, and chemical plants. With ingenuity and hard work, energetic Americans have created industrial empires, often against seemingly impossible odds. Above all, American industry is providing more of the good things of life for more people than any "planned economy" has ever done.

This book has been designed to give a condensed but comprehensive view of industry in the United States. Beginning with those industries which provide the necessary capital — banking, insurance, and investment — each important segment of the industrial world is presented in text and pictures. Following the section on finance, power, machinery, and raw materials are those industries concerned with food, shelter and clothing. Next are the transportation and communications industries without which the movement of goods and the performance of services would be paralyzed. Other sections are devoted to the graphic arts, entertainment, special products, and retail marketing.

In addition to reviewing the interesting histories of industries and of the great companies involved, each article emphasizes exciting future prospects and the opportunities offered by various fields of endeavor. This is not only a reference book; it is also a monument and a challenge to the aspirations of freedom-loving people everywhere.

DONALD E. COOKE

Acknowledgments

The author gratefully acknowledges the cooperation and assistance of the following firms and associations which contributed to the compilation of this work:

Abbotts Dairies; Air-Conditioning & Refrigeration Institute; Air Transport Association of America; Ajax Manufacturing Co.; Allis-Chalmers Manufacturing Co.; American Association of Advertising Agencies; American Bankers Association; American Cotton Manufacturers Institute; *American Heritage;* American Institute of Steel Construction; American League of Professional Baseball Clubs; American Meat Institute Foundation; American Newspaper Publishers Association; American Petroleum Institute; American Sugar Refining Co.; American Telephone & Telegraph Co.; American Trucking Associations; American Type Founders; Anaconda Co.; Ansco; Armour and Co.; Association of American Railroads; Automobile Manufacturers Association; Batten, Barton, Durstine & Osborn; Black, Sivalls & Bryson; Bostitch; Burson-Marsteller Associates; *Business Week.*

Campbell Soup Co.; J. I. Case Co.; Celanese Corp. of America; Chase Manhattan Bank; Chemco Photoproducts Co.; Chicago Historical Society; *Christian Herald* Magazine; Chrysler Corp.; Ciba Pharmaceutical Products; Cincinnati Lathe & Tool Co.; Colonial Broach & Machine Co.; Columbia Broadcasting System; Consolidation Coal Co.; Craftex Mills; Curtis Publishing Co.; Davidson Corp.; Diamond Crystal Salt Co.; Dow Chemical Co.; E. I. Du Pont de Nemours & Co.; Eastman Kodak Co.; Electric Boat Division, General Dynamics Corp.; Federal Aviation Agency; Ford Motor Co.; Foremost Dairies; *Fortune;* Fur Information & Fashion Council.

General Foods Corp.; General Mills; General Tire & Rubber Co.; Gisholt Machine Co.; B. F. Goodrich Co.; Goodyear Tire and Rubber Co.; Graphic Arts Employment Service; C. S. Hammond & Co.; Harris-Intertype Corp.; Hat Institute; Hearst Magazines; H. J. Heinz Co.; Hershey Chocolate Corp.; Geo. A. Hormel & Co.; International Furniture Division, Schnadig Corp.; International Harvester Co.; International Paper Co.; Intertype Co.; Jantzen, Inc.

Ketchem, MacLeod & Grove; Kimberly-Clark Corp.; Kohler Co.; Krementz & Co.; Kroehler Mfg. Co.; Landis Machine Co.; Lennox Industries; Lever Brothers Co.; Liggett & Myers Tobacco Co.; Lionel Corp.; Lodge & Shipley Co.; P. Lorillard Co.; Ludlow Typograph Co.; Mack Trucks; Macy's New York; Magazine Advertising Bureau; Magazine Publishers Association; Oscar Mayer & Co.; McGraw-Hill Publishing Co.; Merck & Co.; Metropolitan Life Insurance Co.; Metropolitan Opera Association; J. L. Metz Furniture Co.; Miehle-Goss-Dexter; Minute Maid Corp.; Monsanto Chemical Co.; Montgomery Ward & Co.; Mosaic Tile Co.; Mo-Tac Co.

National Aeronautics & Space Administration; National Association of Furniture Manufacturers; National Association of Printing Ink Makers; National Automatic Tool Co.; National Broadcasting Co.; National Canners Association; National Coal Association; National Ice Association; National Paint, Varnish & Lacquer Association; National Ready Mixed Concrete Association; New Holland Machine Co.; New Idea Farm Equipment Co.; New York Shipbuilding Corp.; New York Stock Exchange; New York Yankees; *Newsweek;* Oleg Cassini; Oxford University Press.

Pennsylvania Bankers Association; Philadelphia Electric Co.; Polaroid Corp.; *Practical Builder;* Pratt & Whitney Co.; Printing Machinery Co.; Procter & Gamble Co.; Prudential Insurance Co. of America; Radio Corporation of America; Rath Packing Co.; Raybestos-Manhattan; *Reader's Digest;* Record Industry Association of America; Republic Steel Corp.; Rockefeller Center; *The Rotarian;* Rubber Manufacturers Association; San Francisco Chamber of Commerce; F.A.O. Schwarz; Sears Roebuck & Co.; Sheffield Corp.; Shipbuilders Council of America; Simplicity Pattern Co.; Smith, Kline & French Laboratories; Socony Mobil Oil Co.; *Sports Illustrated;* Spreckels Sugar Co.; Stackpole Carbon Co.; Structural Clay Products Institute; Swift & Co.

Tanners Council of America; Thiokol Chemical Corp; *TV Guide;* U.S. Department of Agriculture; Union Carbide Plastics Co.; United States Rubber Co.; United States Steel Corp.; Universal-International Pictures; Universal Pictures Co.; Vermont Marble Co.; John Wanamaker, Philadelphia; Warner Co.; Western Union Telegraph Co.; Westinghouse Electric Corp.; White Motor Co.; Stephen F. Whitman & Son; Wood Office Furniture Institute; York Corp.

Contents

Picture Credits

Picture Credits

1 Finance

All industry begins with finance. Across the United States, from East to West, from Canada to Mexico, the giant mills, the humming factories, and the broad stretches of farmland are dependent upon a continuous flow of their life blood—*capital*. If the sources of money and credit were to dry up, the wheels of industry would soon cease to turn. Millions of workers would be idle. The mills would be silent and deserted while most of the farms would lie fallow.

We in the United States have built the greatest industrial complex on earth, and we have done it on our own account as free, private individuals. We have financed it with our own privately accumulated wealth—our savings and investments. The system we have evolved is Capitalism. But it is a special, peculiarly American brand of capitalism which has been variously described as free enterprise, private enterprise, and people's capitalism. It is all of these things and more. Though we are justifiably proud of it, it has grown so rapidly and advanced human welfare at such a fantastic rate that we ourselves have difficulty comprehending its vast complexities. Our financial system is an intricate and delicate mechanism which is at the same time a mighty force that must be treated with respect and controlled with care and wisdom.

BANKING THROUGH THE AGES

Modern banking had its beginning in thirteenth-century Renaissance Italy, where enterprising traders developed a system of caring for other people's money, making loans, granting credit, and charging interest. Letters of credit, issued by these early bankers, were honored in exchange. Eventually the notes became known as bank money.

Over the centuries a few of the successful banking houses grew into huge international financial institutions, and the great houses of Rothschild and Fugger are still operating in Europe.

U.S. BANKING . . . YESTERDAY

In the colonial period of America, there was only a small amount of money of domestic origin in circulation. The New England Colonies experimented with issuing paper money secured by land values and there were a few coins minted such as the pine tree shilling, for local use; but the money in most of the colonies consisted only of Austrian thalers supplied by the British government and Spanish and French coins secured in trade. The lack of American money reflected the English government's concept that the American Colonies existed only to serve British commercial interest, and every effort was made to

9

The first Bank of New York Building, whose cornerstone was laid June 22, 1797, at 48 Wall Street.

stamp out colonial competition with home industries. Most manufacturing was prohibited, and American trading was restricted to territories within the British empire. Naturally, these economic restrictions were a major cause of friction which led at last to open rebellion and war. With the outbreak of the Revolution, the need for finances was serious; in order to pool public and private sources of money and to collect taxes, the Bank of North America was founded in 1781. This bank not only accepted deposits of coin but also traded in commodities such as grain, flour, iron, and cloth. Banking in America had taken its first major step.

... AND TODAY

Growth of American banking has of necessity kept pace with the mushrooming of all U.S. industry. But it has followed a somewhat different pattern from the banking systems of Europe. There, most banks are agencies for accumulating industrial capital, sharing the ownership and management of industries. Our banks are more like those in England, banks of deposit and credit. It is our system of deposit and credit that makes U.S. banking the dynamic, flexible force it has become in our economy.

It is important to examine the different types of financial institutions and their functions. There are approximately 14,000 commercial and mutual savings banks in the United States and some 60 trust companies. Specialized institutions similar to banks are the savings and loan and the building and loan associations of which there are 6,000, and the 19,000 credit unions. There are also a large number of mortgage companies and investment firms.

Commercial banks offer the widest variety of financial services, which include savings and checking accounts, trust services, money transfers, collections, safe deposit boxes, travelers' checks, and many kinds of loans to meet the needs of individuals, businesses, farmers, and the gov-

ernment. They are organized as corporations, privately owned by stockholders, but are chartered and regulated either by the federal government or by the government of the state in which they are located.

Mutual savings banks are specialized banks owned by their depositors and administered by trustees. Their services are generally limited to savings accounts and mortgage loans.

Trust companies or the trust departments of commercial banks specialize in the administration of estates and special funds.

Savings and loan or building and loan associations are federal or state chartered, mutually owned institutions, formed to promote thrift through investment in their shares. Their chief functions are the making of real estate loans.

Another type of mutual society is the credit union, formed by private groups such as the employees of a large industry, who pool finances for the purpose of making loans available to their members.

Banking in America today is a well organized, smoothly efficient industry which is becoming more streamlined and more highly mechanized every day. New electronic devices are being used in handling checks and in making calculations. Though banks work in close cooperation on a national scale, locally they are keenly competitive, seeking to attract customers with modernized services, such as drive-in deposit windows, convenient bank by mail arrangements, and higher interest rates on savings.

WHAT IS CREDIT?

The most important word in the business and industrial communities is credit. Few people fully understand the principle of creating new money through bank credit, although this is the way 90% of all American commerce and industry is financed.

The word itself is derived from the Latin *credo,* meaning, "I believe." The grantor of credit says, in effect, "I believe you will repay me." A comparatively simple form of credit is consumer credit, which is extended by banks to individuals for the purchase of homes, automobiles,

New head office of The Chase Manhattan Bank, opened May 17, 1961, rises 813 feet in the historic Wall Street area of New York City.

TV sets, and so forth. However, the issuing of bank credit can be a more complex transaction, and it sometimes involves millions of dollars. For example, Trans-World Airlines at one time borrowed seventeen million dollars for new planes, and fourteen banks took part in making the loan.

When commercial banks lend funds, they enter deposit credit in the borrower's checking account. This action has the effect of creating money which did not previously exist. In the creation of "checkbook money" by lending, the Federal Reserve System plays an important role. The Federal Reserve is a system of regional central banks serving other banks in the broad geographical areas of the country. The System, acting as the fiscal agent of the government, cooperates with the Treasury in issuing and supplying paper money as well as coin to the banks in each Federal Reserve District. The regional banks hold the reserves of their member banks. By raising or lower-

in the control of monetary policy. To meet a deficit, the Treasury may raise funds by selling government bonds to commercial banks. By thus increasing commercial banks' investments, the effect is to increase bank deposits. A reverse action occurs when the Treasury retires some of its debt. In brief, a Treasury deficit has an inflationary effect on the economy; a Treasury surplus tends to be deflationary.

HOW CHECKS ARE HANDLED

The most fascinating operation in modern banks is the clearing of checks. At least 90% of all business transactions in the United States is handled by checks. In 1960, more than thirteen billion checks were written. This represented about 72 checks for every man, woman, and child in the country. By 1970, it is estimated that at least twenty-two billion checks will be written annually.

Suppose we follow a single check on its journey from

The Burroughs B 301 Magnetic Document Processing System is the heart of the automatic electronic bank bookkeeping system installed in the First Pennsylvania Banking and Trust Company. The system reads, sorts and edits information encoded in magnetic ink on checks and other documents. Shown here are two Burroughs sorters, a control unit in the background, magnetic tape transport unit at left and the electrostatic printer at right.

ing the reserves, which member banks are required to maintain against their deposits, and by increasing or lowering the rate of interest, which banks are required to pay on loans, the Federal Reserve Banks can control the amount of loans and also the cost of borrowing. A simple explanation of the creation of "credit or checkbook" money follows:

Suppose the Ajax Company placed $1,000 on deposit in its checking account. If the reserve requirement was 20%, the bank would be required to deposit $200 in its reserve account at the Federal Reserve Bank. It would then have $800 available which it might lend to Brown and Company. When this amount was deposited to the credit of the new borrower, the bank would have to increase its reserves by $160, and would again have $640 which it could lend to a third borrower. This process of adding to reserves by lending can expand the effective money supplied by the original deposit about five times. However, as a practical matter, banks do not expand the money supply through credit to that degree, because of the investments, cash, and operating reserves needed to maintain liquidity.

The U. S. Treasury Department is also a major factor

Mr. Hoffman, through the banking system, and back to Mr. Hoffman again. Although Mr. Hoffman lives and banks in Pennsylvania, he writes his check in San Francisco to pay a hotel bill. The hotel deposits the money at its San Francisco bank, where the check is recorded on microfilm before it is forwarded to the local branch of the Federal Reserve System.

In the upper right-hand corner of the check are some numbers which identify Mr. Hoffman's bank. This code also indicates that the check must be sent for collection to the Third Federal Reserve District in Pennsylvania, and that it should clear through the Philadelphia Federal Reserve Bank.

In the San Francisco Federal Reserve Bank, a sorting clerk puts the check with others destined for Philadelphia, and the bundle is flown out on an eastbound plane.

At the Philadelphia Federal Reserve Bank some 400 operators, working with electronic machines, sort over a million checks per day. Within six hours of its receipt, Mr. Hoffman's check is processed, recorded, and forwarded to his own bank. There a signature clerk examines the check to verify Mr. Hoffman's signature, and the amount of the check is charged against his account.

The entire transaction has taken from two to three days.

Should the check be lost, it could be traced by the microfilm record which was made in the first stage of its processing.

At no time has any cash changed hands; this has been entirely a credit transaction. First, the hotel deposited Mr. Hoffman's check in its own bank. Then, the Federal Reserve Bank in San Francisco credited the hotel's bank with the amount of the check. Next, the Philadelphia Federal Reserve Bank charged Mr. Hoffman's bank the same amount, and Mr. Hoffman's bank, in turn, deducted the amount from his account.

CLEARING HOUSE OPERATION

Clearing houses have been established in about 600 U.S. cities for the clearance and exchange of local checks. The idea originated in London about 1775. Before that, messengers would make the rounds of the various banks, exchanging checks at each stop. Eventually, someone hit upon the idea of having the messengers meet at a coffee house, where all the exchanges could be made at one time. Not until 1853 were clearing house associations established in the United States.

This is the way a clearing house operates. Before the time established for the daily clearing house exchange, member banks sort the checks, which they have received, and designate envelopes for each of the other banks. At the proper time, the envelopes are distributed at the clearing house. Then, after tabulation of the totals, a "settlement clerk" determines the debit or credit balances. These net balances are settled either through a special account maintained in one bank for this purpose, or by adjusting balances of the members in the Federal Reserve. In the latter case, the "settlement manager" wires the nearest Federal Reserve office, stating the day's debit and credit balances.

MONEY IN YOUR FUTURE

As the economy expands, banking operations will inevitably accelerate. Actually, the use of banking services seems to be increasing at even a greater rate than the general expansion of industry. This may be explained, at least in part, by the fact that banking techniques are improving and people are becoming better informed about bank services. The electronic methods of handling checks make possible a more rapid processing of greater volume

Here, on the southern tip of Manhattan Island, is New York's financial district, the finance center of the world.

than ever before. Characters and numerals on checks are being imprinted with a special magnetic ink which contains particles of iron oxide. As the checks pass through an electronic sorting machine, the magnetized iron particles can be read by the machine, which sorts the checks, makes lightning automatic calculations, and records the required data.

Further automation is being planned, but far from reducing career opportunities in the financial world, these modern developments are opening exciting new vistas. Banks are hiring about one hundred thousand new employees annually, and the total number of persons engaged in this field has increased 65% to nearly six hundred thousand people in the past 16 years. Banks are currently transferring two trillion dollars through checking accounts each year. The most automation can hope to achieve is to keep pace with the tremendously increasing demand for banking services and with the need for more and more speed in carrying out transactions.

INSURANCE

One of the great sources of capital accumulation is the insurance industry. This fascinating business not only protects people and businesses from devastating losses, but provides a great reservoir of funds for investment. Thus it is one of the three principal elements in America's financial structure. It is also big business in its own right. In the United States more than six hundred thousand people are employed by insurance companies. Americans buy about ten billion dollars' worth of insurance every year. Its complex operations require the services of doctors, lawyers, accountants, transportation experts, builders, actuaries, and many different types of engineers.

Insurance is one of the oldest of businesses, for the ancient Chinese, Normans, and Romans worked out methods of pooling wealth and resources as a protection against loss by fire, robbery, or the hazards of sea voyages. As long ago as 1500 B.C., the Syrians used communal funds to cover losses from disastrous fires and droughts. An important insurance concept was written into Rhodian law in 916 B.C.; the Emperor of Rhodes ruled that a ship owner and all cargo owners should share on a pro rata basis the cost of any cargo thrown overboard in a storm for the safety of the ship. This historic ruling is the basis for present-day "coinsurance" in the maritime field.

An English guild in 1218 offered financial help to any of its members in the event of loss by fire or robbery, "provided such loss came not through his own lust, gluttony, or dice play, or other folly."

The history of insurance is tied closely to the history of sea voyages, because loss of ships at sea, even today, is a hazard that cannot be borne without financial protection. Near the close of the seventeenth century, Edward Lloyd's coffee house in London became one of the most colorful and exciting meeting places in the annals of commerce. Sea captains, ship owners, and merchants gathered here to discuss cargoes, bargain for ships and crews, and invest in voyages. They soon hit upon the scheme of organizing syndicates to share both profits and risks of trading voyages. Documents known as policies were drawn up, and the participants were called underwriters. The formal

12

organization of underwriters, established at Lloyd's in 1769, is still operating under that name.

INSURANCE IN AMERICA

The earliest fire insurance company in America was a mutual company founded in 1735 at Charleston, S.C. Many other American insurance companies were formed shortly afterward; one was established in Philadelphia by Benjamin Franklin. In 1794, the first capital stock insurance company was chartered by the state of Pennsylvania. This was the Insurance Company of North America, whose headquarters are in Philadelphia today.

The idea of life insurance was a comparatively recent one in the insurance field. Although in 1759 the Presbyterians set up a corporation to insure the lives of their ministers so as to provide for their families, commercial life insurance was virtually unknown until the middle of the nineteenth century. By 1947 the largest U.S. corporation was Metropolitan Life Insurance Company.

KINDS OF INSURANCE

Insurance falls into five major divisions: life, fire, casualty, marine and surety. Each of these is a broad, general classification covering a number of functions. For example, the category of *life* insurance includes annuities, and various forms of health insurance. *Fire* (and *theft*) covers direct loss by fire, wind, flood, earthquake, hail, explosion, and riot—as well as fire, theft, and collision on vehicles. *Casualty* protects the assured against damages for injuries, or property damage caused by him. *Marine* insurance not only includes coverage of ships and their cargoes, but merchandise being carried by rail, airplane, or other means of transportation; it covers injury of the transport company's employees and of the general public. Finally, *surety* companies offer bonds guaranteeing that individuals or business firms will fulfill contracts. In addition they write fidelity policies to protect businesses and banks against embezzlements or dishonest acts of employees.

As in banking, insurance firms may be mutual companies, owned by the policyholders, or capital stock companies which raise basic capital by selling shares of common stock. Generally, when an insurance company is formed, shares of insurance stock are sold for more than par value; thus the company is provided with a surplus which may be used to pay operating expenses without touching "paid up capital," representing the stock's par value.

HOW DOES INSURANCE WORK?

Let us follow a typical insurance case from the time of issuing the policy to the collection of a claim. A company has bought a factory building originally valued at one hundred fifty thousand dollars. Since the building is 10 years old, and the insurance agent figures depreciation at 2% a year, he establishes its present sound value at one hundred twenty thousand dollars. The machinery's depreciated value is set at $20,000. On the structure, the fire insurance rate is $1.75 per $100 of insurance; for the machinery, $2.00 per $100.

A policy is drawn up to cover the real or sound values

The busy office of a modern life insurance company, where thousands of policies are processed and reviewed every working day.

of the building and machinery. Since the building is mortgaged, the policy includes a mortgage clause making any loss claim payable to a specified bank, and the policy is filed with that bank. Three additional copies of the policy provide a mortgager's certificate: the factory owner's copy and two copies known as daily reports which go to the agent and to the insurance company.

When the daily report reaches the insurance company's office, a complex procedure for underwriting begins. The new policy and the risk it covers are recorded on a large form called a bordereau, or on a business-machine record card. In either case, the record includes an abbreviated list of pertinent details: name of agency, location of the property, amounts of the insurance and premium, dates of issue and expiration.

Now the daily report is passed on to the "impairment department." Here the factory owner's financial rating is checked with Dun and Bradstreet. This firm provides information as to the financial condition of businessmen. Also, any past records of fire losses, both in respect to the building and its present owner, are carefully investigated and recorded. At the insurance company are maps of every major community where the firm issues insurance. These remarkable maps show every building in the area, drawn to scale. They include symbols which give type of construction, type of roof, thickness of walls, size of water mains, location of fire hydrants, and so forth.

The investigation not only involves the insured building but covers adjacent structures as well. Nearby fire hazards are important factors in determining the extent of risk.

After all factors are studied, a staff of experts determines that the insurance firm must retain $40,000 as its "net line" on the property. Because the policy covers a total risk of one hundred forty thousand dollars, an additional one hundred thousand dollars must be provided in the form of reinsurance from other insurance companies. Through agreements called "treaties" with two reinsurance companies, the policy-issuing firm may request coverage from each of the other companies up to double the "net line." In this case that amount would be $80,000. It is possible, therefore, to obtain reinsurance of $50,000 from each of the other firms.

The daily report is now filed and the policy is in force.

Insurance records which must be maintained for each policy contract, may cover a period of more than 100 years. Microfilm in the modern office at the right makes it possible to reproduce and retain millions of documents in an area only a tiny fraction of that required when file boxes rose to the ceiling and ladders were needed to reach them.

PAYMENT OF A CLAIM

Several months later, a fire loss claim of $25,000 is filed with the insurance company. After reviewing the policy, an adjuster employed by the company goes to the scene of the fire. If he is satisfied that the claim is an honest one, he makes up an itemized list of property destroyed. He has the factory owner sign a "proof of loss" form which is forwarded to the insurance company. When the company has approved the claim, it sends a draft for $25,000 to the factory owner. The draft is made payable to the claimant and his bank, due to the fact that there is a mortgage clause in the policy. After both parties have endorsed the draft it is deposited in the bank for collection.

At this point, the claim is still not paid. It will actually be paid only on final acceptance by the insurance company, and during the time between issuance of the draft and its presentation for payment, the insuring firm still has an opportunity to uncover any possible fraud.

In this case, as no fraud is found, the draft is paid. However, the insurance investigators find that illegal machinery being used in a neighboring building caused the fire. Immediately, the insurance company enters suit against the offending firm; the suit is won and the insurance company is awarded damages.

A "WHODUNIT" BUSINESS

It may be seen that an important and fascinating part of insurance operations is investigation and real detective work. Insurance investigations can, and often do, involve crimes as serious as murder. Unscrupulous people may set fires to houses or buildings for the sole purpose of collecting insurance. Sometimes what appears to be a jewel robbery will turn out to be an owner's trick of hiding the valuable jewelry so as to collect a claim. Accidents must be carefully traced to determine cause, for in many cases large amounts of liability, casualty, and property insurance are involved.

Although the routine of handling different types of insurance varies, basic procedures are similar. Casualty insurance, for example, would be handled in much the same manner as a fire insurance policy. Adjustments are made by a claims department. The primary difference is that a casualty policy deals with intangibles. As a result, a fair award for damages must usually be negotiated, often in a court of law.

Life insurance rates are figured mathematically on the basis of mortality tables—painstakingly recorded statistics and thousands of case histories. While there are always exceptional cases when insurance must be paid long be-

Speed and accuracy are necessary to maintain data about the current status of Life insurance policies owned by 118 million Americans. The electrically operated rotary files illustrated at the right, each with three quarters of a million punch cards, permit immediate reference service impossible with handposted ledgers and policy cards of the 1890's.

One method of identifying a personal Life insurance policy is by its contract number. Hand stamping each policy number was the method used 75 years ago, as pictured at the left. During 1960, however, more than 21 million individual policies were issued in the U.S. Electronic units such as those at the right not only permit policies to be stamped, but note their premiums, record commissions, and compile other data at the rate of 700 an hour.

fore premiums have covered the amount of the payments, over-all averages provide ample margins for the payment of claims as well as dividends to shareholders.

Originally, life insurance was strictly a gamble, underwritten by individuals who actually placed wagers on the chances of the insured persons living beyond specified dates. The usual rate was 5% a year. But about 1843, American life insurance companies began to appear, providing payments to the insured's family in the event of his death. The companies grew gradually and, as they gained experience, became more successful. By the 1960's, some one hundred twenty million people in the United States owned life insurance with a value of close to six hundred billion dollars.

EXTRA BENEFITS

Not only do insurance companies protect policyholders against loss, but their great reserves of capital are put to work for American enterprise. Employed by each insurance company are financial experts who select sound investments for the reserve funds. These high-grade securities form what insurance men call an investment portfolio for the company. Among the investments sought by insurance firms are railroad, public utility, government and municipal bonds; large building or housing projects. Although such securities seldom pay large dividends, they are solid, long-range investments. A great deal of America's heavy industry relies upon insurance capital for growth and expansion.

But the insurance industry benefits the public in other ways. It supports a number of organizations which are working constantly to improve health, reduce mortality rates, accidents, and destruction of property. For example, fire insurance companies set up Underwriters Laboratories, Inc., in Chicago, to test all types of building materials, construction techniques, electrical installations, and so forth. Using some of the world's most advanced equipment, they can determine the effects of stresses and strains and of heat and cold on various materials. Manufacturers pay for such tests, and when their materials have passed certain standards, they carry the Underwriters Laboratory label, a highly respected seal of approval. As a result of the testing and the high standards set by Underwriters, safety factors in all types of building and construction are being steadily increased.

Insurance is much more than a big and profitable industry. It is a vital factor in our economy, a safeguard against disastrous losses, and a powerful force for the improvement of human welfare.

INVESTMENTS AND SECURITIES

The third major segment of the American financial system is the investment field. The trading of securities is certainly big business, and it has become so well organized and regulated that it is today an efficient, modern industry.

In no other country is the buying and selling of stocks and bonds handled on so wide a scale or by such a large segment of the general public. It has been estimated that of the approximately 15 million stockholders in the United States, about 77% have incomes of less than $10,000 a year and 30%, less than $5,000. There has been a startling increase in the number of small investors in the past 10 years. The result is the emergence of a true people's capitalism, in which average people are gaining increasing ownership of American industry, not by legislation but by investing a part of their savings in stocks and bonds.

Focal point of this gigantic activity in the investment field is the New York Stock Exchange, where liquid capital represented by the listed stocks, amounts to over three hundred fifty billion dollars. Other U.S. exchanges include the American Stock Exchange, also in New York, the Mid-West Stock Exchange in Chicago, Philadelphia-Baltimore Stock Exchange, and the Pacific Coast Exchange in Los Angeles and San Francisco. Most great cities in the Western world have stock exchanges.

WHAT IS A STOCK EXCHANGE?

In order to make it easy for people to buy and sell their shares of stock, which are shares of ownership in corporations, it was necessary to establish market places for these securities. A modern exchange is organized by professional stock merchants, or brokers, who purchase "seats" on the exchange. A seat entitles the owner to execute buy and sell orders on the floor of the exchange. As the membership in the New York Exchange is limited, and seats have been in great demand in recent years, the price has been very high. In 1961, seats were being sold for close to a quarter of a million dollars. In the past they have commanded a price as low as seventeen thousand dollars (1942) and as high as six hundred twenty-five thousand dollars (1929).

When someone wishes to buy stock in a large corporation such as General Motors, Monsanto Chemical, or Du Pont, he places his order with a reputable stock broker or banker in his community. He indicates the top price per share he wishes to pay. The broker then teletypes a message to his New York office, if he has one, or to another broker who acts as his contact there, and who is a member of the New York Stock Exchange. As the New York office maintains a private phone on the trading floor of the Exchange, it is easy to place the order with a telephone clerk: "Buy 500 GM at so much." The clerk immediately transmits this message to the firm's floor member who goes to one of the 18 trading posts. This post handles some 75 or 80 stocks of which General Motors is one. Now, the broker's representative must compete in a two-way auction market with other floor members who are trying to buy or sell GM stock. His aim is to get the best possible price for his customer.

When a transaction is completed, the various floor members participating jot down the price. So far, everything has been done by word of mouth. Soon, however, the sale is flashed on a huge screen at one end of the floor while, simultaneously, it is recorded on ticker tapes—special teletype machines—at stock exchanges and brokerage offices in all parts of the country. Within a few days, the actual stock certificate is issued and delivered to the purchaser.

KINDS OF SECURITIES

Most people are familiar with common stocks. These are actual shares of ownership in businesses. Generally they have voting rights on the basis of one vote per share. If a corporation makes a profit, the common stockholders may receive a portion of the profit in the form of dividends. If the business does badly no dividends are paid.

Preferred stocks are usually priced higher than common stocks and carry a fixed, cumulative dividend, often 5% or even higher. In any case the preferred shares

give the holders what the title suggests—*preferred* status in the payment of dividends. They are the first to receive their share of profits and the first to be repaid if the business fails or is liquidated.

Bonds are also traded on the stock exchanges. These are certificates of debt, usually bearing a maturity date when the value of the bond must be repaid. Holders of bonds also receive a stated amount of interest regardless of the issuing organization's earnings. In this category there are government bonds, corporate bonds, and municipal bonds. The latter are issued by state, county, or city governments. There are many different types of common and preferred stocks and bonds, with various rates of interest, special voting, or monetary privileges.

OVER-THE-COUNTER STOCKS

Stocks listed on the major exchanges must conform to certain strict rules, which call for a prolonged record of good management and profits. The New York Stock Exchange requires that shares of a listed corporation be owned by at least fifteen hundred people who hold a minimum of five hundred thousand shares valued at ten million dollars or more. However, hundreds of smaller companies are unable to meet these standards. Their stocks are traded on other exchanges or through brokerage houses by direct telephone or wire. In the latter case, no public announcement is made of current bids or sales. Actually over-the-counter stocks represent the largest securities market in the country.

Another important aspect of the securities industry is the recent growth of mutual funds. These are companies organized by stock specialists who buy and sell what they consider worthwhile investments for their stockholders. Members buy shares of the funds, leaving it to professionals to build an over-all investment portfolio that will make the funds prosper. In the 1960's there were nearly two hundred mutual funds in the United States with total assets of eighteen billion dollars and over two million five hundred thousand shareholders.

Transactions in stocks, bonds, and other securities are rigidly controlled by State and Federal laws. Under the Securities and Exchange Act of 1934, the Security and Exchange Commission establishes and enforces rules for the operation of stock exchanges. The rules are designed to safeguard the public against manipulation, fraud, and unhealthy market fluctuations.

No more exciting market and auction place can be found than the imposing colonnaded building at Broad and Wall Streets in Manhattan, for it is here at the New York Stock Exchange that the pulse of industry's lifeblood may be felt. Here, where hundreds of millions of dollars in shares of great companies are traded every day, capital flows in and out again in a continuous stream. The industrial heartbeat may throb strongly, sluggishly, or with feverish excitement, in time with the vast machinery of a nation at work. The billions of dollars exchanged in the securities industry represent the wealth and energy of a free people—ordinary Americans whose savings in banks, insurance premiums, and personal investments are furnishing the fuel for the proudest achievement of mankind—American Industry.

On the floor of the New York Stock Exchange, trading posts are besieged by brokers' representatives who bargain to buy and sell blocks of stock.

2 Power

What appears to be a space age loop-the-loop at an amusement park is part of the filter section of a transmission line that was energized at 775,000 volts. A number of large firms participated in this record-breaking test to help determine the feasibility of transmitting power at more than double maximum voltages now in use.

From his earliest days on earth, man has sought power to do work beyond his own limited capabilities. First, he harnessed animals to pull heavy loads and to turn grinding wheels and spits. Then, he learned to turn wheels by the force of running water. He built windmills with sails large enough to catch the slightest breeze. In the course of utilizing these forces of nature, he discovered the principle of gear ratios to increase the efficiency of the power at his disposal.

Finally, steam became the driving force of industry. From 1711 when Thomas Newcomen developed the first steam piston engine, and from the 1760's when James Watt began experimenting with steam engines, the burgeoning Industrial Revolution could count on power to drive its heavy machinery. To this day, steam is the primary source of industrial power, although gasoline engines and other types of internal-combustion engines are used for some purposes.

Steam power was known and used in Greece 2,100 years ago when Hero of Alexandria turned roasting spits with a steam-driven sphere called an aeolipile. The sphere was rotated on the reaction principle, being propelled by jets of escaping steam. Although the ancient Greeks had thus discovered the principle of jet propulsion, as well as steam power, many centuries passed before there was further development of importance. In 1629, Branca used steam on the impulse principle to turn a many-bladed wheel. This was the origin of the steam turbine, which is driven by the force of steam striking beveled vanes, much

as a water wheel is propelled by the rushing of water, or a windmill by the passage of wind.

Possibly, the first industrial use of steam power was made in 1699 when Thomas Savery's steam engine pumped water from mines in England.

While steam power was being employed as a direct power source in mills and factories, experiments were being conducted with the mysterious force known as electricity. Benjamin Franklin in America; Galvani and Volta, in Italy; and Hans Christian Oersted in Denmark had been studying the properties of electricity and magnetism. In 1831, Michael Faraday, an Englishman, and Joseph Henry, an American, each working independently, demonstrated that an electric current can be produced in metal by moving it in the field of a magnet. This was the discovery which led to the modern electric dynamo.

POWER FOR MODERN INDUSTRY

Today's power industry is primarily an electrical industry; yet 80% of the electricity generated is produced by steam turbines; the other 20% comes mostly from hydroelectric plants. Thus, in spite of electrical progress, steam power is still the fundamental workhorse of industry.

In order to produce steam, heat must be created, and this requires fuel, enormous quantities of fuel. The major concern of power industries is the conservation of our dwindling coal and oil supplies. Present calculations estimate that by the year 2000, if power consumption continues to increase at its present rate, the amount of coal needed by the United States for one year's supply of power would be one-eighth of our entire present coal reserves and more than our entire supply of oil.

Two solutions to the problem are being explored. First, the development of atomic power plants. Second, a steady increase in the efficiency of conventional plants in order to produce more power for each ton of coal consumed. Progress in this area has been remarkable. In 1889, when the Philadelphia Electric Edison station went into operation, its production of 460 kilowatt-hours per ton of coal astonished experts of that day. By 1900, the Hartford Electric Light Company was able to install a 2,000 kilowatt unit which turned out 1,050 kilowatt-hours for each ton of coal consumed. In the 1960's, modern power plants were approaching an output of 4,000 kilowatt-hours per ton.

ATOMIC POWER

Progress is being made in nuclear power. Five atomic power plants were already operating in 1960. These included the Duquesne Light Company's plant in Shippingport, Pa.; the Vallecitos plant operated by the Pacific Gas and Electric Company in Livermore, Calif.; the Santa Susana plant constructed by the Southern California Edison Company; the Dresden plant in Joliet, Ill. operated by the Commonwealth Edison Company and by the Nuclear Power Group, Inc.; and the plant of the Yankee Atomic Electric Company in Rowe, Mass.

Other atomic plants are under construction. Among them are plants in Monroe, Mich.; Indian Point, N.Y.;

These giant fuses for electric utility companies are being assembled at the Westinghouse plant in Trafford, Pa., where high-voltage power circuit breakers are made on automated assembly lines.

Sexton, Pa.; Eureka, Calif.; Big Rock Point, Mich.; Parr, S.C.; Sioux Falls, S.D.; and Peach Bottom, Pa.

An atomic reactor does not drive the electric generators directly. Its function is to produce heat for the building of steam pressure which, in turn, drives the steam turbines.

DEMAND FOR POWER

Our power facilities are already gigantic. With only 6% of the world's population, the power industry of America is producing approximately 40% of the world's electricity. Russia follows the United States with 13% of the world production; then the United Kingdom with 6%. Why is so much power needed? The growth of industrial and home electrical consumption is so rapid that the industry is anticipating a use of one thousand three hundred billion kilowatt-hours by 1970.

To meet this demand, long-range plans by investor-owned power companies provide for additional investments of one hundred forty-three billion dollars in new plants and construction over the next 20 years. Among major industries, electric companies lead all others in expenditures for new equipment.

Where will this power go? To homes, commercial firms and offices, industries, government installations, and farms. The average household consumer in 1960, using about 4,000 kilowatt-hours a year, is expected to need 8,000 by 1970. For the service to light his house, heat his electric range, operate his TV set, run his washer, dryer, refrigerator, and so on, he pays less than 25 cents a day. Edison's first customers paid 10 times that or approximately 25 cents per kilowatt-hour. Some four and a half million farms, 98% of the farms in the United States, receive electrical service. In industry, the daily electrical power consumed is equal to 429 extra men for each individual worker employed.

To finance this gigantic industry some four million individual stockholders own shares of electric companies; twenty-five million bank depositors and one hundred thirty million owners of life insurance have an indirect interest in the power industry because the banks and insurance companies are heavy investors in utilities. (See *Finance*) The total capital investment represents between forty and fifty billion dollars. This figure is expected to double by 1970. With over three hundred fifty thousand people employed, the power industry's capital investment per employee is approximately one hundred twenty-five thousand dollars.

HOW IS ELECTRICAL POWER PRODUCED?

Thomas Edison's first electric power plant was designed and constructed on principles that are in use today. His steam dynamo for supplying power to a section of New York City was constructed at the Edison Machine Works on Goerck Street, and in September 1882, 400 lamps were turned on in a mile square area encompassing Wall, Nassau, Spruce, and Ferry Streets in lower Manhattan. Edison and his assistants worked night and day, supervising the laying of conduits in trenches under the streets and the installation of machinery at the Pearl Street generating station.

18

Westinghouse engineers check the performance of "R-1," the tenth 108,000-kilowatt generator to be installed at Grand Coulee Dam, making this the greatest generating capacity at any single location in the world, even surpassing Hoover Dam.

A massive turbine spindle for the world's first full-scale nuclear power plant at Shippingport, Pa. is prepared for shipment. A complete turbine unit of this type weighs one million three hundred thousand pounds and is 81 feet long.

Edison used steam engines to furnish power for his generators. These, of course, have long since been replaced by high-speed steam turbines, but the principle of the electric generator remains the same.

A modern steam turbine generator is a massive machine containing a rotor weighing many tons. On the shaft of the rotor is a series of vanes, called buckets, resembling hundreds of windmill blades. Directed against the vanes, a tremendous blast of steam pressure rushes to escape the confinement of superheated pipes. As the vapor forces its way through the buckets, the rotor begins to turn more and more rapidly until it begins to hum like a spinning top. At full speed, the sound becomes a shrill whine. The turbine is turning the electric generator and producing power. Between the spinning rotor and giant stator coils electricity is created. This, on a large scale, is an application of the principle which Faraday and Henry demonstrated when they set a piece of metal in motion in a magnetic field. The power of steam, used to set the rotor in motion, is transformed into the electric energy that runs our industry and lights our homes.

Hydroelectric power is used wherever a power plant can be located conveniently close to a natural falls, such as Niagara; or large dams are built where practical. In the majority of communities, however, steam is still the most economical and dependable source of power.

A FUTURE TO STAGGER IMAGINATION

The future of power industries is brighter than the blazing lights on Broadway, for the development of efficient electrical plants and the rapidly growing demands of American consumers call for unlimited expansion. To find ways of satisfying this hunger for power, the industry is calling for young people with talents and training in many fields. Wide-open opportunities are available for engineers to develop supercritical pressure electric generating plants, nuclear power plants, and electronic controls. The firms of Westinghouse and General Electric, who make much of the giant electronic equipment for power plants, are seeking personnel for planning, designing, constructing, and advancing research. Power companies need management for improved production and distribution.

Typical of the perpetual increase of efficiency in plant operations is the electronic load dispatcher recently developed by the Philadelphia Electric Company and the Minneapolis-Honeywell Regulator Company. This automatic system computes and controls each generating unit's share of the total power load. An electronic brain, with lightning rapidity, solves complex mathematical equations, and makes automatic adjustments in the output of widely scattered stations. Simultaneously, it controls power loads of twenty-seven steam and seven hydroelectric generators. The job was formerly done by the power director who, working with a loading schedule, telephoned instructions to the various stations. Now, the power director merely adjusts dials and the electronic load dispatcher does the rest.

The ultimate in automation was achieved when the Little Gypsy station of Louisiana Power and Light was installed in 1961. This two hundred thirty thousand kilowatt unit is the world's first fully automatic generating station.

How much power will America need? How much can its power industry produce in years to come? No one knows the exact answers to these questions, but if the advances made in the past 10 years are indicative, the possibilities are almost beyond calculation.

EXPLOSIVES

There are times when the smooth, silent power of an electric crane or the throbbing power of a diesel locomotive will not suffice. Often, men need more than a mighty push or pull—they need a real wallop. Power to blast rock or power to crumble mountainsides requires the use of high explosives. Most people think of explosives as instruments of war; yet modern industry would slow to a walk without their daily use for commercial purposes.

The discovery and use of gunpowder dates back several centuries. Reference to "the spear of vehement fire"

This 1881 view of the Du Pont gunpowder mills near Wilmington, Delaware shows pulleys at the right of the picture. They supplied waterpower to buildings some distance from the Brandywine Creek.

Rock and water are hurled 1,200 feet into the air as nearly three million pounds of "Nitramex" 2H rip the peaks from an underwater mountain which had wrecked over 100 vessels in British Columbia.

is made by a Chinese writer about the year 1259. Apparently, this was a bamboo "gun," containing a black powder charge and having somewhat the effect of a Roman candle. Firecrackers were known to the Chinese at least 200 years earlier.

There are numerous types of explosives. Many are aware that the explosive force of gunpowder has been used for lethal weapons, but few stop to consider that gasoline and steam are also utilized as explosives. The rapid fire explosions of ignited gasoline, in the internal-combustion engine, drive pistons; the steam engine runs by explosive puffs of vapor trapped in cylinders.

Gunpowder is composed of saltpeter, sulphur, and charcoal. These ingredients may be mixed in various proportions and still be explosive if ignited in a confined space. Saltpeter is the key. Although originally this chemical was recovered from animal dung, modern chemical plants produce tons of synthetic saltpeter by a process known as atmospheric nitrogen fixation.

U. S. EXPLOSIVES INDUSTRY

The story of the manufacture of explosives in America begins with the story of Du Pont, for this giant among America's mighty corporations began as a gunpowder

mill on the banks of the Brandywine Creek near Wilmington, Delaware. Éleuthère Irénée Du Pont founded the Eleutherian Powder Mills with a capital of $36,000 in 1802. He did not have immediate success. For years, he struggled to get his enterprise out of debt and suffered through some disastrous explosions in his plant. The mills had played an important part in supplying powder to the army during the War of 1812, and the demand for good quality gunpowder on the frontier was great. For this reason the company ultimately prospered. Today, of course, the name of Du Pont is preeminent in the chemical and explosives industries. (See *Chemicals*)

While gunpowder is still in use, modern high explosives have far outstripped it for war as well as for peaceful purposes. In Switzerland in 1846, Professor Christian Schönbein, using his wife's kitchen as an experimental laboratory, discovered that cotton when soaked in distilled nitric and sulphuric acids and ignited, produced a clean, smokeless explosion. His invention was guncotton. In the same year Ascanio Sobrero, a professor of chemistry at the University of Turin in Italy, added glycerin to nitric and sulphuric acids; then poured the compound into a basin of water. A pale yellow oil sank to the bottom. He soon found that this was the most fearful of all

This streamlined Du Pont dynamite plant eight miles from Martinsburg, West Virginia supplies the biggest markets of commercial explosives — the coal mines of West Virginia and Pennsylvania.

explosives, nitroglycerin. Sobrero was so alarmed by his findings that he urged scientists to ignore his discovery.

Alfred Nobel, founder of the Nobel Peace Prize, first dared to manufacture "Nobel's blasting oil," or nitroglycerin. His use of a percussion cap of gunpowder to set off a nitroglycerin charge opened the way for the use of modern high explosives in mining, quarrying, tunneling, and building. After a series of tragic explosions of his crated cans of blasting oil, Nobel invented dynamite, a mixture of earth and nitroglycerin. This safe, yet powerful explosive is, literally, man's power to move mountains.

In 1880, Du Pont built the world's largest dynamite plant near Gibbstown, New Jersey. It was named Repauno after the Repaupo Creek. Until the plant was converted to chemicals in 1954, it produced over three billion pounds of dynamite. Now, Du Pont has seven other automated dynamite plants. The largest is near Martinsburg, West Virginia. In underground bunkers, robot machines, electronically controlled, manufacture the dynamite. They are considered among the safest of industrial plants.

Dynamite is sometimes made in a waterproof gelatinous form which is especially useful for blasting in damp, rocky crevices or under water. "Blasting gelatin" was another of Nobel's inventions.

TNT, or trinitrotoluene, was a German development introduced in warfare during the first World War. This is basically a coal tar derivative containing toluene, a product of benzene. TNT is shock proof, may be melted, cast in various shapes, and handled safely under most conditions.

The power of dynamite and other explosives can be controlled to a remarkable degree. When the "Big Inch" transcontinental oil pipeline was being laid, 31,000 lb. of dynamite opened up a trench in the bedrock of the Susquehanna River in a single blast. In another case, Du Pont experts were called upon to solve a problem of damming the Saguenay River in Canada for a hydroelectric power plant. So swift was the current that engineers had been unable to complete the job. Finally, the dam was constructed on one bank of the river. The massive block of steel and concrete, 95 ft. high, 45 ft. wide, and 40 ft. in depth, was built standing on end. This had to be dropped exactly into place. With 1,000 lb. of gelatin dynamite, the Du Pont experts blew out the supports with such accuracy that the dam fell precisely on the appointed spot.

All of these conventional explosives are children's toys in comparison with the force of nuclear bombs. The extent to which atomic explosions may be developed for industrial use remains to be seen. Possibly, even this terrible weapon can have peaceful uses. The manufacture of explosives is not strictly an industry for war. The contribution of explosives to industrial progress is invaluable, because gunpowder, dynamite, TNT, and atomic bombs are *power*. Power to benefit mankind if properly channeled, to destroy it if uncontrolled.

This giant electric generating station, completed in 1960, houses two 325,000-kilowatt turbine generators capable of furnishing enough power for a city of five million people.

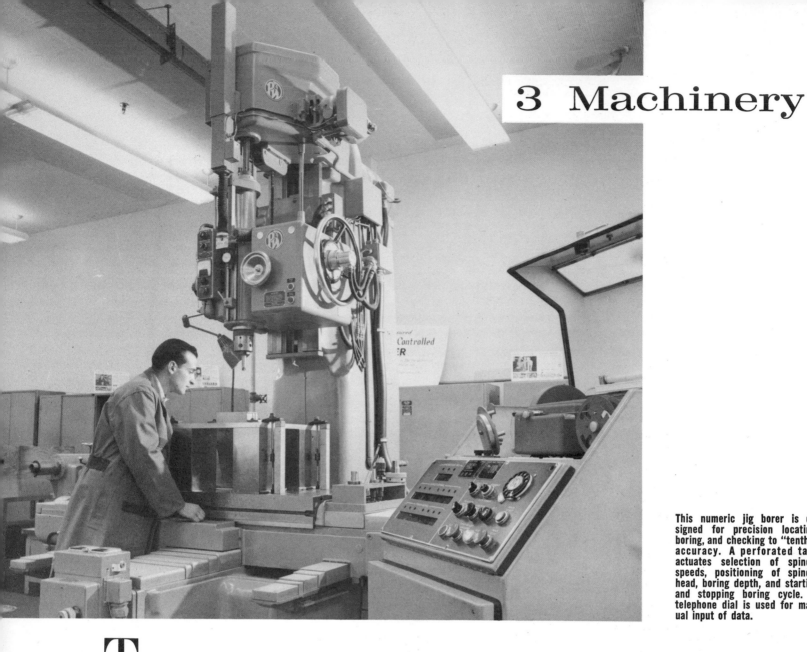

3 Machinery

This numeric jig borer is designed for precision locating, boring, and checking to "tenths" accuracy. A perforated tape actuates selection of spindle speeds, positioning of spindle head, boring depth, and starting and stopping boring cycle. A telephone dial is used for manual input of data.

This is the age of automation and mechanization. Machinery has given men thousands of extra arms and hands, the power of millions of horses, and the incredible skill of fairy tale magicians. Because of its fabulous machines, modern American industry outproduces the rest of the world, and the production of these machines is an industry in itself.

To tell the full story of machinery would necessitate going back to prehistoric times when people first thought of using tools and implements to make work easier. But power-driven machinery is a comparatively recent development. By utilizing water and wind, men began to power their grinding mills several centuries ago. Then, the invention of steam engines in the seventeenth century literally set the wheels in motion for the Industrial Revolution. (See *Power*) English textile mills began using power-driven spinning and weaving machines early in the 1700's.

An American introduced the great concept that made mass production possible. Eli Whitney, inventor of the cotton gin, gave the world something far more significant than a machine to separate the seeds from cotton when he devised machine tools, interchangeable parts, and the jigs or patterns which guide power-driven machines through repetitive motions. In his New Haven gun factory, he was able to turn out the stocks, barrels, triggers, flash pans, and every other part of a musket in record time to fulfill a government contract. Each part was machine-tooled and therefore was identical to and interchangeable with other parts produced by the same pattern. This was in 1800. During the course of the next century, machinery revolutionized the world.

MODERN MACHINE TOOLS

Generally speaking, the term, machine tools, applies to cutting and drilling machinery which can be used to build other machines. They include lathes, drill presses, boring machines, shapers, gear cutting machines, planers, milling, grinding, forming, sharpening, polishing and broaching machines. They may be employed not only to produce other machines and parts, but also to reproduce themselves. Virtually everything we use in our homes, offices, or industrial plants is processed by machine tools or made on equipment that was manufactured by such tools.

The machine-tool industry comprises some 375 firms most of which are located around the eastern part of the

North Central section of the United States. More than half are in Ohio, Michigan, and Illinois. New York, Massachusetts, and Connecticut are also important machine-tool states. Total annual volume of business fluctuates considerably from year to year, but generally it amounts to approximately a billion dollars.

Modern machine tools are usually automated, complex mechanisms, yet they are often compact and easily operated. One type of milling machine, for example, by the use of push-button controls, will provide a multitude of operating cycles; thus producing a wide variety of parts. During a given operating cycle, a cutter is placed automatically at three different depths, while the feed mechanism is also automatically controlled for cuts of three lengths. As soon as the operator presses the starting button, the machine goes through a prescribed sequence of functions. The parts, such as electric motor armature shafts, axles, or rods of multiple diameters, are precision-tooled for microscopic tolerances.

Machine tools may be tiny mechanisms small enough to fit on a card table, such as machines for fashioning delicate tracery in the design of a piece of jewelry. They may also be monstrous creations that must be shipped from the machine plant in sections, one section to a railroad flatcar.

Grinding machines are made for utmost precision. Parts may be tooled to allow a deviation of five-millionths of an inch.

The variety of work performed by machines is infinite, from milling aluminum slabs into precisely formed airplane wings to cutting brass gears one-eighth of an inch in diameter.

Most specialized machine tools are custom made and are designed to a manufacturer's requirements. The parts are milled, shaped, and cut on the machine-builders' own tools. Nearly all machinery parts are machine finished today; however at some time in the past, the master machines had to be built virtually by hand. First came machines to make parts, then the parts were assembled into machines to make other machines. Today's automation has been evolutionary until now we may create by machinery.

In addition to mechanical cutting, grinding, and stamping machines, there are metalworking machines designated as flamatic or inductron which, by means of heat or energy, braze metal parts together or harden the materials for special uses. Flamatic machines are those which employ flames of acetylene, propane, or other gases to produce heat. An inductron machine generates heat by means of electric induction.

The hydroform machine shapes parts by means of a rubber blanket under hydraulic pressure, which squeezes metal into a desired form. Sheet metal, foil, and even thick steel plate can be molded by this method of chipless machining. Cincinnati Milling Machine Company also produces a "Hydrospin" to form metal. This hydraulic pressure machine employs two rapidly spinning, opposed rollers to spin a workpiece into the shape of a revolving mandrel. Although the metal being formed may be a tough, high tensile alloy, it flows ahead of the rollers like soft clay and rapidly conforms to the prescribed shape.

23

Two steps in the forming of a metal piece as it is "flowed" on a horizontal Floturn machine. A rapidly revolving mandrel shapes high tensile alloys as easily as though it were molding soft clay.

A horizontal spindle-milling machine like this can produce precision tools, dies, and prototypes. It reproduces the shape of any two-dimensional template or three-dimensional model quickly and accurately.

An operator uses a dial to preselect the next spindle speed while a "Hydrashift" lathe is cutting. Gears are shifted automatically by hydraulic power when the machine is put in neutral and started again.

Present-day technology has placed exacting demands on the manufacturers of machinery. To make one part in the automatic transmission of an automobile, for example, requires a machine that performs 171 different finishing operations. Holes with a .040-in. diameter must sometimes be ground in ball bearings smaller than houseflies. At a rate of one every 15 seconds, such miniature parts are drilled by a machine which develops one hundred thousand revolutions per minute.

Because such operations generate tremendous heat from friction, the machine-tool industry has developed special cutting fluids which cool the machinery and the parts being milled. Here, as in many other segments of industry, chemistry and chemical research play a vital role. Machinery companies employ physicists, chemists, biologists, bacteriologists, metallurgists, ceramists, as well as mechan-

This double-end precision-boring machine performs boring, counterboring, and chamfering operations on tractor cylinder heads. A cross slide indexes the workpiece into position for machining holes at selected points.

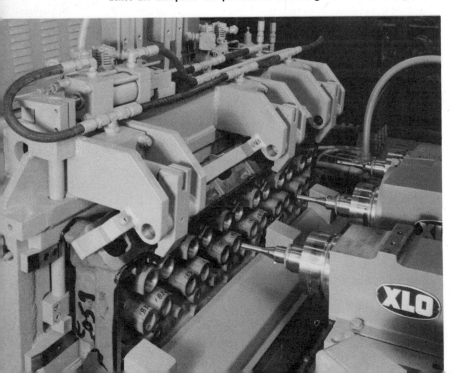

ical, electrical, hydraulic, and electronic engineers. The advance guard of all big industry today is research.

PRODUCTION MACHINERY

Machinery to mold, cut, drill, and press parts for other machines represents the beginning of the story. Machine tools are the parents of a host of complex machinery used by industry to do everything from shelling peas to handling radioactive isotopes. To describe all of the ingenious devices used for automatic operations found in the millions of plants and factories in all parts of the country would be impossible. Box-making machinery prints, cuts, folds, and assembles paper containers while other machinery fills the boxes with various products. Woodworking machines cut and form furniture parts; bottling machines cast molten glass into the shape of bottles, fill and seal them; sorting machines separate various sized objects. Automated robots, with amazingly versatile hands, can handle tiny objects with the delicacy of their human counterparts.

Descriptions of a great many specialized machines and their operation will be found in the chapters on other industries throughout this book.

Who makes the thousands of specialized fabricating and assembling machines that keep our mass production system running at high speed? Most machines for specialized purposes are made by specialized firms. Harris-Seybold Company, Intertype Corporation, Mergenthaler Linotype Company, and Miehle-Goss-Dexter Company are manufacturers of printing and typesetting machinery. Other machinery companies make looms and special equipment for the textile industry; still others specialize in packaging machines. So vast is the field and so varied is the demand for equipment to do particular jobs that a catalog of the machines, even for a single industry such as food canning, would make a book in itself. The motors and engines that drive machinery are produced by another segment of the great machine industry. Many of these heavy electrical units are made by Westinghouse Electric Corporation and by General Electric Company.

CALCULATING MACHINES

The most fascinating aspect of the machine industry is in the realm of calculating and "thinking" machines, and in the various electronic controls used for the operation of production machines. This is the ultramodern phase of the machine age which has started a new industrial revolution. In a sense, automatic computers had to be created to keep pace with the speed of manufacturing machines. Men had created mass production industries so vast and so complex, that the human brain required mechanical aids to analyze and tabulate records. The use of various types of business machines is known as data processing. Leaders in this field are RCA (Radio Corporation of America), General Electric, Remington Rand, and IBM (International Business Machines) Corporation.

Data processing generally consists of combined units for gathering, storing, processing, and reporting information. They can handle business, scientific, and other mathematical data at fantastic speeds and with absolute accuracy. Self-checking units virtually eliminate possibility of error. With their high-speed electronic computers, these data processing systems have been developed since World War II. Most experts agree that their application has only begun and that the changes they can bring to civilization are more momentous than those of the nineteenth century Industrial Revolution.

As American technology has advanced, industry has seen a tremendous increase in clerical work while the number of production workers has declined. To meet the staggering demands for paper work, automated data processing has become a major industry.

Possibly, one of the greatest challenges to the manufacturers of business machines is the banking industry. With machines for magnetic character sensing, the billions of checks that are exchanged annually in the United States can be read, recorded, and sorted automatically with the speed of light. (See *Banking*) Data processing machines are used in scientific research, business administration, and compilation of statistics of all kinds.

HISTORY OF DATA PROCESSING

Only 30 years ago, data processing machines were little more than scientific curiosities. Punched card systems with 80 columns of information began to appear in the early 1930's. Automatic multipliers also came into use at about that time, along with key-operated accounting machines. Although these innovations represented major advances, the operations were slow compared to up-to-date systems. Prior to World War II, the printing units in business machines were considered fast if they turned out 150 lines per minute. Now 1,000 lines per minute are not unusual.

The first large scale computer, the ENIAC, was built at the University of Pennsylvania, and it became popularly known as the "electronic brain." A major technological advance, which made possible much more rapid calculations, was the introduction of electronic vacuum tubes for switching and control functions. These replaced the relatively slow mechanical movements of the older electromagnetic switches, and made calculation speeds 1,000 times faster than had heretofore been possible.

Another important advance was made in the memory units of the machines. The stored-program computer records data for future reference simultaneously with the machine's other functions. The first computer containing this internal memory unit was built in 1948. Today, these amazing mechanical memories not only follow instructions fed to them by human operators, but also modify the instructions and issue their own on the basis of new data.

A further improvement of the memory device came in 1950 with the invention of the magnetic core. This is a small ring of ferromagnetic material. The cores are strung on fine wire mesh. Some are magnetized in one direction, some in another. Each stores an item of information. Within a few millionths of a second, information contained in a core storage can be located and started through processing units.

IBM's Ramac machine contains a stack of magnetic disks, which store ten million digits of information. Rotating at 1,200 revolutions per minute, the disks can receive or give back data through access arms. These arms move rapidly to any point on any disk as they file or retrieve items of information.

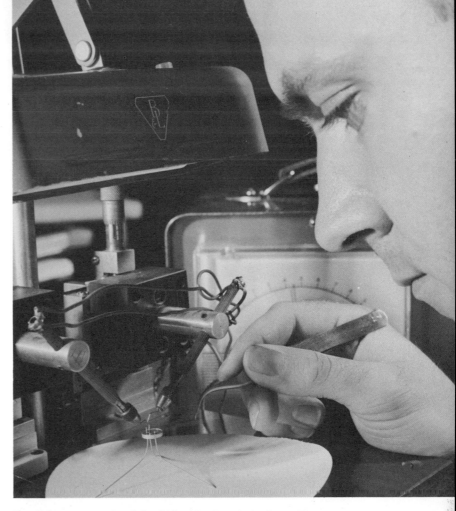

Now being mass produced by RCA, this tiny electronic workhorse — a silicon transistor — can perform the jobs of up to several hundred types of transistors previously devised. It is used in military weapons, communications, control devices, and data-processing equipment.

To speed drilling operations when workpieces require several accurately spaced holes, this machine automatically positions the table. A drilling cycle can be punched into an eight-track tape which controls the positioning of the table.

Further improvements were made on switching functions with the development of a semiconductor diode, which is smaller, requires less power, and gives off less heat than vacuum tubes.

One of the greatest of all electronic advances is the transistor. This amazingly simple, tiny mechanism, no bigger than a man's thumbnail, has given civilization a gigantic forward stride. What is a transistor? It is a germanium or other type of crystal. It resembles a tiny pellet of paraffin at the junction of a number of wires. Without generating any heat, it does the work of a vacuum tube approximately 50 times its size. Since the crystal is a semiconductor of electricity, it allows the excess or deficiency of electrons freedom to move and to conduct current which may be precisely controlled by the application of voltage. Similar to a radio tube, the transistor can

nism on modern papermaking machines can spot microscopic changes in the thickness of the paper web, and automatically adjust the machinery to maintain a uniform production run. Similar spotting devices are used to warn of trouble or flaws in almost every manufacturing process today. The engineering and production of control mechanisms constitute a large segment of the machinery industry and are represented by such companies as Minneapolis-Honeywell Regulator Company, Brown Instruments (a division of Minneapolis-Honeywell), and major electronics firms such as RCA, Westinghouse, and General Electric.

Machinery is one of the most advanced of American industries from a technological standpoint. It presents challenging opportunities. Recent electronic breakthroughs clearly demonstrate that the Machine Age is still in its infancy.

The Univac III is a high-performance electronic data-processing system designed to meet the needs of business and science. The system is highly flexible in the variety and numbers of peripheral units, like those at the right, which can be attached.

transmit more power than is applied to it; in other words, it is an amplifier. As far as is known, a transistor is virtually impervious to wear, shock, or extremes of temperature.

Not content with the original transistors, electronics experts have worked steadily toward still smaller units. RCA engineers have developed a series of "Micromodules," electronic components so tiny that equipment already considered to be miniature was reduced to one-tenth the size of earlier models. A standard of .350-in. square has been adopted for the various microelements. On wafer-thin material, the transistors, semiconductor diodes, capacitors, resistors, and inductors are mounted and assembled into complete, hermetically sealed circuit units forming .350-in. cubes. An entire unit may be placed within the area of an average person's thumbnail.

For use in space satellites, and in the increasingly complex computors needed for everything from nuclear physics equations to inventory control, the new field of miniature electronic machinery is looking well into the future.

Meanwhile, electronic controls for all types of machinery are accomplishing minor miracles. An electric eye mecha-

A scene in the first full-range electronic data-processing center designed to serve all types of businesses. Located in New York's financial district, it is air-conditioned to insure accurate humidity control. It provides data processing for banks, brokerage houses, insurance companies, and other firms.

4 Mining

In strip mining, giant power shovels scoop up 65 cubic yards, or 98 tons, of earth and rock in a single bite. This shovel in use near Georgetown, Ohio is one of the largest mobile land machines in the world. Towering 160 feet high, it dwarfs a bulldozer at its base.

Digging in the earth, a favorite pastime of children in all times and places, may well have been one of the first industries of man. Certainly, his use of clay and stones dates before the earliest recorded history. People soon learned that some areas were rich in special types of earth and in minerals of various kinds.

When the usefulness of metal ores and the beauty of gem stones were discovered, mining became a primary source of wealth for enterprising individuals and for entire nations. Discoveries of rare crystals or of precious metals have, throughout history, stirred men's greed. Wars have been fought and untold numbers of people have died in struggles to control the earth's important mineral deposits. Others have worked tirelessly to make constructive use of nature's resources for the advancement of civilization. Mining through the ages has been a colorful, exciting, and often tragic drama.

COAL MINING

Locked in secret places below the surface of the earth, coal lay hidden for millions of years before men discovered its value as a fuel. Probably, much of the coal used today was formed between three hundred million and four hundred million years ago. The earth's first vegetation began to grow during the Carboniferous Age. In an atmosphere of poisonous gases, strange plant life thrived. Luxuriant ferns, thick mosses, and giant trees grew in the

steaming swamps, and dropped their leaves, leaving thick deposits of partially decomposed vegetable matter. As the earth's crust cooled and shifted through eons of unrecorded time, this mass became compressed under heavy coverings of silt and sand. Intense heat and pressure drove out oxygen from the layers of decomposed vegetation, leaving concentrations of carbon squeezed in the rock strata and in the seams and folds of the earth. In its early stages of formation, the soft carbon mass is called peat.

During millions of years following the Carboniferous Age, earthquakes and convulsions of the earth's outer layers tossed the coal deposits, twisted them, buried them deep in the earth, or sometimes left them close to the surface.

Ages passed and still the secret storehouses of power lay untapped. Coal was not mentioned in human documents until early Biblical times. There were some references to it in Greek writings approximately 300 B.C., but what little coal was brought out of the earth was used to burn in small braziers and stone fireplaces. The first real coal mining was done in England. There, some of the earliest, quarry-type mines were worked in the eighth and ninth centuries.

COAL MINING IN THE UNITED STATES

Although there is speculation that American Indians knew about coal before Europeans came to North America,

27

An underground coal cutter with a nine-foot blade of steel bites and chews into coal seams like a mechanical dinosaur.

At a loading point, this shuttle car dumps tons of coal into a mine car which will transport the load to the surface.

no positive evidence of this can be found. But as early as 1673, the French explorers, Marquette and Joliet, located deposits in what is now Illinois. However, wood was so abundant in early America that a need for coal, as fuel, was insufficient to encourage coal mining.

The first Colonial mine was established in 1750 near Richmond, Virginia, where Negro slaves were employed to dig bituminous coal. The harder anthracite was mined in Pennsylvania approximately 40 years later. As an industry, American coal mining really started during the Revolution, when fuel was needed for the iron foundries making munitions. Yet growth of the industry was retarded by a superstitious belief that fumes from burning coal caused epidemics of disease.

As the Industrial Revolution gathered momentum, a number of coal mining companies sprang up in the Appalachian regions, in Ohio and in Illinois. Although many of the early companies failed, by 1840 American mines had produced their first million tons of coal. The industry has been of primary importance ever since.

HOW COAL IS MINED

Coal mine productivity has greatly increased in recent years. This is due to improved machinery and coal preparation technology. There are two basic methods used: strip mining and subterranean or deep mining.

Strip mining is generally found where the coal lies close to the earth's surface. Immense power shovels are used to uncover the coal bed. Some of these machines can remove 3,500 tons of earth and rock per hour, carrying off the waste on 500-ft. booms and piling it away from the coal seams.

As soon as the coal is exposed it is loosened, usually with high explosives. (See *Power*)

Underground mining requires carefully engineered tunnels, the design of which depends on the location and depth of the coal to be mined. To reach coal beds far below the surface, shaft mines are dug and the coal is brought up on elevators. Ventilating shafts are usually required, as some mines are as deep as 2,000 feet. Modern shaft mines have forced-air ventilating systems as well as electric blowers to spray "rock dust" against the walls. This dust, a whitish limestone powder, keeps down coal dust to prevent accumulation of gases and subsequent explosions.

Where coal is found in steep hillsides, drift-mine entrances are bored close to the vein. The mine is then tunneled, more or less horizontally, along the course of the coal bed.

A slope mine, another type of underground mine, is dug to reach coal beds that are comparatively near the surface. In this case, tunnels, often extending for several miles, slope downward into the coal deposit.

Most American mines are dug on the room-and-pillar principle. The coal is excavated from a series of rooms whose ceilings are supported by pillars of coal. When a room is worked over, the miners move out of the area, remove the pillars and allow the roof to cave in. Longwall mines are dug along the mine face, with wooden beams or other artificial supports constructed in place of the natural coal pillars.

Breaking the coal has become increasingly mechanized in recent years. Replacing the honored but backbreaking pick and shovel are an assortment of fantastic machines that resemble mechanical dinosaurs. Undercutting machines with long, endless-chain cutters saw slots in coal seams to start the breaking process. More dangerous, but often used, is blasting. Special safe explosives, such as compressed air or liquid carbon dioxide, have replaced dynamite; thus eliminating the possibility of gas and coal dust fires.

Coming more and more into use are complete continuous-mining machines. These are monstrous power-driven dragons that bite into the mine face, chew up seven or eight tons of coal a minute, and load the broken chunks onto conveyor belts or waiting cars. Many types of automatic loaders, cutters, and drillers are made for the various operations.

Above ground, the coal chunks are sorted for size in a large structure known as a breaker in anthracite mining, or a tipple in bituminous operations. As the coal is drawn out of the mine on conveyors, it is dumped onto sizing screens which act as sieves to sort various grades, such as pea coal, nut coal, and stove coal. The graded coal is also washed with water during the sorting process, while finer sizes are produced by a crushing apparatus.

LOCATION OF COAL DEPOSITS

The largest U. S. coal deposits are in West Virginia, which produces over one hundred forty million tons a year; in Pennsylvania with an annual production of one hundred ten million tons; in Kentucky, seventy-one million tons; in Illinois, forty-seven million tons; in Ohio, thirty-six million tons; in Virginia, twenty-seven million tons. Other impor-

Power, Primary Metals) These two industries are increasing their use of coal at a steady rate. They consumed half of U.S. tonnage in 1959. By 1975, electric power requirements, which took one hundred sixty-five million tons of coal in 1959, are expected to be four hundred million tons per year. The use of steel is expected to jump from ninety million tons to one hundred twenty-five million tons in the same period.

Industry uses coal as a fuel for a great variety of manufacturing processes. For example, a ton of coal must be burned for every ton and one-half of paper produced. (See *Paper*) To make 15 lb. of aluminum requires 100 lb. of coal; 300 lb. of cement requires 100 lb. of coal.

Filled with coal, a hopper car leaves a preparation plant and will join a train for transport to consumers. The modern preparation plant breaks up, washes, and sorts coal chunks into various grades, such as pea coal, nut coal, and stove coal. Finer sizes are produced by a crushing apparatus.

tant coal mining states are Indiana, Alabama, Tennessee, and Utah.

Though Britain has always been one of the world's leading coal producing nations, American mines produce four times as much coal per worker as those in Great Britain. This is due partly to the high degree of mechanization in U.S. mines, and partly to the fact that most North American coal beds are close to the surface.

USES OF COAL

Despite the fact that railroads have virtually eliminated coal-fired steam locomotives, and that fewer homes are heated by coal each year, the market for coal is still very large. Electric power companies and the steel industry both consume gigantic quantities of the black fuel. (See

Even with the enormous consumption, reserves of bituminous coal have been estimated to be sufficient for centuries at the present rate of depletion. The future of anthracite is less optimistic. Experts believe that the highest grades of Pennsylvania anthracite may not last beyond the turn of the next century.

The most interesting uses of coal, and probably the ones with the most promising future, are its by-products. Many unlikely articles are made from coal and coal tar derivatives: perfumes, dyes, fertilizers, fingernail polish, mothballs, medicines, soaps and detergents, explosives, piano keys, crush-proof fabrics, phonograph records, paints and varnish. These are only a few of the products which use chemicals derived from coal.

Several processes are employed to obtain coal by-

Rockdust, or finely powdered limestone, is blown with terrific pressure on the main haulageway in a modern coal mine as a major precaution against the spread of a coal dust explosion.

products and chemicals. Through carbonization, coke is made. This consists of baking coal in a sealed, airtight oven, which converts about two-thirds of the charge into coke, and the remainder into tar and gas. Coke is an important industrial fuel, particularly in the production of iron and steel. Hydrogenation is the process used in the production of various hydrocarbon gases, such as ethane, butane, and propane. When the coal is subjected to heat and pressure and treated with oil and hydrogen, a resulting liquid product is the source of miraculous chemicals. These include aniline for dyes, benzene, phenol, and naphthalene —basic ingredients for paints, plastics, perfumes, and other useful items.

Another process called the Fischer-Tropsch process, or gas synthesis, extracts chemicals from coal by oxidation. When pulverized coal is subjected to oxygen and steam, it turns to gas. This gas, in turn, is converted into other valuable forms as it passes over certain catalysts, such as cobalt or iron. Diesel fuel and gasoline can be produced in this manner.

Although coal mining is still a hazardous occupation, beset with the dangers of cave-ins, explosions, mine flooding, poisonous fumes, and occupational diseases, great strides have been made in the development of safety measures. Major mine tragedies, which were frequently in the news only a few years ago, are becoming rare. Not only have technological advances improved mine safety, but the miners themselves are thoroughly trained in safety measures. The United States Bureau of Mines, unions, and the mine owners cooperate in studying hazards and in giving miners adequate safety instruction.

MINING ORES AND OTHER MINERALS

On a spur of the Rocky Mountains and at the headwaters of the Columbia River, rises the "richest hill on earth." This bleak elevation in an almost barren Montana plain held its secret treasure while the westward settlement of America moved past it on the way to California. Prospectors rushed in search of California gold. But some stragglers drifted back to the Idaho country and into what is now Montana. Placer mining, consisting of washing sands and gravel in stream beds in search of gold or silver particles, uncovered some silver ore in the Butte district. About 1850, miners and prospectors endured every imaginable hardship including the danger of Indian attacks in order to reach this remote district. Several important gold strikes were soon made and Montana became the center of a new gold rush.

In 1864, William Allison and G. O. Humphreys, searching for gold and silver in the Butte region, sank a mine shaft and thus opened up what was to become known as the Original Lode. By 1865, Butte was a roaring mining camp of lawless men who labored, fought, and killed one another in their quest for gold. The gold, recovered by placers, was soon worked out. But Humphreys and Allison continued to extend their mine shaft into the Original Lode and had reached a depth of 80 ft. by the end of the first year. Though they uncovered some copper, they paid little attention to it. Their quest was primarily for gold. Another miner, Joseph Ramsdell, made a copper strike in Butte, and his Parrot No. 2 mine began taking out copper ore in 1866. Soon veins of silver, manganese, and copper were being worked in nearby claims. For a time, the copper ore was shipped all the way to Swansea in Wales where the world's leading copper smelting and refining plants were located; however, by 1867 and '68 smelting operations were set up around Butte.

Prospecting for ores fills the annals of American history with many colorful stories, and the names of some of the early Butte mines are curious. Two men who had sunk a shaft were working in shifts. One slept while the other dug. Finally, the man on the day shift blasted open a silver vein. He rushed to the cabin, shouting, "Wake up, Jim. We struck it!" Their find was registered as the Wake Up Jim claim. In 1875, Michael Hickey staked out a claim on a large outcropping of rock on Butte hill. A Civil War veteran, Hickey, remembered reading an editorial by Horace Greeley in the *New York Tribune,* which stated, "Grant will encircle Lee's forces and crush them like a giant anaconda." Hickey named his Butte claim, Anaconda. The name has made mining and metal history. This was the beginning of the great Anaconda Company, the world's largest nonferrous mining and metal fabricating corporation.

Fabulous fortunes have been made by miners and mining interests. Homestake, greatest of all gold mines, was located in South Dakota in 1876. William Randolph Hearst obtained a 30-day option on the property for $70,000. Since that time, the mine has produced one hundred sixty million dollars' worth of gold and is still producing.

Similar stories can be told about gold and silver strikes in many parts of the West. Yet the long-range production of Butte hill dwarfs any single mining operation in the country. Since 1880, fifteen billion pounds of copper, four and one-half billion pounds of zinc, three and one-half billion pounds of manganese and seven hundred eighty-four million pounds of lead have come out of this one small patch of earth. In addition, this region has produced over six million ounces of silver and two and one-half million ounces of gold.

GOLD MINING

Prospecting and mining for gold in the United States and in Alaska have given men the drama and excitement of the wildest fiction. Actually, as an organized American industry, it has been of comparatively slight importance. U.S. gold production has been far below that of the Union of South Africa, Russia, or Canada.

Gold is generally found in rock formations or in the sand deposits of streams. The latter, known as placers, may be surface deposits or buried deep in the earth as remnants of streams that flowed in ancient times. The simplest type of placer mining is panning, which consists of washing the sand and silt and allowing heavy gold nuggets to sink to the bottom of a pan. This favorite method of our Western prospectors was practiced in Egypt 4,000 years before Christ. Panning on a larger scale is accomplished by the construction of sluices, through which the gravel is carried by a rush of water. Walls of the sluices have ridges holding mercury, to which grains of gold will adhere.

Where gold is found in rock deposits, the ore is pulverized in a stamping mill. Water carries the powdered ore over mercury-coated copper plates, and a gold amalgam forms on the plates. Another gold extraction method is the cyanide process. Crushed gold ore is placed in a solution of sodium cyanide. The gold combines with the cyanide to form sodium gold cyanide, and the gold is then precipitated by aluminum or zinc shavings. Final refining by the electrolytic process is necessary before gold may be cast into bars of pure bullion.

URANIUM MINING

For 150 years after the discovery of uranium in 1789, virtually no practical or commercial use was found for it. Scientists studied it, measured its atomic weight, and found it to be radioactive. The process of darkening photographic film by exposure to the radiation of uranium salts was discovered in 1896. Excited chemists took a new look at this element.

Uranium oxide in glass produces pastel colors from light shades of yellow to green. Some uranium has been used in tool-steel alloys. But it was not until 1939 that fission of an uranium isotope, U-235, was accomplished; this led to controlled chain reaction, and subsequently to the atomic bomb.

Suddenly, uranium production became a vitally important industry. Although in the mining of pitchblende at Great Bear Lake, Canada, large amounts of uranium ore had been uncovered, it had been discarded for years as a useless by-product of radium. Only one grain of radium could be extracted for every one-half ton of uranium concentrates, yet the mining had continued on a small scale. In 1943, U.S. demand for uranium ore made Great Bear Lake one of the most valuable mines in the world.

Uranium is found in four chief types of deposits. The best are veins of pitchblende or uranite. These are found presently in Great Bear Lake, Czechoslovakia, and France. Conglomerates, containing thorium and other minerals with uranium ore, are found in Canada, Madagascar, Africa, and, possibly, the U.S.S.R. A third type may be recovered from sedimentary rocks and sandstones, most of which are mined in the Western states of Arizona, Colorado, Utah, Wyoming, New Mexico, Washington, Oregon, Texas, and South Dakota. Finally, there are uraniferous shales and phosphate rocks which contain as little as one-fifth pound of uranium per ton of ore. Fortunately, enough phosphate is mined in the United States to make the extraction of uranium a practicable by-product operation.

Prospecting for uranium is not as simple as the old-time panning of Gold Rush days. Modern scientific instruments are required, such as portable geiger counters and small ultraviolet lights to reveal fluorescence in radioactive ores. By means of highly sensitive scintillation counters, prospecting for uranium may be done from automobiles or airplanes.

Recent estimates indicate that there may be twenty-five

This ultramodern coal preparation plant of the Old Ben Coal Corporation near Sesser, Illinois handles 50,000 tons of coal daily. Coal enters the five-story tipple from the mine hoist at the right and is crushed, screened, washed, dry-cleaned, blended, and finally loaded into rail cars for shipment.

million tons of uranium ore scattered over various parts of the world. Of this, probably only two million tons are readily available. Major known reserves include four hundred thousand tons in Canada, four hundred thousand in South Africa, two hundred twenty thousand in the United States, and one hundred thousand in France. Russia's deposits are not known.

The mining and processing of uranium is one of the newest, most intriguing, and potentially important of mineral industries. An idea of its significance may be gained from the fact that the energy released from the fission of one pound of uranium equals the energy output of 1,650 tons of coal. (See *Power*) The long-range future of power industries may well be tied to the future of this rare, but potent, element.

IRON MINING

More than three-quarters of the iron ore used by the steel industry in the United States comes from the Lake Superior region. In the Mesabi Range of Minnesota is located the world's largest open-pit iron mine, the Hull-Rust-Mahoning mine. It is nearly four miles long, a mile in width and 450 ft. deep.

Iron sediments, deposited at the bottom of an ancient sea more than a billion years ago, were accumulated in layers hundreds of feet thick; then, massive shifts of the earth's crust heaved up the iron-bearing masses, and formed mountains containing iron deposits. Sometimes, great cracks or fissures allowed water to carry off soluble matter, and caused a chemical change which produced iron oxides, the richest of iron ores.

America's high-grade ores are expected to last only another 50 or 60 years. Two World Wars seriously depleted some of the best reserves. However, the search for new deposits and better methods of extracting iron from inferior ores is meeting with considerable success. In addition to the Lake Superior iron region, Alabama, New Jersey, New York, Pennsylvania, California, Wyoming, Virginia, and Texas have some iron deposits.

Most of the ore mined in the great Mesabi Range is transported to iron foundries in ships which ply the Great Lakes during all, except the coldest, winter months. Huge ore barges, each capable of transporting over 11,000 tons, are loaded at special docks where ore is stored in bins.

FOREIGN INTERESTS

American metal industries and mining interests have necessarily explored outside sources of important minerals and ores. The largest known reserves of copper ore are in the Republic of Chile, where the Anaconda Company has built huge mining and smelting operations. Field geologists, employed by large American companies, are constantly engaged in a worldwide hunt for new ore and mineral deposits. Important iron mines have been developed in Venezuela by the U. S. Steel Corporation and the Bethlehem Steel Corporation. Surface rock and earth formations furnish clues to the geological detectives who track down possible mine sites. After a geological survey is made, indicating that ore or mineral veins can be tapped, drill teams move in and take out test cores which show the rock formations at various levels below the surface. When a core reveals a valuable mineral deposit, a new mine is opened up.

OTHER IMPORTANT MINERALS

Although metals such as iron, aluminum, and copper involve major mining operations, many people do not realize that the mining of nonmetallic minerals constitutes an even greater portion of the mining industry. Compared with some 70 known metals, there are approximately a thousand nonmetallic minerals. Among them are such useful substances as gypsum, asbestos, mica, talc, borax, sulphur, graphite, diatomaceous earth, feldspar, asphalt, diamonds, and the familiar condiment, salt. (See *Sugar, Salt*) All of these mineral substances are mined in large quantities.

Gypsum is a crystalline rock composed of sulphur and calcium. Large gypsum quarries are found in the southwestern part of the United States. The U. S. Gypsum Company lists over 750 industrial uses of this mineral. One of the best known of the gypsum products is a powdered variety known as plaster of Paris. Building plasters are also made from gypsum. Between five and six million tons of gypsum are mined in the United States every year.

Asbestos is a silicate rock composed of fibers which can be separated and woven into ropes and various types of fabrics. It is fire and heat resistant and is used in the making of insulations, roof shingles, fireproof clothing, and many other fireproof items. (See *Fabrics and Textiles*)

In the electrical industry, a huge quantity of mica is used for making magneto condensers. Highly resistant to electric current, mica is an excellent insulating material for wires used in heating units. The wires of electric toasters, for example, are generally wound over sheets of mica.

Thousands of tons of borax are mined annually from deposits in California. This familiar mineral is important in manufacturing soap, glue, and glass, and for putting high glaze on paper.

One of the most beautiful of commercial minerals, bright yellow sulphur, is in abundant supply. There are vast deposits in Texas and Louisiana. Sulphur mining is carried out by an unusual process. A number of concentric pipes are sunk into the ground until they penetrate the sulphur deposit. When superheated steam is forced into the outer rim, the sulphur melts. Air pressure then forces this frothy yellow mass of molten sulphur to the surface through the center pipe. The largest use of sulphur is in the production of sulphuric acid, an essential chemical in a host of manufacturing processes.

Mining industries remain one of the basic activities of mankind. By extracting the many elements which make up the earth's crust, we have learned to transform the wealth stored by nature into thousands of useful products. Research in geological, chemical and mining engineering abounds with unlimited future opportunities. As known mineral deposits are exhausted, new ones must be found. Meanwhile, the laboratories must explore more efficient ways of using the natural treasures available to us.

In the early days of the petroleum industry, wooden barrels were the only means of transporting oil. Here a wood-burning locomotive hauls three cars loaded with barrels from a Pennsylvania oil field. Today diesel-powered locomotives pull long trains of steel tank cars at high speed.

5 Petroleum

Nature has stored up solar energy in the earth in many forms. Probably the most versatile of the earth's treasures is the "liquid sunshine" which we call petroleum. Gasoline and other liquid fuels derived from petroleum are the most practical means of producing power for transportation. Because it flows through pipes, is easily stored and transported, and has a high degree of energy-producing efficiency (25% greater than coal), oil in various forms is being used more and more to power our railroads. It is, as of now, the only fuel that can be used for airplanes. It is the energy source for automobiles, trucks, buses, and ships, and is the fuel which drives millions of machines in factories, mills, and on farms. But petroleum's use, as a fuel, is only the beginning of its fabulous service to mankind.

HOW THE INDUSTRY BEGAN

Although the raw material was being formed by nature four hundred forty million years ago, and though the newest of petroleum deposits are at least ten million years old, the industry itself has just completed its first 100 years. Why did men fail for so long to realize what treasure lay under their feet? They knew that oil was there, but until fairly recently, they did not fully understand or appreciate the properties of crude oil.

Just how oil was formed still remains something of a mystery. We know that petroleum is found only where there are marine deposits, and that it is the result of decayed marine and plant life. But the chemical synthesis, the actual transformation from living matter to underground masses of oil and its pockets of natural gas, is something over which scientists are still puzzling. Some bacterial and chemical action, combined with changes in the earth's crust over millions of years, have created these miraculous storehouses of energy, and to this our modern civilization is eternally indebted.

Man's ingenuity and the enterprise of American oil men also had something to do with petroleum's contribution to better living.

In the ancient world, people dug pits to collect oil seepage. From this slow accumulation they were able to obtain some lamp oil and to make pitch for calking wooden ships. Nebuchadnezzar actually paved roads with a sort of asphalt made from petroleum. Early Egyptians, the Chinese, and the American Indians learned the soothing quality of oil on burns and wounds.

In American Colonial times, George Washington acquired a tract of land in western Pennsylvania because he had found "a bituminous spring of so inflammable a nature as to burn freely as spirits, and nearly as difficult to extinguish."

Throughout the first half of the nineteenth century, tallow candles and whale oil lamps furnished illumination: then in the 1850's some lamp oil was made from petroleum. A few adventurous businessmen set up small refineries to distill rock oil which they collected laboriously from seepages.

Meanwhile, most people looked upon oil only as a nuisance, an unwanted substance which occasionally spoiled water and brine wells in certain areas. Nobody thought of drilling wells in order to obtain this obnoxious, oily fluid until George H. Bissell, a New York lawyer, became intrigued by the possibilities of the kerosene business. After some investigation, he purchased a tract of land on Oil Creek near Titusville, Pa. He helped to organize the Pennsylvania Rock Oil Company, later changed to the Seneca Oil Company, which drilled the first oil well.

The man put in charge of this momentous operation was 40-year-old Edwin L. Drake, an unemployed railroad conductor. He erected a wooden tower, containing a pulley arrangement to raise and lower drills, and a steam-driven walking beam to pound the drill into the ground. Local residents dubbed his preparations "Drake's Folly."

Drake's greatest problem was to overcome cave-ins. His solution was a major contribution to the new industry. He lined the well with sections of pipe. As the drill sank deeper, the pipe liner was driven farther into the ground. This idea of lining oil wells with casing is still practiced today.

After two months of drilling, in August 1859, Drake's Folly struck oil. He had sunk his well to a depth of 69½ ft. With oil selling for $20 per barrel, the production of 15 to 20 barrels a day stirred up as much excitement as a gold mine might have done. Overnight an industry was born, as the news spread to all parts of the world. Oil was found in Ohio, Oklahoma, California, and Texas. At first, eager well diggers would drill to a depth of 70 ft., simply because that was the depth of Drake's well; then, if no oil was struck, they would abandon the effort and move to another locality.

While all this was happening and while a boom town was springing up at Titusville, a young man named John Rockefeller traveled the rutted, muddy roads to western Pennsylvania to visit the six-month-old oil field. He saw the horse-drawn wagons, loaded with barrels of crude oil, rolling eastward; saw the noisy saloons and rough gangs of workmen; watched the steam dinkeys working the derricks and the drills. Rockefeller made an important decision. Since drilling for oil was risky, the way to make a fortune was to set up a refinery. Let others gamble in the wild search for oil. His advice to the produce firm, where he worked, was to wait for the oil supply to be assured; then find capital to build a refinery.

In 1862, Rockefeller formed a company for refining oil and producing kerosene and axle grease, two items desperately needed by the Union armies. The firm prospered. He bought out his partner, and through a policy of eliminating waste and setting up high standards, he built the greatest oil company and one of the greatest of all U. S. corporations, The Standard Oil Company.

During this time, the demand for oil was increasing. While American oil was being exported all over the world, American engineers were hired by European firms to search for oil and to drill wells. Most of the world's great oil fields, including those in the Middle East abandoned by other drill teams as worthless areas, have been found by Americans. American oil experts hacked their way through Bolivian jungles where U. S. oil firms spent millions of dollars before oil was found. They did much the same thing in Venezuela and in the East Indies.

PERPETUAL SEARCH

The hunt for oil still goes on, but today, petroleum geologists work with scientific instruments, using knowledge gained over many years. They study aerial photographs, rock formations, and soil. Fossils and shells furnish important clues. Using gravity meters, magnetometers, and seismographs, they determine whether or not the chances are good for an area to have oil deposits. Even so, many wells are drilled without success. Only one well out of nine produces oil, and the average drilling costs from two hundred thousand to one million dollars.

Taken near Titusville, Pa., in 1861, this photo shows Edwin L. Drake, in top hat and frock coat. It was Drake who conceived the idea of drilling for oil. The world's first commercial oil well is seen in the background.

HOW WELLS ARE DRILLED

When, after studying all scientific data, drillers decide to "spud in," as they call opening up a well, a derrick is built at the selected site. Usually this is a steel-frame tower, nearly 200 ft. tall. The two principal methods used to sink wells are known as cable tool drilling and rotary drilling. By the cable tool method a heavy drill, suspended by a cable, is raised and dropped repeatedly into the hole, driving the well deeper with each drop. Most wells today are opened by rotary drills which bore into the earth as a power drill bores holes in wood. Drilling bits are steel rollers with large teeth which chew into earth and hard rock. Considerable skill is required to keep the bore straight as the hole is deepened. A lubricating substance known as drilling mud, composed of clay, water, and certain chemicals, is forced down into the drill shaft to keep the bit cool, to lubricate the drill, and to hold back gas or oil which might cause a blowout. It also flushes out the loose earth and rock as the bit advances.

(Left) A drill bit is guided into the hole by a driller in Southern Louisiana. Thousands of feet down, the drill may find oil. (Right) The unique riggings of pipes and valves at the mouth of an oil well are what petroleum industry men call "Christmas trees."

The hole is lined with strings of steel pipe as the well is extended downward. This is the casing which Drake had found necessary to prevent cave-ins. Cores, or cylindrical samples of the earth and rock at various levels, are cut with a specially designed bit. The cores are sent to laboratories for study. When certain types of rock are encountered, experts know there is no advantage in drilling further. The drill team may as well "pack its suitcases" and go home. For this reason the telltale rock is known to oil men as "suitcase rock."

Because underground oil reservoirs are usually subjected to great pressure, the oil tends to gush to the surface when tapped. This is what causes gushers. But contrary to popular notions, gushers occur rarely, and care is taken to avoid them. As soon as the drill bites into the rock, it is withdrawn. Drilling mud holds back the oil's natural flow. Tubing is now lowered into the hole, and at the upper end of the tube, an instrument known as a "Christmas tree" is attached. This tree has a number of valves which can control pressures and allow the oil to flow into storage tanks.

As technology has improved drilling methods, oil wells have been dug considerably deeper than Edwin Drake's 69-ft. strike. Wells, two to three miles deep, are common today. Modern techniques enable the maximum amount of oil to be obtained from deposits with much less waste than occurred in the early days of the industry. Efficiency has increased to the point where 80% of the oil in a field may be brought out, compared with only 25% some years ago. Some abandoned areas are now being re-tapped. This is called secondary recovery, and it involves injecting water or natural gas into the oil sand to force it to the surface.

Although oil is being consumed at an alarming rate, the petroleum industry's program of exploration for new reserves has actually increased the amount of proved reserves in the United States. In 1920, known reserves were approximately seven billion barrels. Since then some forty-two billion barrels have been brought out of U.S. wells, yet proved reserves are now at least four times as great as they were in 1920.

REFINING

Oil refineries are intricate mazes of tanks, cylinders, pipes, and weird, towering structures. Their operations change crude oil into many valuable petroleum products.

Petroleum, made up of hydrogen and carbon molecules, may be broken up and reconstituted to form a variety of hydrocarbons. Crude oils vary; some are thick and dark; others are clear and light; still others are green, yellow, brown, or black. Many processing steps are required to extract such products as gas, gasoline, asphalt, lubricating oils, kerosene, and so forth.

Fractionating towers, many stories high, receive crude oil which has been heated in a brick furnace to 800° F. As the heated crude oil leaves pipe coils inside the furnace, it vaporizes inside the base of the fractionating tower. This vapor rises through a series of perforated trays. At each stage, the vapor cools, gradually condensing certain fractions, which are then drawn off as liquids through connecting pipes. At the first, lowest tray, the heaviest fractions are collected. This would be a heavy fuel oil or asphalt. Higher up, lubricating oil is formed; then heating oil, kerosene, gasoline, and, finally, the gasoline vapors which become gas. As each fraction is drawn off, it goes to other equipment for further refining.

Most crude oil yields only 20% of its volume in gasoline. This would be insufficient to supply our needs in this automotive age. A process known as cracking is used to increase the percentage of gasoline production. Latest methods employ gigantic fluid catalytic cracking units, consisting of huge metal drums and towers. Oil vapor is introduced into the unit and comes in contact with a clay-like catalyst which has a chemical effect on the vaporized oil. Though from outside nothing appears to be happening inside the cracking unit, oil vapor and the powdery catalyst are rushing through miles of pipes and tanks. Gradually, the catalyst gathers carbon from the oil. The ultimate

At a modern oil refinery, catalytic-cracking units like these change crude oil into many valuable products. Chemical action results in producing more than double the amount of gasoline achieved by ordinary refining.

chemical action has the effect of breaking up large molecules into smaller ones, and from a given quantity of crude oil, more than double the amount of gasoline is produced than could be achieved by ordinary refining.

Other oil refining processes are employed to rearrange the atomic structure of petroleum. One of the most recent is called reforming. This is a catalytic process for the production of high-octane gasoline. Polymerization causes small molecules to link up and form larger ones. Alkylation joins different types of molecules, while isomerization rearranges the atoms within a molecule to create a new product. For each process, complicated refinery equipment is constructed, and various mechanisms are required to refine different types of crude oils.

PETROLEUM PRODUCTS AND BY-PRODUCTS

Chemistry has unlocked more than 2,000 useful products from crude oil's molecular storehouse, and scientists estimate that half a million materials could be derived from this amazing Pandora's box. To accomplish such miracles as synthetic rubber, synthetic fabrics, fertilizers, insect sprays, antiseptics, adhesives, and plastics, some 42,000 U.S. oil companies spend over three hundred fifty million dollars a year on research. The huge chemical industry is, likewise, exploring new uses of petroleum. (See *Chemicals*) Petrochemicals are developed in multimillion dollar pilot plants after laboratory studies have been completed.

Some of the more familiar petroleum products are paraffin wax, detergents, vaseline, cosmolene, lubricating oils, fuels, and gasolines. Also, from petrochemicals come such products as alcohols; solvents; Buna-S, synthetic rubber (made from a petrochemical called butadiene); Buna-N, a rubber material which is not damaged by oils and acids; and Butyl which is used for tire inner tubes, and which holds air about 10 times as effectively as natural rubber. Various fibers come from petrochemicals, among them are nylon and dacron. (See *Rubber, Plastics*)

The future of petroleum chemistry is impossible to envision, for its possibilities appear to be endless. A day may come when people will be appalled to think of burning such a miraculous substance for fuel. Even petroleum-derived fuels, themselves, will probably undergo radical changes as scientists working in the oil company research laboratories discover new and better ways to extract energy from oil.

Meanwhile, the petroleum industry continues to do business at an astonishing rate. U.S. oil consumption was more than a billion barrels in 1938, rose to one and one-half billion in 1941 and hit a wartime peak of nearly two billion barrels in 1945. Yet by the 1950's, consumption was still rising. In 1953, it was nearly three billion barrels, and the increase has continued, year after year. Today, America is using nearly ten million barrels a day as engine and motor fuel alone. To satisfy this enormous appetite for oil and natural gas, the great oil companies are drilling in the seas, in the deserts, and in the jungles.

Here, as in the chemical industry, there is an ever growing need for men and women of science and technology. Geologists are needed to find new oil reserves; chemists to develop new petrochemicals and to find new uses for known by-products; engineers to build the refineries needed to keep pace with chemical research, and to construct pipe lines for the transportation of crude oil from distant oil fields to the industrial plants.

The petroleum industry is a huge complex of many different types of companies, each requiring a great variety of human talents. Some companies specialize in drilling for oil; others sell or transport oil products; still others make petrochemicals or specialize in fuels. There are many small companies as well as the familiar giants. But Standard of New Jersey is without question one of the world's greatest corporations. With over three hundred thousand shareholders and some one hundred sixty thousand employees, it supplies approximately 20% of the petroleum used in the world, outside of Russia. Its affiliated companies are spread throughout the United States, Canada, Latin America, Europe, North Africa, the Middle East, and the Far East.

Linked as it is with the chemical industry, the petroleum industry offers unlimited opportunities to imaginative people, for much of the world of tomorrow will be created in its plants and laboratories.

(Left) Scientists plan to explore whether the Van de Graaff "atom smasher" holds one of the keys to the future of the oil industry. The instrument is being used for many petroleum research projects. **(Center)** Once almost forbidden to man, Louisiana's bayou country is now the scene of oil well drilling projects. **(Right)** Offshore drilling is the new frontier being explored to meet the increasing demand for oil.

6 Rubber

This Koylon foam rubber mattress of United States Rubber Company is made in one complete unit and each one is cured in an individual mold. The full-size mattress is shown being removed from the mold.

An inventive genius working under free enterprise is not always crowned with financial success. A free individual, in a competitive system, must accept the risk of failure along with the hope of great personal reward. Unfortunately, it cannot be said that the man who made the modern rubber industry possible was another of America's self-made industrial magnates. Charles Goodyear's lifetime efforts to demonstrate the value of rubber ended in failure and debt. Yet billions of dollars have been earned and all the world has enjoyed untold benefits because of Goodyear's discoveries.

HOW IT BEGAN

The earliest known use of rubber was purely for fun and recreation. Unlike so many of our vital raw materials, rubber was little used for practical purposes until comparatively recent times. In ancient Egypt, as we know from early picture writing, crude rubber balls were made for playing games. How long ago the South and the Central American Indians played games with rubber balls is not known, but Christopher Columbus reported watching such games. He related that the balls were made of a milky liquid drawn from trees. Later Spanish conquistadors learned that the Indians called the material *caoutchouc*. Some of the Spaniards experimented with latex waterproofing of clothing, but they soon found that the rubber melted in the hot tropical sun. Absorbed in their quest for gold, the Spanish and the Portuguese explorers paid little attention to the curious, elastic material.

More than two centuries later, in 1770, an English scientist, Dr. Joseph Priestly, found that the Indian *caoutchouc* would erase pencil marks when it was rubbed over them. He named it rubber. Some further experiments in making boots and shoes out of rubber failed because the substance

softened in hot weather, became brittle and hard in winter. In 1823, a Scotsman named Macintosh succeeded in waterproofing cloth with rubber, and to this day the English raincoat is known as a macintosh. Still, the elasticity and lasting quality of rubber left much to be desired.

The perplexing problem was solved by Charles Goodyear in 1839, after several years of discouragement and frustration. He had gone into business for himself, making rubberized mailbags for the Government. But as in all similar efforts, the project failed because of the rubber's instability under various weather conditions. Virtually penniless, Goodyear continued his experiments at a relative's home in Woburn, Mass. At some point, probably by accident, he discovered that the mixture of sulphur and raw rubber became tough and elastic when it was spilled on a

A workman places a green tire into a Bag-O-Matic machine. At the left is a cured tire. As molds close, steam inflates a bag at the bottom of the green tire. This forces the tire into the proper shape.

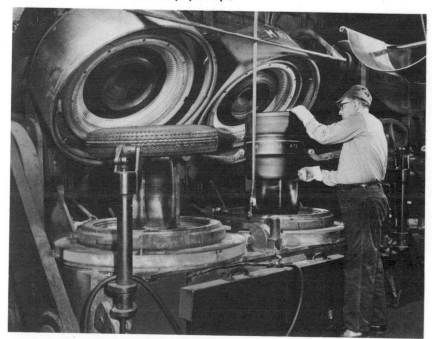

Charles Goodyear, discoverer of rubber vulcanization in 1839, never found enough of a market for his product to establish a prosperous business.

The *Hevea* or Para rubber tree whose useful life is from 25 to 30 years requires about five to nine years to mature. When it is tapped by making slantwise cuts in the outer bark, the milky latex trickles into a spout and thence into a cup. After workers collect the full cups, the latex is placed in large, open tanks where it coagulates. It is formed into sheets, rolled to squeeze out excess water, or smoke dried and pressed into bales.

American rubber companies own plantations in many tropical areas. The Goodyear Tire and Rubber Company, named for the inventor of vulcanization, has plantations in Sumatra, Costa Rica, the Philippines, Brazil and Guatemala. One of Firestone's major enterprises has been the development of rubber plantations in the African republic of Liberia. This industry has become one of the mainstays of Liberia's economy. The American company has furnished huge funds for schools, hospitals, and medical research, and has contributed greatly to the economic stability of the country.

Today, most natural rubber comes from carefully tended plantations rather than from the wild jungle trees. Cultivation and care have increased both the volume and the quality of latex produced by rubber trees.

Rubber comes to the United States as a concentrated liquid latex, as smoked sheets, or as "pale crepe." Liquid latex is concentrated by a process of creaming or by the centrifugal method. Creaming is accomplished by the addition of certain chemicals which cause rubber curds to rise to the surface of the latex mass as cream rises to the top of a milk bottle. The centrifugal method whirls the latex in a machine which performs in the manner of a cream separator. The machine drains off water while separating the concentrated latex.

To prepare raw rubber sheets for shipment, they are hung on large racks and subjected to smoke at high temperatures. This smoking process protects the rubber against mildew and decay.

hot stove. Further, when the charred bits of rubber were left outdoors overnight in extreme cold, they still remained firm, yet flexible. Goodyear worked out additional refinements of his new process, which he called "vulcanization" after Vulcan, the god of fire.

Goodyear knew he had made an important discovery, although he never succeeded in finding enough of a market for rubber to develop a prosperous business. At his death in 1860, he was two hundred thousand dollars in debt.

SOURCE OF LATEX

Hevea Brasiliensis, the rubber tree, grew originally in Central America and in the steaming Brazilian jungles. In 1876, Sir Henry Hickham took thousands of seeds of the Amazonian trees to England. After seedlings had been started in greenhouses, some young plants were shipped to Ceylon and Malaya and replanted. The present rubber plantations in those countries, as well as later plantings in Sumatra, Java, and Borneo, grew from that original crop.

PROCESSING RAW RUBBER

Rubber is no longer a uniform material which is easily identified. In the world of chemicals, rubber has become the raw material for hundreds of formulations. Some 1,300 chemicals are used for a variety of products. These basic compounds are concocted and blended to even substances in huge milling machines called Banbury mixers, which

(Left) Each day, tappers of rubber trees make fresh cuts from which latex will flow. (Right) A native worker from The Goodyear Tire and Rubber Company's Costa Rica plantation brings new latex to a collection station where it will be converted into commercial rubber.

(Left) Workmen weigh out rubber and other materials before putting them on a conveyor that will carry them to a banbury mixer. (Right) Butadiene, one of the principal materials of synthetic rubber, is manufactured by applying a dehydrogenation process to butane gas at this Firestone petrochemical plant in Orange, Texas.

may be three stories high. The various mixtures are shaped or molded; they are then "baked" or "cured" in the vulcanizer. This final process strengthens the rubber and enables it to retain a permanent shape.

SYNTHETIC RUBBER

As far back as 1860, an Englishman by the name of Greville Williams discovered that a spongy, rubberlike substance could be produced from isoprene which had been distilled from natural rubber. A few years later Sir William Tilden made isoprene from turpentine. Serious efforts to produce synthetic rubber on a large scale were not made until the 1940's, however, when major rubber supplies to the Western world were cut off by Japanese occupation of Far Eastern plantation areas. The U.S. rubber industry, in cooperation with the Government, rapidly developed a number of synthetic rubber factories. The advance of technology in this field has been so swift that, by 1959, 65% of all the American rubber produced was synthetic.

Today's synthetic rubbers are generally tougher than natural rubber, though somewhat less resilient. Chief ingredients are styrene and butadiene, both by-products of petroleum. (See *Petroleum*) To these chemicals, others are added to produce a variety of rubbers which are designed for special purposes. The chemicals are mixed in a reactor under pressure and instrument-controlled temperature until they form a liquid latex. Unused butadiene is removed in a "flash tank" by evaporation. Excess styrene is eliminated by steam distillation in a "stripping column." This is a high, multi-chambered tank containing a series of perforated metal plates, through which the latex is allowed to drip. Meanwhile, steam is forced up through the base of the tank, causing unwanted styrene to vaporize.

Now, the latex enters a tank containing brine and acid. The effect of this solution is to coagulate the latex. Pellets of rubber, called "crumb" are formed, and the water drains off through rotating filters. The crumb is washed, dried, and then pressed into blocks or bales.

Synthetic rubbers are called "polymers," since the process is one of co-polymerization, by which hydrogen and carbon molecules are reformed in a pattern closely resembling that of natural rubber molecules. There are a number of important rubber polymers, each having unique qualities for special purposes. Butyl is used, mostly, for tire inner tubes because of its superior ability to hold air; Buna-N serves as a base for many plastics, since it is resistant to oils and solvents; Neoprene is oil-resistant, waterproof, and fireproof. Those synthetics which stretch well and can be vulcanized like the natural product are known as "elastomers." Among the more recent synthetic products are urethane and Natsyn. Urethane, an amazing material which can be as soft as cotton or as hard as ivory, is made through the reaction of a chemical called isocyanate with a synthetic resin. Natsyn, a Goodyear product made from isoprene, has virtually the same molecular structure as tree rubber. Developed in 1955, Natsyn has been used to make airplane tires which can endure landings at speeds of 250 miles per hour. A highly elastic, heat-resistant synthetic is the new polybutadiene, one of several polyisoprene rubbers.

The speed of synthetic rubber production is one of its great advantages. Whereas natural rubber requires an average of six years from planting of seedlings to the first tapping of latex; modern polymerization plants can produce large quantities of synthetic rubber in a matter of hours.

TIRE MANUFACTURING HIGHLIGHTS

By far the greatest use of rubber is in the manufacture of vehicle tires. This industry had its start in Scotland in 1846. An engineer named Robert Thompson invented a rubber-coated canvas tube which he covered with leather and filled with air. Although it did not wear well, Thompson's creation had the honor of being the first pneumatic tire. In 1888 Dr. John Dunlop, an Irish veterinarian, contrived bicycle tires for his son by encasing rubber tubes in canvas jackets. From these homemade models, Dunlop developed a successful bicycle tire business. Unknown to him, his enterprise was a forerunner of one of the world's greatest industries. Only five years later, in 1893, the first gasoline powered American automobile chugged through the streets of Springfield, Mass. From that day, the rubber industry boomed.

The earliest auto tires were made of solid rubber, but it was not long before pneumatic tires came into use, about 1896. They were single tubes. Inner tubes were developed as the weight of cars increased, and the treaded tire was introduced in 1908.

HOW TIRES ARE MADE

Modern tire manufacturing is an operation which involves more than rubber processing and molding. In one section of the plant are looms weaving cord fabric. Rayon, dacron, nylon, and other synthetic fibers are used for this tough, wear-resistant material. Beads, treads, and tire bodies are made in separate operations. While all steps involve elaborate machinery, a certain amount of skilled hand work is required for the "building" of a tire.

First, natural or synthetic latex, sometimes a combination of the two, is mixed with carbon black or with other toughening chemicals. A mixing machine blends the latex and chemicals with rotating blades. Under extreme pressure of a calendering machine, nylon or rayon fabric is fused with the rubber to form the "plies." Meanwhile the treads are molded in metal forms; then the plies are assembled on a revolving drum. Different numbers and types of plies are used for each kind of tire. The tough rubber tread, and a lighter sidewall layer are added, as are the rubber-covered steel wires, known as "beads," which hold tires on the wheel rims. After being removed from the building drum, the barrel-shaped tire is squeezed and formed in a hydraulic press which exerts thousands of pounds of pressure. Finally, the partially formed tire is vulcanized in a mold where steam heat and pressure make it tough, resilient, and ready for duty.

RUBBER ON THE MOVE

The growth of the rubber industry, even since World War II, has been impressive. After the U.S. Government sold the wartime synthetic plants, private owners doubled their capacity to approximately two million long tons per year. More than 1,500 companies are involved in various phases of manufacturing and marketing some 40,000 rubber products. In addition to the long list of rubber's obvious uses are wire insulation, conveyor belts, floor tiling, latex paints, bowling balls, space suits, space balloons, parachutes, luggage, toys, plastics, and medical sundries. One specialized tire made recently by Goodyear for an earth-moving machine measures ten ft. high, four ft. wide, and weighs two tons. A year's production of about 450 rubber trees was required to make one of these giant tires.

Rubber companies, pioneering in space equipment, are engaged in making a space platform, as well as a nuclear-powered airship which should be operational by 1963 or '64.

Rubber was a giant, billion-dollar industry in 1940. It has grown to an annual volume close to eight billion dollars. An idea of the way this industry has been expanded is illustrated by the fact that all U.S. rubber production in 1860 could have been hauled by a freight train a quarter of a mile long. Now 800 miles of freight cars would be needed for a year's production, and experts estimate that a 1,000-mile train would be required by 1970.

A LOOK INTO RUBBER'S CRYSTAL BALL

This is another of the many industries where the great cry is going to be for research, science, and engineering. In the never ending quest for "more bounce to the ounce," rubber firms need experts in physics, chemistry, biology, botany, and plant pathology. Excellent opportunities are offered in production, sales, and administration. Other fields included by this far-reaching industry are medicine, astronomy, oceanography; chemical, electrical, aeronautical and agricultural engineering. More than 12,000 scientists are currently employed in the industry's laboratories.

As an added incentive to anyone seeking a future in rubber, the industry's employees are among the highest paid in the nation.

Rubber is a basic, essential industry where plans for expansion are so extensive and in which new developments are coming at so rapid a pace that its remarkable past is undoubtedly a mere prelude of things to come.

An engineer adjusts an X-ray plate in front of a tire at the Goodyear Tire and Rubber Company in Akron, O. Radiation from the X-ray tube head in the center of the tire will record an image which will be studied by scientists.

7 Chemicals

The first age of exploration reached its climax with the discovery and settlement of North America. By the time of our own Western pioneers, and with the development of railroads and more rapid means of transportation, the earth seemed to hold few secrets. Men continued to roam the ocean, to explore polar regions and to delve below the earth's crust. But the excitement of discovering new continents had passed.

Now, suddenly, in the second half of the twentieth century, a new age of exploration has captured the imagination of people. Man has at last gone beyond the confines of his own planet and has begun to travel into space. Already we are referring to this as the Space Age.

Yet it might be more accurately called the "Age of Chemicals." While daring young astronauts are winning newspaper headlines with their rocket flights, groping their way into infinite space, another group of explorers is advancing into an equally mysterious and fascinating realm —infinitesimal matter. This is modern chemistry. If chemists did not explore the unseen composition of matter, there would be no possibility of space travel. Without chemicals our giant rockets and missiles would be empty shells. They would have no power to reach outer space, and would be incapable of withstanding the heat, the cold, and the other strange forces at work beyond earth's atmosphere.

Strange towers and fantastic mazes of pipes typify the chemical industry. This is a section of The Dow Chemical Company's polyglycol plant at Freeport, Texas.

HISTORY OF THE INDUSTRY

The chemical industry in America goes as far back as 1635 when there was limited production of inorganic chemicals such as potash and tannic acid. These materials had been known for thousands of years. Still, the study of chemistry was popularly thought of as something akin to witchcraft and sorcery. Beginning more than 500 years ago and continuing for some 400 years, alchemists tried without success to turn cheaper elements, such as iron, sulphur, or lead, into gold. The alchemist, who did such experiments, was often in danger of persecution by people who believed this was the work of the devil. Today, modern scientists have actually learned, by splitting atoms, to transform one element into another.

The concept of the atom began to take form in ancient Greece when Democritus wondered how far iron could be broken down into minute particles without losing the properties of iron. Another Greek, Anaxagoras, was convinced that there was no limit to the breakdown of matter. Democritus thought otherwise. He named what he thought to be the smallest possible particle, the atom. Today, the knowledge of atoms is resulting in breathtaking leaps in the exploration of our chemical world. Within half a century the American chemical industry has grown from a minor factor in our economy to what many now consider the foremost U. S. industry.

As recently as 1910 or 1912, other industries looked upon chemical research with disdain. "Leave chemical manufacturing to the Germans; they know the field best," was a popular reaction to those who wanted to build new chemical plants.

In the forefront of the fight against this viewpoint was the founder of Monsanto Chemical Company, John Francis Queeny. With $1,500 in 1901, he had started his business in an effort to produce saccharin, a coal-tar derivative several hundred times sweeter than sugar. Though it was discovered at Johns Hopkins University in 1879, U. S. chemical firms had shown no interest in it. Small as Queeny's plant was, German manufacturers of saccharin tried to stop him by price cutting. U. S. producers of soft drinks, candy, and a variety of products with sugar content were importing saccharin from the Germans at lower cost than it could be made here. While Queeny and other American chemical manufacturers did everything in their power to get tariff aid through Congress, most American companies helped block such legislation. Bankers, businessmen, and congressmen saw no reason to erect complex and costly plants when excellent German chemicals were so readily available.

World War I shocked industrialists into a realization of their shortsightedness. When supplies of German chemicals were suddenly cut off, manufacturers frantically sought American sources, only to find that American know-how and equipment were woefully inadequate. But the demand was too great, the need too imperative. Virtually overnight U. S. chemical plants mushroomed to giant proportions. This was the real beginning of the chemical industry in the United States. For brief periods since World War I, the industry has faced difficulties. After the war, German chemicals flooded world markets again. In 1920, a new tariff threatened to keep American chemicals out of the British markets. But by that time, firms such as Monsanto, Du Pont, and Dow Chemical Company had grown too strong in the chemical field to be seriously threatened.

tion, interests so vast that they reach into every corner of the globe.

A LOOK AT A LARGE CHEMICAL PLANT

What is a modern chemical plant? What does it make? How does it operate? Of course, there are so many different chemicals and chemical products that chemical plants vary according to their specialized production. Certain features, however, are more or less typical. If we visit the plant manager, we will probably find that he is a comparatively young man, a college graduate, and a chemical engineer. Though his day is a busy one, his responsibilities heavy, he is thoroughly absorbed and fascinated by his work. On a quick tour around the plant, he shows us miles of multicolored piping with innumerable valves and controls, all tracing complex patterns and seemingly endless mazes. In one section is a group of high-pressure

This was the chemical industry in 1908. A shipment of bromides is started on its way to Japan in a period when U.S. chemical companies struggled against German competition.

Today U.S. chemicals are supreme. This Celanese Corporation of America plant at Pampa, Texas supplies acrylate esters for paint, leather, paper, and textile industries.

Some idea of the vastness of the industry today may be seen from a few statistics. Monsanto, for example, has grown since 1901 from a shaky venture in the corner of a St. Louis warehouse to a worldwide organization with nearly nine hundred million dollars in assets, over 30,000 employees, 21 plants, 12 research laboratories, investments in five associated U. S. companies, interests in 11 foreign countries, and sales agents in 71 countries. Sales are running over seven hundred fifty million dollars annually. Dow Chemical Company, another giant, lists 19 plants and associated companies, eight division headquarters, subsidiaries and interests in 20 foreign countries and six Canadian plants. In 1961, Dow listed 95,700 stockholders; their 1960-61 net sales were eight hundred seventeen million dollars. E. I. Du Pont de Nemours & Company has many facets to its chemical production, which include industrial chemicals, commercial products such as nylon, orlon, paints, antifreezes, and other commercial chemicals. It has 70 plants, over 90,000 employees and one hundred sixty-eight thousand stockholders and, in addi-

tanks, or reactors. These giant steel tanks, which have lids fastened with six-in. bolts, are cooking chemicals under extremely high temperatures and pressures to produce chemical reactions. The chemical "stew" may be fused to form a new synthetic material, a resin from which a variety of synthetic films, fibers, or other plastic substances will be made.

To insure this "brew" against disaster, an instrument panel is watched closely by skilled operators. The dials tell what is happening inside the reactors, and when the chemical reaction has achieved a desired result. At this point, pressure is released, the mixture is cooled, and studied for impurities. Finally, the product is packaged and shipped to consumers.

Success of such production depends upon absolute accuracy in the amounts of chemicals, temperatures, and pressures. Chemical engineers spend hours making mathematical calculations, working with slide rules, sketching plans, and working out formulas before actual chemical production takes place.

In his office, the plant manager receives a call from one of the control points. A routine check of a product indicates that some foreign matter has entered one of the pipe lines. This calls for immediate action. Production of the material is halted and a thorough chemical analysis is ordered. The report indicates that some part of the line has a leak. A crew works around the clock, if necessary, to locate the trouble and make repairs, since thousands of dollars may be lost during a prolonged shutdown.

In addition to the huge production lines, the chemical plant contains a pilot plant where experiments with new products are made. Testing in the pilot plant follows exhaustive planning in the laboratory. The laboratories of large chemical firms are equipped with millions of dollars' worth of instruments, technical equipment, and testing devices. They are staffed with experts in many fields of chemistry. There are clinical laboratories for finding and correcting imperfections in the company's products; research laboratories for exploring new ideas and creating new materials.

HOW SYNTHETIC MATERIALS ARE MADE

The stories of some of the well-known synthetic products are typical of hundreds of similar examples in American chemical plants.

Nylon production involves the use of chemicals derived from coal, air, water, natural gas, petroleum, corn cobs, cottonseed hulls, and the hulls of various grains. It requires highly complicated chemical operations. One nylon product bears the impressive technical name of polyhexamethylene adipamide. To reach the end product, adipic acid and hexamethylene must first be manufactured. By adding six atoms of hydrogen to a benzine molecule, a chemical known as cyclohexane is produced. This in turn may be used in making adipic acid. Du Pont technicians have found that cobs, grain hulls, and other cellulosic materials are sources of a chemical called furfural. At a Niagara Falls, N.Y. plant Du Pont carries out a process which converts furfural into adiponitrile, which in turn is processed into hexamethylene diamine at a plant in West Virginia. After adipic acid and hexamethylene diamine are produced, they are fused in water solution so that their molecules hook together forming a nylon salt solution. Into one of the reactor tanks, or autoclaves, flows the solution where it is subjected to heat. As a result, the molecules link together to form long, chain-like molecules. This process is known as polymerization.

A thick, syrupy substance flows from the autoclave to the surface of a slowly revolving wheel. There, a spray of water hardens the solution into a translucent, milky ribbon.

Next, the ribbon is pulverized into small flakes, which are melted in heated spinning machines. When the molten nylon reaches the proper consistency, it is forced through tiny holes and drawn out into long filaments or threads.

Cellophane is a household word in every American home today. Its story began in the early 1900's when Dr. Jacques Brandenberger, a Swiss textile chemist, conceived the idea of coating tablecloths with a cellulose solution to make them stain-proof. His first product was stiff and brittle, but later he created a thin sheet of transparent film which he applied to the cloth with better success. He named the

Continuous synthesis and purification of acrylate esters take place in these futuristic distillation towers of Celanese Corporation's Pampa plant. Production in this unit totals fifteen million pounds per year.

At this zone refiner unit of a Dow Corning silicon plant in Hemlock, Michigan, any impurity in the material leaving the machines is measured in fractions of a part per billion.

film cellophane and, by 1911, had begun to produce it with a specially designed machine.

Du Pont acquired American rights to the process in 1923. From that point, Du Pont chemical research began to make steady improvements, the most important of which was moistureproof cellophane developed in 1927. Today, the manufacture of cellophane requires millions of dollars for plant investment. High-grade wood pulp, furnished in sheets or rolls, is soaked in caustic soda to form alkali cellulose. After this material is dehydrated and shredded, carbon disulfide is added to produce sodium cellulose xanthate. A syrupy liquid known as viscose is made from the xanthate. It is piped into a casting machine and forced through a slit into an acid bath. Here the material coagulates and reforms into cellulose. A series of washing, bleaching, and softening operations result in the finished film.

The names of chemically created products are legion in our vocabulary today. Such familiar materials as lucite, dacron, zefran, styrofoam, bakelite, and polyethylene are products of our modern chemical industry.

AGRICULTURAL CHEMICALS

The realm of synthetic materials and plastics is by no means the complete extent of chemical production in the United States. One of the most vital contributions of the industry is in the field of agriculture and food production. Not only are chemicals making our food production abundant, but they are improving the quality and nutrition of the foods we eat. Chemicals play a major role in growing, processing, packaging, shipping, and storing foods. If our chemical industry suddenly ceased to supply vital fertilizers and preservatives, there would be an immediate shortage of foods. Some chemicals are added to the food to enhance the taste, improve color, or to supplement the nutritional value of the natural food. Salts, sugar, baking powder, vinegar, and sodium bicarbonate are well known chemical food additives. In recent years the study of vitamins has resulted in more adequate food nourishment than formerly. Crop yield is improved by agricultural chemicals. These include insecticides, fungicides, fertilizers, plant growth regulators and weed killers. Other chemicals are produced for the health and growth of farm animals and poultry.

Before any new chemical is used in connection with food production, it is thoroughly tested by the biochemical research laboratories of great chemical companies. There is close cooperation between industrial laboratories and those in colleges and universities.

The case of a well-known pesticide is typical of work being done in this field by American chemical industries. Research on toxicity (the possible harmful effects) was begun as soon as the new pesticide was considered to have some application. Tests were made to determine the effects, if any, of the product on human skin, eyes, and mucous membranes. The compound was then tried on crops in a number of localities. The crops were harvested and analyzed to determine the extent of chemical residue in the raw or processed food.

Meanwhile, many studies were conducted with animals.

The treated crops were fed to rats and other animals. So thorough are tests of this kind that they may be carried on for several years and through as many as three generations of animals, while the effects of the diet on blood, skin, hair, and organ function are painstakingly recorded.

Harvested test crops can be analyzed for chemical residue to less than 0.1 part per million. Reports are made to the U. S. Department of Agriculture and the Food and Drug Administration. The Department of Agriculture decides whether or not the new product is useful. Next, the Food and Drug Administration examines the test reports. If satisfied that the percentage of residue is safe, an official tolerance is established. This tolerance is set at the lowest amount of chemical needed to accomplish its purpose as an insecticide, and allows a wide margin of safety.

Thus ends a long pesticide research program conducted by a large chemical company. It may take five years or longer, and may cost as high as three million dollars.

MEDICINAL CHEMICALS

Similarly, the chemical industry in the United States is constantly developing and testing new drugs and medicinal chemicals. New pharmaceutical products are being produced every year. One of the most interesting stories is that of the development of aspirin. This popular pain reliever, consumed by Americans at a rate of nearly twenty million pounds per year, is actually a chemical known as acetylsalicylic acid. Salicylic acid, parent of aspirin, was established in 1826 as an effective medicine for rheumatic pains. Long before that, the soothing effect of salicylates was applied in the form of certain barks, fruits, and herbs. The name aspirin is derived from one of the natural sources of salicylic acid—spirea.

Since large doses of salicylic acid had harmful effects on the human system, it was not until a young German chemist, Felix Hoffman, discovered the beneficial properties of acetylsalicylic acid, in 1899, that the world adopted aspirin as a universal pain killer. Today, it is recognized as one of the safest, most useful drugs known to man, and is produced in huge volume by some of our largest chemical manufacturers.

Many of the so-called "wonder drugs" of modern medicine are produced in volume by the chemical industry. Included among the well-known medicinal chemicals recently developed are chloromycetin, atabrine, penicillin, and streptomycin. But there are many other lesser known drugs and medicines of equal importance. Vitamin K, fibrinogen, and other chemicals for blood clotting have saved many seriously injured patients from bleeding to death. One of the great areas of chemical research is in a family of new chemicals known as nucleic acids. It is possible that these chemicals hold fundamental secrets of life. (See *Pharmaceuticals*)

PROMISE OF A GOLDEN FUTURE

No industry holds more promise for the future nor more opportunities for young people than the chemical industry. It is the fastest-growing among our giant industries. By its very nature it is an industry of pioneering and newness. One of the largest firms reports that one-third of its cur-

In the search for new and more durable coloring materials, tests of plastics, colored fabrics, and painted materials are made in the "Fade-Ometer," foreground, and "Weather-Ometer" to determine durability of pigments. The objective of such chemical research is colors which will outlast the products in which they are used, under normal exposure conditions.

From studies of the basic biochemical reactions within plants, scientists draw data that may someday enable man to multiply the food value of crops and, at the same time, reduce nutrients and water required. Dr. William Pritchard, below, is one of many Du Pont scientists studying the chemical aspects of such problems.

Seeking to develop super-pure metals and alloys capable of withstanding 3000° F. temperatures generated in phases of space flight, Du Pont scientists study chemical reactions of materials under various conditions. The zone-refining apparatus shown above is producing a high-quality silicon by passing a bar of the material through an energized induction coil which melts a segment of the bar. As the bar moves, the molten zone shifts, carrying impurities to the end of the bar.

45

rent sales are of products created during the past 10 years. New chemicals are emerging at an astounding rate. The Manufacturing Chemists' Association listed more than 8,000 different chemicals being made commercially in 1960 with 400 new products being added each year.

Consider what the U. S. chemical industry has recently provided and is promising for the immediate future: Acrylic fibers, made from natural gas and air, have given us suits with permanent creases, dresses with permanent pleats, shirts that will never stretch or shrink, garments that can be washed and dried without ironing.

Because of the "Haber" process which converts nitrogen from the air and hydrogen from water into ammonia, the production of man-made ammonia is now considered unlimited. This means that more and better fertilizers will be made available to farmers at lower price. On this single discovery, the prediction can be made that crop production can keep pace with the world's rapidly increasing population. This is by no means the only chemical breakthrough that is helping to advance food production.

New chemical fuels and sources of power are being developed. Should our supplies of petroleum be exhausted, the chemical industry will furnish synthetic fuels which may, ultimately, be better and cheaper.

Chemically created plastics have scarcely passed their infancy. Synthetic materials may enter every phase of construction in buildings, automobiles, clothing, toys, eating and cooking utensils, and packaging. (See *Plastics*)

Cures for so-called "incurable" diseases continue to be found in new chemical compounds.

In the paper industry one may expect sensational new chemical developments with the introduction of synthetic fibers. Dollar bills made from nylon paper will have a durability five times greater than that of present paper currency.

Natural woods and metals will be replaced gradually by synthetic materials with greater strength and equal beauty.

THE ALADDIN'S LAMP OF CHEMICALS

All of these marvelous creations spring, basically, from nature's simplest and most abundant materials. The chemical industry uses natural brines containing chlorine, bromine, calcium, and magnesium. With these as building blocks and the addition of hydrocarbon from petroleum, hundreds of chemical products are derived. The inexpensive inorganic chemicals in salt, brine, and seawater can be combined in an almost infinite number of combinations. Many of the raw materials for chemical manufacture are waste products of other industries. Oyster shells, waste oil well brines, and by-products of steel and coke manufacture, are among the inexpensive materials from which valuable chemicals are made.

Career opportunities in this fabulous industry appear to be endless. Chemists are needed in every one of the basic chemical fields: organic, inorganic, physical chemistry, analytical chemistry, biochemistry, medicinal chemistry, high polymer chemistry, and the exciting new science of radiochemistry, which is exploring the innermost secrets of our universe.

In addition, engineers, draftsmen, and designers will find high-paid jobs to work on the ever changing design of complex chemical reactors, pipe lines, and instruments. Diversity of products calls for experts in almost every field, including marketing and advertising.

Most intriguing of all, to men and women seeking exciting careers, is the realization that the chemical industry is on the threshold of even greater discoveries. Such discoveries may change the entire course of human existence, and the standard of living for people throughout the world.

In the gas-conditioning laboratory of The Dow Chemical Company, Midland, Michigan, staff and facilities are working to solve problems of the gas industry. Almost every aspect of modern life and industrial activity is being influenced by chemical research, and it is in the laboratory that tomorrow's discoveries and products will emerge.

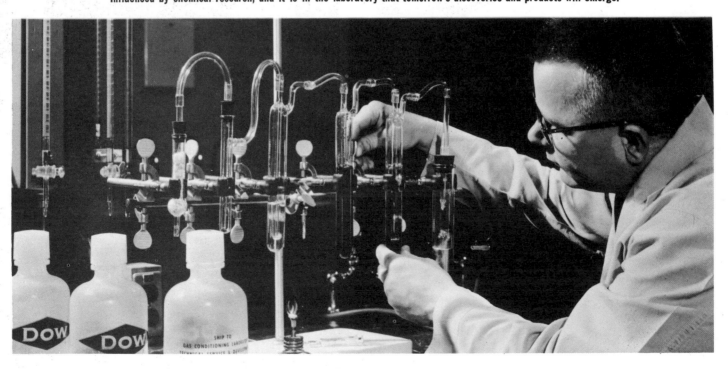

8 Primary Metals

In giant blast furnaces such as this one at Republic Steel Corporation's Cleveland district plant, iron ore is reduced to pig iron.

Although the wonders of our modern civilization sprang in a large degree from man's recent development of the metal industries, the fashioning of tools and implements from metal dates back to the very dawn of history. No one knows exactly when men first began to use copper and bronze, but copper implements at least 10,000 years old have been found in Turkestan. In ancient Egypt, copper was in common use 6,000 or 7,000 years ago. One of the great milestones in human history was the discovery of bronze, a copper alloy consisting, in ancient times, of about nine parts copper and one part tin. Since copper ores sometimes contain tin oxide, the first mixture of the two metals to form bronze may have occurred accidentally. Later, by trial and error, men learned how to achieve maximum strength and hardness with the best alloy. The Bronze Age began about 3000 B.C., probably in Asia, where it is thought that bronze was first developed.

Iron came into use at least 1000 B.C., for it is mentioned in ancient Greek writings. Iron swords, sickles, scythes and axes, as well as many iron ornaments more than 2000 years old, have been found in Europe, particularly at the site of the ancient settlement of La Tène, Switzerland. The Iron Age continued until the invention of steel, and it is here that the story of the modern metal industry begins.

STEEL

Steel! The very word has a cold grandeur that suggests strength. Giant among giant industries in the United States, steel was not a major factor in the economy until the late 1800's. In 1810 scarcely 1,000 tons of steel were produced by American manufacturers. By 1900 steel production was eleven million tons, while in the 1960's the output has been in the neighborhood of one hundred twenty million tons a year. The United States is undisputed leader of steel production in the world.

As early as 1728 a steel process patent was granted to Samuel Higley of Connecticut; nevertheless, steel was rare and costly in the early days of this country. Even the introduction of the crucible process in the 1830's did not make large scale production possible. Almost simultaneously, an American and an Englishman discovered a revolutionary process which was destined to catapult the world into the Steel Age. The American was William Kelly, a Kentucky ironmaster. Thousands of miles distant, Henry Bessemer, was working along the same lines. Both had found that when a blast of air is forced through molten pig iron, silicon, manganese and carbon are burned off and the temperature of the metal increases from 2,300° F. to 2,600-3,000° F. Bessemer was granted patents in 1855.

However, Kelly was able to prove that he had used the process eight years earlier, and eventually the two interests were merged. The method is known today as the bessemer process.

BESSEMER FIREWORKS DISPLAY

Steelmaking is one of the most dramatic of all manufacturing processes, and a visit to a steel plant is an unforgettable experience. The bessemer converter, for example, puts on a colorful show. This huge, pear-shaped tilting vessel is made of steel and is lined with heat-resisting bricks and clay as much as 16 in. thick. The converter may hold up to 25 tons of molten metal. This red glowing mass of liquid iron is poured from a mixer, into the mouth of the converter. Next, air is forced by blowing engines at a pressure of 30 lb. per square inch through a blast line and into the bottom of the converter. When the blast of air is turned on, a spectacular shower of sparks erupts from the mouth of the converter. This is followed by reddish flames and a cloud of brownish fumes as the silicon and manganese are ignited in the iron. Yellow silicon flames soon appear and continue for about five minutes, after which comes a dazzling white carbon flame. While the escaping gases produce a deep roar, the flame

47

One of the most spectacular steel-making processes is the bessemer converter. When air is forced into the bottom of the converter, escaping gases produce a deep roar and a flame 25 to 30 feet high.

reaches a height of 25 to 30 ft. After a few minutes the flame drops suddenly and the air blast is cut off.

Manganese and carbon must be added to the blown metal in order to make it forgeable. This is generally done as the molten mass flows from the tipped converter into a giant ladle. All that remains in the bessemer converter is slag, the waste residue resulting from oxidation.

SIZE OF STEEL INDUSTRY

Today, the American steel industry consists of nearly 300 companies with plants located in 35 states. Mammoth steel mills with towering blast furnaces are familiar landmarks in many industrial communities. There are about 85 companies making raw steel. The rest are engaged in rolling and drawing steel or in producing pig iron. In all, the industry represents an investment of over nine billion dollars supplied by seven hundred fifty thousand stockholders and by reinvested profits.

Everything about steel is big. A modern blast furnace may be 125 ft. tall and may cost ten million dollars. There are about seven hundred thousand men and women employed in iron and steel production; many more in related operations. Most steel mills occupy many acres with their stockpiles of ores and minerals, furnaces, rolling mills, and offices.

ORIGIN OF IRON ORE

Without the help of Father Time, and marine creatures of a prehistoric period, American steel production would not be as extensive as it is today.

In the Lake Superior region and the great Mesabi Range of Minnesota, where 80% of U. S. iron ore originates, there are vast iron deposits, formed during the course of a billion years. At some period of the earth's dim past, great seas covered this area. Layer by layer, iron-rich

sediments gathered on the sea bottom. When the waters receded, the earth shifted, wrinkled, and folded until, in the resulting land mass, concentrated deposits of iron oxides were created.

The demand for steel in World War II was so great that there was fear that our high-grade iron ore reserves might be nearing depletion. A recent technological development, however, has made practical use of another type of ore known as taconite. This is found in a hard, rock formation in the Lake Superior region. Though it holds only about 32% iron, the iron content may be magnetically separated after a series of crushing and grinding operations. The taconite-bearing rock is so hard that blasting holes must be bored into it with jet piercers. Large fragments are dynamited free, then crushed and ground to the consistency of a muddy sand. Magnets are used to separate the iron from waste rock.

PRINCIPAL STEEL PROCESSES

BLAST FURNACE: In this towering cylinder occurs the first step in the conversion of iron ore into steel. Coke, limestone, and iron ore are dumped into the furnace in alternating layers, and the heating process begins. Gas is burned in huge stoves to heat the firebrick linings to about 1,250° F. Then air, pumped through the stoves, becomes the hot blast which promotes combustion in the furnace. As the raw materials melt, their bulk decreases and new layers of ore, coke, and limestone are poured in at the top of the furnace. Meanwhile, the charge descends through increasing heat. The reaction releases oxygen from the ore, causes the limestone to crumble and to form a molten slag of impurities.

Still lower in the furnace the iron becomes a porous mass. It then passes into the melting zone and liquefies. Ash from the coke is absorbed into the slag while the iron takes on silicon and carbon.

There is now a pool of iron five feet deep in the lowest

Blast furnace operation. One car of the skip hoist charges raw materials into the furnace while the other is being filled at the stockhouse hopper below. Molten iron is shown running into a mixer car.

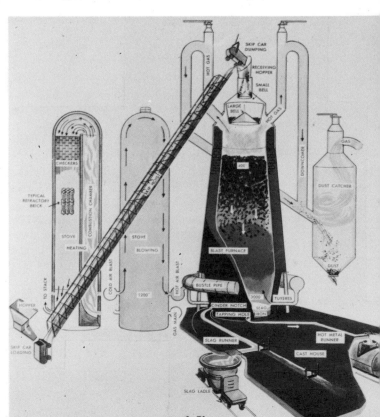

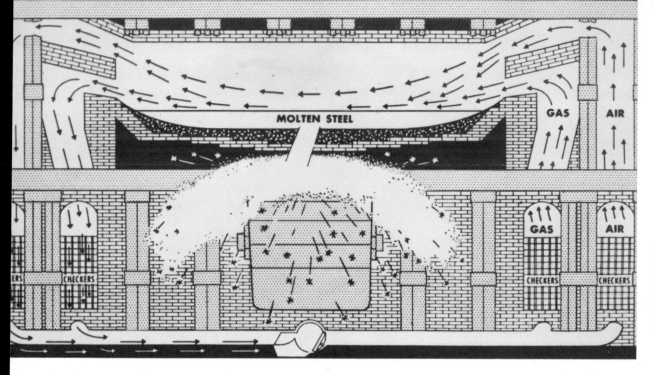

This diagram shows an open-hearth furnace in operation. Incoming air and gas are preheated in brickwork checker chambers. The hearth of the furnace is open to flames which melt the charge. Steel is being tapped into the foreground ladle. Slag overflows into another ladle.

part of the furnace, or hearth. Every few hours the iron and slag are drawn off. As much as 300 tons of iron are tapped at a time. The red-hot material gushes forth in a fiery mass accompanied by a shower of sparks, and flows through a trough into a ladle car. These hot metal cars are like tremendous thermos bottles. Lined with heat-resistant material, they can transport the molten iron as far as 20 miles without cooling and congealing it.

Constructing a modern blast furnace requires over 4,000 tons of iron and steel, some three million firebricks, 5,130 cu. yd. of concrete. Such a furnace can produce 1,200 tons of iron per day.

OPEN HEARTH: The process, known as open hearth, was developed in the 1860's by William Siemens in England and by the Martin brothers in France. In this case the hearth, in the shape of an elongated saucer, is directly exposed to the furnace flames. Fuel, such as gas, tar, or oil, is blown into the furnace through a large

opening at one end of the structure. The huge flame heats the furnace to 3,000° F. and melts the charge of pig iron, scrap, and limestone beneath it. As in the blast furnace, molten iron is drawn off the hearth into ladles. Because of its efficiency in melting scrap and old junk iron and steel, the open-hearth process is used in about 90% of U. S. steel production today.

A skilled supervisor called the "melter" is in charge of the open-hearth furnace. He has three assistants, or pit-men, who, as a team, generally operate a battery of several furnaces. It is the melter's responsibility to control the amounts of alloying minerals to be added to each batch of steel. He decides when the steel is ready to be tapped and what kind of molds will be used when the molten metal is poured from the ladle. Many different types and qualities of steel are created through the controlled proportions of carbon, manganese, phosphorus, and other elements which are introduced into the furnace by the

(Left) An ingot is withdrawn from a soaking pit. Soaking in this case means that the ingot has been exposed to heat until it is sufficiently plastic to be run through blooming rolls. (Right) With this modern electron microscope, U.S. Steel scientists can study ultra-small structural features of steel. Subjects can be magnified up to 250,000 times. A penny enlarged this much would be nearly three miles across.

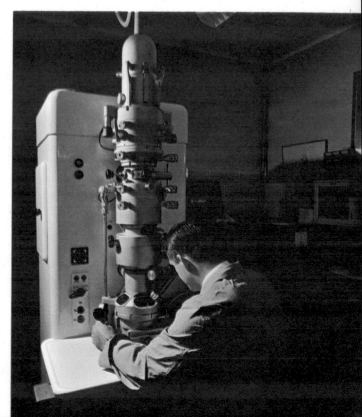

melter. Nowadays, most of these operations are scientifically controlled from instrument panels.

PNEUMATIC PROCESS: This is the bessemer process which has already been described. In 1954, the method was improved by the oxygen process which involves the use of a jet of pure oxygen shot onto the molten iron in the converter. This burns out more impurities and keeps unwanted nitrogen out of the steel.

ELECTRIC FURNACE: Like a gigantic tea kettle on rockers, the electric furnace is heated by means of large carbon or graphite cylinders—electrodes, which carry electric current into the charge. The electricity merely provides heat; it has no chemical effect on the steel. One advantage of this type of furnace is its ability to generate high temperatures, very rapidly, up to 3,500° F. Also, since oxygen is not needed for combustion in electrically created heat, the amount of oxygen entering the furnace may be precisely regulated. This is important in the making of certain fine steels. Electric furnaces are capable of producing steel with fewer impurities than is possible by any other steel-making processes.

ROLLING AND FINISHING

A major segment of the steel industry is devoted to rolling bulky steel ingots into slimmer forms known as blooms, billets, and slabs. A bloom is square or rectangular, having a cross-sectional area of 36 in. or more. Billets are generally the same shape, but smaller, while slabs are flat and vary greatly in size.

The rolling operation is another spectacular phase of steel production. Ingots are heated to 2,200° F. These glowing blocks of steel are rolled between huge steel rollers

At Republic Steel Corporation's Cleveland district plant, this 45-inch Universal slabbing mill rolls steel ingots weighing 25 tons into steel slabs up to 75 inches wide and 4 to 7 inches thick.

which squeeze the soft ingots flat, as they are sent back and forth at high speed. Vertical rollers keep the edges true. From a control point called the pulpit a skilled operator, using push buttons, occasionally turns the ingot so that it is rolled equally on all sides. Many different shapes and sizes can be made, depending on the number of passes through the rollers and whether or not grooved rollers are used. Steel plates, beams, and rails are rolled and shaped by the amazing skill of experienced steelmen.

Sheet and strip steel are turned out from slabs. In three minutes, a six-foot slab of steel can be rolled through a hot strip mill into a thin strip a quarter of a mile long. In another five minutes, a cold reducing mill will flatten the steel into a ribbon more than a mile in length.

USES OF STEEL

It is almost impossible to picture life today if there were no steel industry. The framework of every great city is steel: steel bridges, steel reinforcement in concrete highways, steel automobiles, steel cabinets, desks, chairs, refrigerators, springs for watches and for locomotives, cans, nails, and hundreds of household utensils. All are vital and so much in evidence wherever we turn that there would, literally, be no civilization as we know it without steel. In addition to the products themselves, the machinery which manufactures them is made almost entirely of steel. Yet the uses of steel have by no means reached their limit. New technology has made possible a variety of special steels never imagined even a decade ago. Chrome and vanadium steels are well-known. Stainless steel was a sensational breakthrough. Now there are steels soft enough to be whittled with a penknife; steels so hard that they can be scratched only with a diamond point. Steel can be formed into any shape, welded, magnetized, and alloyed in hundreds of combinations.

In the research laboratories of the great steel companies, chemists and technicians are working on new alloys and new uses of this versatile metal. At U. S. Steel alone, more than 1,700 scientists are engaged in research. Latest scientific equipment is used to test samples of steel—bending, stretching, twisting and breaking the metal to establish its durability under all possible conditions.

As in the chemical industry, steel research is exploring nuclear chemistry and the atomic structure of the metal with a view to learning the fundamental secrets of its properties. With electronic microscopes, steel samples can be magnified two hundred fifty thousand times. An area the size of a penny, enlarged to that extent, would measure about three miles in diameter. Using such equipment, research laboratories of the steel industry have learned how to tailor steel for specific uses. Today, the large user of steel can ask for special properties to be built into his particular order. For example, a manufacturer of stoves wants a steel that can be enameled directly with a single coat. A user of steel pipe needs a lightweight steel that will stand 60% more pressure than was possible a short time ago. If steel research centers have not already solved such problems, they go to work on them and generally come up with the answers. Thus, new types of steel are born.

THE FUTURE

With new methods of extracting iron from low-grade ores, and with sensational discoveries in the laboratories, steel appears to be opening a vast range of future possibilities. In space exploration, the demand for special steels is only beginning. For rocket launching devices, the skins of space vehicles, special bolts, and rivets, steel is finding a vital place. Modern styles in architecture call for new structural steel components. Only a few years ago, structural steel having a breaking point at 50,000 to 60,000 lb. per square inch was acceptable. Today, steels with three hundred thousand pound tensile strength are being produced. In the future, technicians say that a steel with a breaking point of a million pounds per square inch will be possible.

Young people entering the steel industry whether in the mills, the sales and marketing departments, research laboratories, engineering, design and planning divisions, or in any other phase of this mammoth endeavor, are assured an exciting future of expansion, pioneering, and discovery.

ALUMINUM

Despite the fact that aluminum is the newest of commercial metals, it now ranks second only to steel in importance. It is the fastest growing of all metal industries. Since World War II, while steel production increased 10% and copper 50%, aluminum production in the United States increased an astounding 600%. The U. S. aluminum market is the largest in the world. There are more than 20,000 companies, directly or indirectly, involved in the industry. These include primary producers, smelters who melt aluminum scrap and reprocess it, fabricators, jobbers, and sales organizations.

HISTORY OF ALUMINUM

Not until 1888, two years after Charles Martin Hall had discovered the secret of extracting pure aluminum from the ore in quantity, was there a significant aluminum industry. Previous to this, the metal was little more than a costly scientific curiosity. In 1825 a Danish physicist, Hans Christian Oersted succeeded in producing a tiny sample of aluminum. Twenty years later a German, by the name of Wöhler, performed similar experiments and was the first to demonstrate the light weight of the metal. When a French chemist, Henri Sainte-Claire Deville, exhibited a bar of aluminum at the 1855 Paris Exposition, Napoleon III became interested in the possibility of using it for military purposes. Sainte-Claire Deville went to work on the problem. Although he succeeded in reducing the price of aluminum from $545 to $17 per pound, it was still too costly for extensive use.

In 1859, the world's aluminum production was two tons. Today, this amount can be produced in two minutes!

Young Charles Hall, just out of college, was convinced that electricity could be used to separate aluminum from natural compounds. He started his experiments in a woodshed in Ohio, using alumina, or aluminum oxide, as the cheapest available ore. Because he could not melt the alumina in his furnace, he set out to find a material which could dissolve alumina. Cryolite, a mineral found in Green-

Bottle cars like this are used for transporting hot metal from blast furnaces to open-hearth furnaces. The engineer's cab is equipped with two-way radio communication with the yard master's office.

land, did the job. He dissolved alumina in the melted cryolite, inserted two carbon electrodes in the solution and, after a couple of hours, poured the solution into an iron skillet. When it had hardened, he broke up the material with a hammer and found several pellets of pure aluminum. At 22 years of age, Hall had learned a secret which had eluded scientists for many years. This was the beginning of a great new industry. Basically, Hall's electrolytic smelting process is used throughout the aluminum industry today.

Hall's discovery did not immediately bring him success. For two years, he sought capital. Finally, in 1888, he was able to establish the Pittsburgh Reduction Company, financed with $20,000. This plant began turning out 50 lb. of aluminum per day and the price quickly dropped from eight to two dollars a pound. The problem was to find markets for the product. Users of other metals were skeptical. They resisted change. One member of the new firm, Arthur V. Davis, spent his time in efforts to demonstrate uses of the new metal. Finally, he found a manufacturer of cooking utensils who ordered 2,000 aluminum kettles. Unfortunately, the manufacturer was unwilling to work with the strange material. As a result, the Pittsburgh Reduction Company itself had to borrow the molds and do the casting.

Unlike the steel industry, the young aluminum company had to create its own products. When the Snoqualine Falls Power Company of Seattle ordered one hundred forty thousand pounds of aluminum wire, nobody could be found to do the fabrication. The Pittsburgh Reduction Company promptly built a wire and cable mill. The necessity of fabricating aluminum products has forced the aluminum industry into a more rapid growth than might otherwise have been possible.

In 1907, The Pittsburgh Reduction Company became Aluminum Company of America and adopted the world-famous trade mark, ALCOA. Other important firms entered the picture as time went on. Reynolds Metals Company, which began with the U.S. Foil Company in

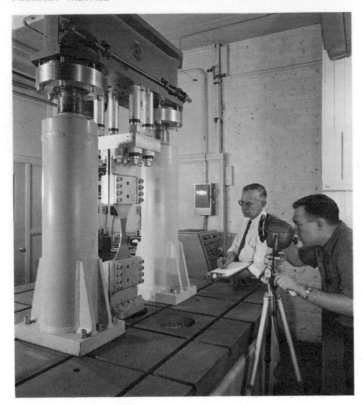

Testing of aluminum plate specimens under dynamic tensile loading at Reynolds metallurgical research laboratories. Differential strain is studied by observing color differences in a photostress plastic coating.

Aluminum foil is produced by rolling aluminum sheet in this 78-inch-wide rolling mill, is used for packaging grocery, drug, and cosmetic products.

1919, is now one of the major producers of aluminum and aluminum products. Kaiser Aluminum and Chemical Corporation, Anaconda Aluminum Company, and Olin Mathieson Chemical Corporation have joined the competition in the past few years. However, ALCOA has from its inception held a preeminent position in the field, largely because Hall and his associates created not only the company, but also the entire industry.

ALUMINUM PRODUCTION TODAY

A modern aluminum mill is in many respects similar to a steel plant, in that the ore is fed into a furnace, molten metal is drawn off and cast into ingots, and the ingots or scrap aluminum are converted into sheets, plates, bars, rods, wire, or tubes. There are hot and cold rolling mills as in the steel industry.

Most of the alumina needed for conversion by the Hall process comes from bauxite, a mineral found in large deposits in Africa, Australia, Brazil, China, France, British Guiana, Jamaica, Surinam, Russia, and many other parts of the world including the United States. The largest source of bauxite in the United States is Arkansas. Bauxite comes in many forms. It may be as hard as rock or as soft as clay. Its color may be buff, yellow, pink, red, or white.

The process of refining bauxite to remove impurities from the ore results in a fine, white powder. This is alumina, a compound of aluminum and oxygen. The refining is done by a process invented by Karl Bayer. In a steam-heated digester, a caustic mixture of soda ash and ground lime causes the alumina to dissolve, whereas the impurities do not. The solution is forced through cloth filters which hold back the solid impurities, known as red mud. Next, the liquid alumina is fed into tall, silo-like tanks, or precipitators. Here, small amounts of crystallized alumina seed particles are stirred into the solution to promote the precipitation of solid alumina as the mixture cools. Because water is chemically combined with the aluminum oxide, in this form it is called hydrated alumina.

Finally, the hydrated alumina is filtered and washed, then dried in a long, slowly revolving kiln where the temperature is 1,800° F. This dehydrates the mixture so that it emerges from the kiln as a white powder. By much the same procedure that Hall used in his early experiments, but on a far greater scale, the smelting is carried out in large steel cells, or furnaces, with carbon cathode linings. Within these furnaces, alumina is dissolved in a cryolite bath at about 1,800° F; then giant carbon anodes are lowered into the bath and a powerful electric current is applied through a "bus bar" to the anodes. A slag crust of electrolyte and alumina forms on the surface of the bath while pure molten aluminum is produced in the furnace.

Aluminum production requires a great deal of electricity. For that reason, most plants are located near sources of hydroelectric power. There are large mills at Massena near Niagara Falls, N.Y.; Alcoa, Tenn.; Listerhill, Ala.; Vancouver, and Wenatchee, Wash. The search for adequate electric power is one of the major concerns of the aluminum industry. Possibly atomic generators will provide the answer in the future, but nuclear power is still too costly for general commercial use.

USES OF ALUMINUM

When the Wright Brothers launched their clumsy aircraft on Kill Devil Hill, N.C., in 1903, aluminum became a vital factor in a new and fabulous age of flight. Aluminum parts in the engine of that first Wright plane had been made by the Pittsburgh Reduction Company. From that day forward, more and more lightweight aluminum was specified by aircraft designers and engineers. In two World Wars, American aluminum flew in hundreds, then thou-

and pigments. Seals, caps, labels, signs, pipes, and aluminum-coated steel are only a handful of some 5,000 uses listed by the industry.

A GLEAMING FUTURE

The concept of creating new markets for a new metal has been one of the hallmarks of this creative industry. Nature made aluminum light, but human technology and research has developed the alloy to make it strong and versatile. Research laboratories of the great companies are busy seeking new processes, new products, and new uses. The futuristic approach of this ultramodern industry

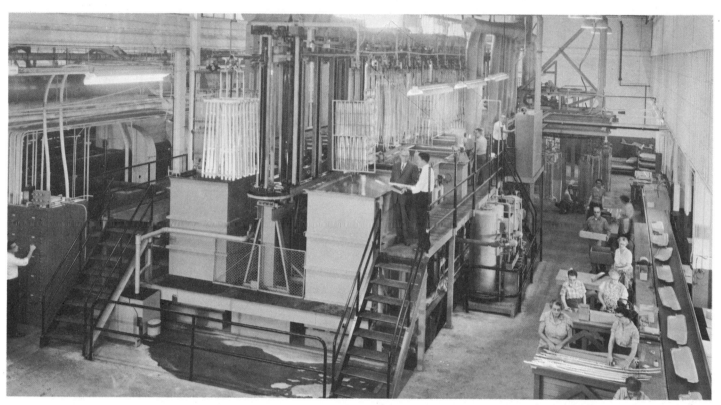

This giant anodizing machine occupying 10,000 sq. ft. of floor space contains 21 different sequence solutions and processes 5,000 sq. ft. of aluminum an hour. Through this process of anodizing aluminum an almost unlimited number of textures and colors may be created.

sands of missions. Aircraft production in the war year of 1943 reached a peak of 86,000 planes, with three-fourths of their weight comprised of aluminum. Other military uses of the metal included canteens and mess gear, time fuses for shrapnel, automotive and marine engine parts, and chemical equipment.

Nowadays, the uses of aluminum are becoming so widespread that it would be foolish to attempt a prediction as to its limitations. A glance at the skyline of almost any American city reveals a dazzling display of glass and aluminum. Some of the newer office buildings have complete facings of stamped aluminum panels. Aluminum window sash and frames are familiar in homes and offices. Aluminum roofing, railings, ducts for heating and air conditioning, nails, screws, bolts, and insect screening are becoming commonplace in the building trades.

Aluminum household appliances, aluminum foil wrappings and kitchen utensils are familiar to every housewife. Aluminum is being used for furniture, jewelry, toys, paints,

is through design. Some of the best opportunities, for young people seeking careers, exist in this field of design. Through modern design of buildings, boats, household appliances, furniture, and so forth, aluminum is being introduced on the drawing board where all new construction begins. For example, the industry's design experts have created hundreds of beautiful mesh patterns, formed from sheet aluminum. These are used as decorative elements in walls or partitions, rails, chair backs, door panels, and screens. Special finishes and colors can be produced to simulate wood, gold, wrought iron, or brass. Automobile design, from the dash to the taillight is utilizing increasing amounts of aluminum for style and practicality.

As in many fields today, chemical research will open up countless applications of this metal. Structural aluminum with a tensile strength of 90,000 lb. per square inch is already in use, although most commercial aluminum tests at about 13,000 lb.

The future of aluminum in transportation is as bright

as the polished surfaces of modern railroad coaches. Indeed, the future of aluminum may well be linked to the future of railroads, where lightweight passenger and freight cars can offer the economy needed to keep the rails in competition with other forms of transportation. In aircraft, of course, the importance of aluminum has been well established, but future automobiles, trucks, and buses will have aluminum castings in cylinder heads, wheels, bumpers, and many working parts of their engines. One of the fastest-growing markets for aluminum is the electrical industry, where applications are being found in generator and motor windings, cable sheathing, conduits, switch gear, and related items.

In this fast-moving age, the demand for lightweight, portable products is growing daily. Aluminum not only meets the technical demands of the Space Age, but can be molded and finished in forms of unique beauty. To build its gleaming future, the industry needs civil engineers, chemical engineers, electrical engineers, industrial engineers, mechanical engineers, metallurgists, sales administrators, sales engineers, development engineers, accountants, research scientists, and many different categories of skilled craftsmen. It is an expanding industry with the far reaches of outer space as its limit.

COPPER, BRASS, AND OTHER NONFERROUS METALS

By no means as spectacular in size or in scientific advances as the steel and aluminum industries, the copper industry is nonetheless vital to civilized progress. Primary reason for this is the high conductivity of copper, which makes it indispensable in the electrical field. Copper wire, as well as small copper parts in motors and electronic machines, is required to carry much of the power which keeps our entire industrial complex in operation.

HISTORY OF COPPER

Thousands of years before man learned to make iron and steel, copper was extracted from the earth, softened in fire and hammered into the shapes of tools, weapons, and other implements. As mentioned earlier, copper is the basic ingredient of bronze, which was man's primary metal for many centuries. Copper ore is not as abundant in supply as iron and aluminum, but it is more easily processed. It is the only metal found in pure form in large deposits. In ancient times, the "red metal" was used by virtually all peoples, including the Egyptians, North American Indians, Phoenicians, Chinese, and the Peruvian Incas. Since large copper mines were on the island of Cyprus, the ancient Greeks called the metal *Kyprios,* meaning "of Cyprus." Later derivations were *Cyprium, cuprum,* and finally copper.

SMELTING AND REFINING

Modern smelting and refining of copper has been largely an American development due to the great demands of the U. S. electrical industry. First a "charge" of copper ore is melted in a long, shallow furnace. Impurities and lightweight minerals rise to the top and are drawn off in the form of slag. The remaining mass of metal, mostly

Lifting cathodes of pure copper from an electrolytic refining tank. The anodes are suspended by dark copper lugs, and the cathodes are suspended from copper bars placed through two narrow loops fastened to the top of each cathode.

iron and copper, is called matte. The matte is poured into huge ladles which, by means of overhead cranes, discharge their molten contents into converters. Air is then forced into the converters along with a small amount of silica. The resulting oxidation of foreign substances leaves the copper almost pure, and it is cast into bars and ingots of "blister copper" for shipment to refining plants.

Most copper smelting plants are located near mines, whereas the refineries are concentrated in the East in the heart of industrial areas. The refining process takes the final, minute portions of silver, gold, and other unwanted minerals out of the 99% pure copper. Small as the percentage of impurities may be, further refining is essential to convert the copper into an efficient electric conductor.

A modern copper refinery is a model of scientifically precise processing. Here, we see copper bars remelted and cast into plates known as anodes. The anodes, suspended in a solution of sulphuric acid and copper sulphate, are dissolved under the influence of an electric charge. The pure copper is redeposited on plates called cathodes. Generally, the cathodes are melted in a furnace and cast into various shapes for ultimate fabrication.

At the electrolytic refining plant of Anaconda Copper Company in Perth Amboy, N.J., both domestic and foreign copper is cast into 525-lb. anodes. The copper is deposited on a "starting sheet" which weighs only eight pounds. The process produces 99.95+% pure copper, which is ultimately cast into parallel-sided copper cakes weighing 1,800 to 3,000 lb.

Refining by fire yields a slightly less pure grade of copper. Blister copper is melted in an agitated, silica-lined vessel. The agitation causes sufficient air circulation to oxidize most impurities, leaving cuprous oxide still in the solution. When the slag is removed, the molten mass is stirred with green wood poles. At this stage the cuprous oxide is reduced, due to the release of hydrocarbons from the wood.

SOURCES OF COPPER

One of the richest mineral deposits ever discovered is at Butte, Montana, where in 79 years from 1880, nearly fifteen billion pounds of copper have been mined. In addition, the mines in this area have produced four and

At the Telephone Cable building, Hastings-on-Hudson, New York, is equipment for manufacture of paper-insulated and thermoplastic-insulated telephone cable. As many as 2,121 pairs of insulated copper wires may be assembled in one jacket.

most modern automated equipment. Brass strip is produced at speeds up to 1,000 ft. per minute, rolling 24-in.-wide coils weighing 2,400 lb. At the Ansonia, Conn. plant of American Brass Company, a flat wire rolling mill winds 1,000-lb. reels and spools of wire at an astonishing speed of 2,000 ft. per minute. Brass ferrules, eyelets, washers, grommets, and dozens of other small metal items are stamped or extruded at a rate of 10,000 units per hour. Other machines can turn out brass or copper tubes with a minute .032-in. diameter.

Through a large, complex extrusion press, a heated cylindrical copper billet passes from a furnace, is forced into the press and emerges as a hollow tube, or "blank." In order to reduce the comparatively thick walls of this extruded blank, and to increase the length at the same time, it is rolled, then drawn on "draw benches" to the desired size.

one-half billion pounds of zinc, three and one-half billion pounds of manganese, seven hundred eighty-four million pounds of lead, six hundred nineteen million ounces of silver and nearly two and one-half million ounces of gold. Until 1887, Michigan was the leading copper producing state; then Montana was the richest U. S. source; recently Arizona has taken the lead. The world's most important copper mines are located in Chile, where U. S. engineers have worked closely with the Chilean Government in the development of modern mining methods and in the exploration for new sources of copper. (See *Mining*)

COPPER ALLOYS

Because copper combines with zinc, tin, aluminum, silicon, silver, nickel, and cadmium, the red metal is used in a great many alloys. Brass and bronze are the best-known copper alloys, and therefore the copper industry is involved in the production of zinc, tin, and nickel.

America's brass industry is nearly as old as the nation. Early producers made small quantities of the metal for the manufacture of such domestic items as kettles, pins, buttons, and various types of hardware. It was the rapid rise of the railroad and electrical industries which caused major expansion of brass production. Brass resists corrosion, and is an excellent conductor of heat and electricity. At the same time it is tough and malleable.

One of the best-known brass producers is The American Brass Company. Organized in 1899, this company was the result of merging several Connecticut brass firms, some of which originated as far back as 1812. Today, American Brass, a subsidiary of Anaconda, has plants across the nation, located in such cities as Buffalo, N.Y.; Ansonia, Torrington, and Waterbury, Conn.; Detroit, Mich.; Kenosha, Wis.; Los Angeles, Calif.

Constant research has developed a variety of special alloys for different uses. "Alpha" brasses contain 30% zinc. Though they retain most of copper's high conductivity, they are both stronger and cheaper than pure copper. Alpha brass is used for tubes, sheets, cartridge and shell cases as well as for a variety of plumbing fittings. Adding 40% zinc produces "beta," or "alpha plus beta" brass, used principally for brass castings.

Today, copper and brass fabrication is handled by the

WIRE PRODUCTION

Since the demand on U. S. electrical power increases about 7% a year, the use of wire and cable has grown accordingly. This does not mean merely more production of wire. Ever larger voltage loads must be carried underground by heavy cables. Huge testing laboratories, equipped with giant electrical devices, like a scene out of science fiction, have been built by the Anaconda Wire and Cable Company to experiment with extra-high-voltage cable. Here electrical energy is generated and transmitted through cables designed to carry up to three hundred forty-five thousand volts. Doubtless even higher-voltage cables will be developed and tested in such laboratories.

Meanwhile ultramodern electronic and missile devices are requiring not only special types of wire and electrical parts, but new super-temperature insulations. The copper wire industry must also develop the insulation materials to keep pace with technology of the Space Age. Rubber and thermoplastic insulations, as well as various cotton and paper coverings, are fabricated for different types of wire.

In the making of cables, as many as 2,000 pairs of insulated wires may be drawn from a battery of spools, twisted, and covered by a single jacket.

CAREER OPPORTUNITIES IN COPPER

As stated previously, the perpetual increase of electrical output and the recent phenomenal strides in electronics point the way to further growth of copper industries and increased production of other nonferrous metals, such as zinc, lead, nickel, and tin. Metallurgists will be in great demand. As consumption of the metals increases, new sources of ore, new and better methods of extracting pure metal will have to be found. This will require the services of experts in the fields of geology, chemistry, and engineering.

The large copper-producing companies are seeking technical specialists for an expanding future.

All of the primary metals industries are big, dynamic, and vital to the nation. No field of endeavor offers a more assured future nor more challenging opportunities for exploration and discovery.

9 Lumbering

Using long poles, loggers with spiked boots assemble logs at "booming grounds" for rafting. Skill and strength are required for these difficult and dangerous operations.

The story of America began as a story of forests. When the early settlers pushed westward into the wild country of what is now New England, New York, Pennsylvania, and Virginia, vast, seemingly endless forests lay before them. In this natural hunting ground, the American Indians roamed. As white men cut down the stately trees to build cabins, to burn as fuel, to make furniture, and to clear the land for planting crops, the Indians seethed with resentment. They saw their source of wealth and happiness being ruthlessly decimated without any consideration of the consequences.

Looking back, we, the descendants of those hardy settlers, are proud of many of their accomplishments and of the courage they showed in the face of hardships. But we wince at the terrible waste of vast natural resources that continued for nearly two centuries. Now at last, we realize how precious are the remaining forests. Fortunately, the modern lumbering industry is taking the necessary steps to protect its own future, along with that of the entire nation.

TREE FARMING TODAY

The richest forest area in the United States today is the Pacific Northwest, especially the states of Oregon and Washington. The Southern United States is also an im-portant production area for wood products. Canadian production is very high, although many of the forests in Canada are still virtually untouched. Alaska has vast forested areas where the lumbering industry is becoming increasingly important.

Yet with all this mass cutting of trees, our timberlands are not decreasing. This is because the modern industry carries on a carefully planned program of tree farming under the "sustained yield" plan. The plan is based on the principle of cutting about $1/80$ of a given forest area each year and immediately reforesting in the harvested section. In this way, during the full cycle of 80 years, the entire original forest is harvested, but at all times there remains a balanced crop ranging in age from one to 80 years.

Today, most of the lumbering is done on controlled tree farms, where the harvesting cycle is based on the maturing rate and habits of the tree species. Douglas firs, for example, grow best on mountainsides. Their tall, dense stands are comprised of trees approximately the same age. When areas are selected for cutting, nearby stands of mature trees are marked to be left standing. These will scatter their seeds and a new crop of seedlings will soon appear on the open slope. If a natural source of seeds is not provided, the land is reforested by artificial planting, either on the ground, or by seeding from helicopters.

Ponderosa pine farms, most of which are located east of the Cascade Mountains in southern Oregon, are handled quite differently. Over dry, level areas, these trees grow in unevenly scattered stands, with trees of all ages intermingled. Harvesting must, therefore, be done by individual selection. Foresters mark for cutting only those trees which have reached marketable maturity.

Other important lumber trees are the western red cedar, which is found along the damp coastal regions of the Northwest; western hemlock, abundant in wet areas of Oregon and Washington; loblolly pine, one of a number of southern yellow pines; and California redwood.

There are now about 9,500 private owners of timberland, whose holdings exceed forty million acres of tree farms and many more millions of acres in unregulated forestland. Less than 25% of U. S. forests are public property.

HISTORY OF LUMBERING

Lumbering is credited with being the first major industry in America. The first sawmill is reputed to have been built around 1608 at Jamestown, Va. The industry moved rapidly westward, due to the demand for virgin timber and the depletion of forests in the thickly settled East. It is said that the word, lumber, is derived from the people of Lombardy, France, who were known for their bartering and banking practices, and who sometimes used lumber as a medium of exchange.

Early American lumbering was carried out along waterways, since the logs could be floated downstream to riverside sawmills. Meanwhile, impatient settlers might be clearing out huge inland forest areas, burning and cutting indiscriminately, with the sole thought of opening up farm land.

About the turn of the last century, private industry cooperated with government agencies in plans for forest conservation. Unfortunately some property tax laws are not designed to encourage sustained yield tree farming, since they do not recognize the industry's risks from fire, disease, and insects or the slow return on investment when self-imposed harvesting restrictions decrease annual yields.

MIGHTY MEN AND TALL TALES

Logging camps are traditionally colorful places, and the typical lumberjack himself is tough, boastful, and proud of his physical prowess in work and sport. Lumbermen often dress in bright-colored, plaid, woolen shirts; in many camps warm clothing is essential, because the cutting is done in cold, northern regions and at high elevations in the mountains. Some of America's most entertaining legends have originated in logging camps where tall tales are part of the industry's stock in trade. Best known of these stories are the Paul Bunyan tales, the hero of which has supposedly accomplished astonishing feats of cutting timber, lifting impossible weights, and outfighting the roughest men of the Northwest. With his monstrous blue ox, Babe, he carries out exploits that would put Superman to shame.

A typical Paul Bunyan story tells how he made an axe handle of woven grass, swung the blade in a circle around his head and chopped down 100 trees in a single sweep. So heavy were the blue ox's shoes that a man who tried to carry one sank knee deep into solid rock. According to Paul Bunyan yarns, most of the West's natural wonders were caused by this amazing woodsman's exploits. Among his creations were such well-known landmarks as Old Faithful Geyser, the Rocky Mountains and the Grand Canyon.

Tall tales aside, lumbermen have to be hardy and skillful. The cry of "Timber-r-r" comes after axes and saws have prepared a tree to fall precisely in a prearranged spot. Often very large trees are first "topped." This is done by daring lumberjacks who climb to great heights to cut off upper sections of the trees.

MOVING THE LOGS

Transporting logs to sawmills can be a difficult and hazardous operation. Wherever possible, great masses of logs are floated to their destination in rivers or streams. Loggers with spiked boots balance on the rolling lumber, guide the logs with long poles, and prevent or break up log jams. This is frequently at the risk of their lives. Log rafts are assembled in large streams. One type is known as the Benson raft—a cigar-shaped arrangement used in the Columbia River region. Benson rafts are often 1,000 ft. long and 50 to 60 ft. wide. Bound with iron chains, one of these rafts may contain several million board feet. Ocean tugs tow them some 2,000 miles along the West Coast to San Diego, California.

Tractors and a variety of prime movers are used to drag logs on land. In winter, sledges may be employed, with a tractor pulling a long train of log piles, mounted on runners. They may be hauled to a railroad and loaded on flat cars for further transport to the mills.

A deep-sea tugboat on the Nass River in northwestern British Columbia pulls a four-boom tow (four river booms lashed together) containing about one million board feet of logs. Logs will be converted to dissolving wood pulp.

THE SAWMILL

At the sawmill, logs are moved through powerful jets of water on conveyor belts called jack ladders. This washing operation serves to remove stones and other foreign matter from the bark. Next the logs are brought on moving carriages to trimmers which square the ends and cut desired lengths. Giant circular saws, revolving at tremendous speeds, bite into massive logs as though they were cutting soft cheese; then slice off boards of various thicknesses. Other machines are used to finish the rough boards into smooth, high-grade lumber.

WOOD PRODUCTS

Nowadays, wood is used for many more purposes than for building houses and making furniture, although these uses still rank high in importance. Modern science looks upon wood as a mass of fibers and chemicals which, similar to metals, rubber, coal, or petroleum, can be broken down and reconstituted to make an amazing variety of products.

A log is made up of the outer layer, the bark; the cambium, a thin layer of cells which manufactures the wood; the sapwood which carries the sap up to the leafy branches; and the heartwood. Walls of wood cells are composed of cellulose and are cemented together with a substance called lignin. A carbohydrate, cellulose is made up of carbon, hydrogen, and oxygen, elements which the tree draws from the earth, water, and air.

Cellulose is used in the manufacture of many items, among which are cellophane and a number of other plastics and films. Wood pulp, made by dissolving lignin chemically, from the fibers, is the raw material for most of the paper we use. (See *Paper*) The forest products industry lists more than 5,000 items made from wood, wood fibers, and wood chemicals. These include lumber, plywood, many kinds of paper, fabrics such as rayon, chemicals, dyes, explosives, paints, and a host of building materials.

Modern architecture employs beautiful new finishes and textures which the industry is making available. Particularly interesting are the new plywoods which come in handsomely laminated panels for rich interiors.

Research in the chemistry of wood offers great career opportunities for young people. Studies of wood pulp are leading to new cellulose products, while forestry research is improving methods of growing, protecting, and harvesting timber. These fascinating fields offer travel and outdoor life in addition to work in the laboratories of major lumber companies.

Forestry is fast becoming one of our essential sciences. It is the lumber industry's hope for the future. Our once dwindling timberlands are staging an important comeback. This is due, in part, to increased knowledge of fire prevention, entomology, pathology, and silviculture, which is the development and cultivation of trees.

Heavy logs being transferred from truck to railroad flat cars. Logs are transported to the railroad reload area both by truck haul and over water. Logging is carried out on a year-round schedule.

When logs are delivered to the mills, they may be converted to boards or beams for building purposes or to chips for wood pulp. Here a huge circular saw bites into logs as a knife cuts butter.

10 Farming

The American farmer has more power at his command today than ever before in the history of mankind. Here a disc harrow, mounted to a tractor, does a back-breaking task with ease. In a span of 50 years, farms have undergone more changes than occurred in the previous 50 centuries.

Before the streams of work-bound traffic clog freeways into the cities on a summer day; even before the sun has cleared the early morning mists, farmers are busy feeding their livestock or starting up their tractors for a day in the fields. The broad meadows are drenched with dew; the green rows of sprouting crops are glistening in the dawn light, and in the barnyard a cock is crowing. While the industrial world of rocketry, plastics, and atomic energy roars and thunders with explosive new progress, the earth continues to give man his sustenance. The sun and the rain give life to growing things, and the farmer continues his age-old struggle with the soil. But the nature of this struggle has undergone great changes in the past few years.

Farming is the oldest industry of civilized man. The cultivation of plants for food and the domestication of animals was, indeed, the very beginning of civilization. Prior to the development of farming, the human race lived a nomadic existence, wandering in search of wild roots and berries, following the game which men hunted with crude weapons. Not until the farmer began to tend his animals and to cultivate his fields did towns and villages spring into being. Only then did people remain long in one place and only then did other industry evolve.

The contemporary American farm is as modern as a missile base and, in its own way, as mechanized as a plastics factory. The smell of new-mown hay is still as sweet

as it was in ancient times, and the broad fields of wheat and corn wave in the breeze as they have always done, while the meadowlark sings his haunting song. But today, the farmer uses machines to lighten the physical toil. One harvesting machine can do the work of a hundred field hands. The farmer rides easily, handling the controls. In a space of 50 years, farms have undergone more changes than occurred in the previous 50 centuries.

FARMING THROUGH THE AGES

Since earliest times, famine has haunted men; it still stalks many areas of the earth. America is one of the few countries in the world where hunger is not commonplace. Even in Colonial America, farming was little different from what it had been in ancient Egypt. Although it is impossible to trace the beginnings of cultivation, most historians agree that the breeding of animals and seeding of food crops began about 7000 B.C. One of the first written records of farming tells of planting summer wheat in Egypt about 5000 B.C. Barley and millet were also grown in Egypt, and it is believed that people learned to plant banana shoots in Asia at a still earlier date.

During Europe's Stone Age, about 8000 B.C., pigs, sheep, goats, cattle, and horses were domesticated. As in Egypt, the chief crops were wheat, barley, and millet. In the Far East, rice has been the great food staple since earliest times, while maize was the basic grain of the Americas. Throughout all these ancient periods and civilizations, terrible famines were recorded again and again. Men could find no way to control or compensate for the ravages of nature. Not until the seventeenth century did farmers begin to experiment with fertilizers and crop rotation. But they had little scientific knowledge and only the crudest of implements to do their work.

FARMING IN AMERICA

It is difficult to realize that, in Colonial America, 85% of the population was engaged in agriculture; for all that, it provided only a mediocre diet. The North American continent was a wild, thickly forested land. Pioneer farmers literally hacked out their farms with axes, and laboriously dug up the stumps and roots. Then, with crude wooden plows, differing little from those of ancient times, they broke up the sod. This they did with their long rifles slung over their shoulders—one eye to the furrow, the other on the edge of the woods where hostile Indians might be lurking. Horses or oxen pulled the plows, which farmers guided by hand.

munal and tenant farming has always existed in most European countries where the old feudal system has had its influence even down to modern times. The American tradition of individualism and free enterprise owes much to the development of private farms, and to the early settler's fierce pride in his land.

GROWTH OF MECHANIZED FARMING

Why is America the best-fed nation in the world? Is American soil more fertile? No; as a matter of fact there are many areas of the world with greater yield per acre. Are there more farmers in America? Actually, there are fewer farmers in proportion to the population (only 12%) than in any other country. The answer lies in an amazingly high rate of production per worker, due to modern farm machinery and to scientific growing methods. Every U.S. agricultural worker produces enough food for 25 people. On farms which do an annual volume of $10,000 or over, each worker produces enough for 45 people. Today, the average farm worker has 80 horsepower at his command compared with 5.3 horsepower in 1920 and a mere 1.6 in 1870. Whereas a man using a steel walking plow

Farmers of 1831 used the cradle to harvest standing grain. With this tool, one man could cut efficiently only about two acres a day. Today's huge combine harvests and threshes wheat mechanically in a single unit. More than a million combines are now operating on American farms.

In 1788, Thomas Jefferson applied mathematics to the designing of a more efficient moldboard. A cast iron plow was patented in 1797.

Despite these attempts to improve farm implements, plowing remained one of the farmer's most difficult tasks. When western settlers tried to turn rich black soil along the Mississippi, the earth clung to wooden moldboards of the plows, making constant scraping necessary. So serious was this problem that many farmers actually returned to the East rather than continue to struggle with the sticky western soil. Finally, steel blades did the job. When John Deere introduced the steel plow in 1837, a major milestone in farm history had been reached.

Because America has so much land, private ownership of farms has become more prevalent in the United States and in Canada than in any other part of the world. Com-

could cover an acre a day in 1860, the modern farmer can plow 15 acres or more, in a day, with comparatively little effort.

During the nineteenth century, plow design and construction underwent constant improvements. In 1868, the plow moldboard and share were made of soft-center steel, with the outer part heat treated and hardened. This prevented cracking or warping.

Harrowing was originally accomplished with a tree limb, having branch stubs serving for teeth. Disk and spring-tooth harrows were introduced in the 1860's. Instead of dragging over roots and grassy clods, disks slice through them and are valuable particularly in hard or sticky soils.

Oddly enough, seeding machines were invented in ancient times. As long ago as 2800 B.C. the Chinese had a wheelbarrow type of seed drill, and wheel seeders with

A step in the evolution of farm machinery was the Marsh harvester in 1858. This machine employed continuous canvas aprons to raise grain to a table, where two men could bind and throw the bundles over the side.

funnels were used in Italy about 1600. But for some reason these mechanical advances were forgotten in later centuries and men endured backbreaking labor with the hoe. An American two-row corn planter appeared in 1860. It was operated by two men; one drove, the other operated a tripping mechanism to release the seeds. By 1875 the machine was made for operation by one person.

Meanwhile mechanical harvesters were being developed. The scythe's only improvement in over 4,000 years was the "cradle," a scythe which American farmers used in the early nineteenth century. This implement had a wooden framework for catching enough stalks to make up a sheaf. But in the 1830's, some mechanical reapers appeared. Their use was resisted by farm workers who feared being put out of work. Nevertheless, the sale of reapers continued to increase until, by 1855, nearly 10,000 were in use on American farms. By 1880, this figure had increased to more than 35,000.

The man who contributed the most to farm mechanization was Cyrus Hall McCormick. He patented his first reaper in 1834. With the help of his father, Robert McCormick, he struggled for ten years to improve and market the reaper, yet by 1842 he had sold only seven of the machines. A rival reaper invented by Obed Hussey was offering stiff competition. In 1847, McCormick moved his manufacturing operations from his native Virginia to Chicago. Realizing that the opening of the West with its vast farmlands would provide a great opportunity for his mechanical reapers, he personally demonstrated the machine at western county fairs. By 1856, he was operating, in Chicago, a five-story factory which was turning out about forty reapers a day.

The McCormick reaper, more than any other single development, was responsible for the greatest revolution in all of farming's long history. Following the reaper came the harvester, the wire binder, the twine binder, and finally the most spectacular of farm machines, the combine, which harvests and threshes wheat or other grain in a single unit. Early horse-drawn models covered 25 acres a day. Attempts to apply steam power to the combine were unsatisfactory, because of the unwieldy equipment required and the excessive amount of grain wasted. Not until gasoline power became available, did combines come

into general use. Today, there are more than a million combines operating on American farms.

FARM EQUIPMENT INDUSTRY

From McCormick's reaper factory and from William Deering's Harvester Company, there grew up in the Chicago area one of the world's greatest industries. These and several other farm equipment companies were merged in 1902 to become the International Harvester Company, one of America's major corporations. International's 1960 annual report showed one hundred four thousand two hundred seventy-eight employees throughout the world, and worldwide sales of nearly one billion seven hundred million dollars. The company is owned by more than a hundred thousand stockholders who hold more than fourteen million shares of common stock.

The age of tractor power, which began just prior to World War I, has brought about a phenomenal growth of the farm machine industry. In addition to International Harvester, makers of Farmall tractors and a great variety of reapers and harvesters, are such world renowned firms as Allis-Chalmers, which manufactures tractors of all kinds, cultivators, cotton strippers, and pickers; Ford Motor Company, which produces many types of tractors and motorized equipment; New Holland Farm Machinery Company, specializing in hay and forage equipment; Windsor Pippin Corporation, makers of backhoes, loaders, and bulldozers, Deere and Company, manufacturers of various agricultural implements.

In the United States there are over 20,000 farm equipment dealers and wholesalers who sell and service agricultural machinery.

SUPERHUMAN MACHINES

Nowadays farmers can find a machine to perform almost any agricultural task. Tractor-drawn plows, harrows, drills, cultivators, mowers, and power-driven harvesters are available for all sorts of soils, crops, and climates. Basic machines are provided with an assortment of attachments and ground rigs which can dig furrows, plant seeds at specified depths, fertilize the soil, cover the seeds with the proper amount of earth, or press the seed into firm, moist soil. Two- to four-row planters can also be used for preemergence spraying to control weeds. All of these steps can be performed in a single operation. Later, mechanical cul-

The McCormick Reaper Works, built in 1847, is on the Chicago River. The McCormick reaper was responsible for the greatest revolution in farming history.

Henry Ford, Sr., is seated on one of his first farm tractors which he called an "automobile plow." The photograph was taken in 1907 when gasoline tractors were rare.

Picking corn is highly mechanized on most large farms today. Here is a two-row corn picker mounted on a tractor and trailed by a wagon, which receives the corn ears from an automatic loading mechanism.

tivators are used to loosen the soil four to six rows at a time, as the wheels of the tractor and its attachments straddle the ranks of growing crops. Accurate row spacing and depth regulation are achieved by means of easy bolt adjustments.

One of the most amazing of modern farm machines is the cotton picker, successful models of which appeared in 1941. Driven by a single operator, this compact unit can accomplish in an hour what formerly required two men working a full ten-hour day. Height of the picking unit is hydraulically controlled so that it follows the ground contour to pick low cotton as well as the bolls on tall plants. A number of "gathering snouts" gently draw the branches of the cotton plants into mechanical picking units. A jet stream of warm air carries the cotton at a mile-a-minute speed from the stripping unit into a large cage-like basket. The air serves to fluff the fibers as well as deliver the cotton into the basket. The entire picker can be re-

moved from an ordinary field tractor which provides the motive power. Seeders, cultivators, and other attachments can be used with the tractor at other seasons of the year.

Combines can be equipped with "corn heads" to harvest corn. After corn ears are automatically picked, husked, and shelled, the kernels enter a grain tank and are finally delivered through a chute into a truck which moves along beside the combine. Corn pickers are also made to pick and husk whole ears which are then automatically loaded into a trailer-type wagon. Each of these machines is operated by one man.

Other important farm machines include milking machines (See *Food Products*); sprayers and dusters to control plant disease and insects; automatic loaders; portable sprinklers for local irrigation. Windsor Pippin Corporation advertises a stump cutter which will process stumps up to 92 in. in diameter and 24 in. in height, and will remove roots 10 in. below ground.

The most important machine of all is the modern mechanical workhorse of farming, the tractor. Production of these versatile vehicles began about 1906. At that time there were 11 tractor companies. Their total output in 1907 was 600 machines. The industry rapidly expanded to comprise 31 manufacturers by 1909 with production in that year reaching 2,000 units. When early steel wheels were replaced by low-pressure rubber tires, the modern tractor really came into its own. (See *Rubber*) Now, conservative estimates indicate that on American farms there are over five million farm tractors and about half a million of the new small-size garden variety. Garden tractors are coming more and more into use in small truck gardens and for a variety of farm chores where the standard tractors are unwieldy. Latest ultramodern tractor designs include such features as electrically controlled magnetic coupling and television screens inside all-weather cabs, to show operators how the equipment is performing at all times.

MAJOR FARM CROPS AND PRODUCTS

America's staple grain crops include corn, wheat, barley, and rice. Another crop which has gained in importance in recent years is soybeans which are used, among other things, in the manufacture of plastics and paints. Tobacco is widely grown in New England and in the South. (See *Tobacco*) In the midwest area, which encompasses Ohio, Indiana, Illinois, and Iowa, we find the richest of all farm areas, the corn belt. Farms of this region are notable for their up-to-date equipment and businesslike management. The people are prosperous; the farms, neat and well tended. From eastern North Carolina, across the lower Mississippi and into western Texas, cotton is the major crop. Cotton growing has suffered from the inroads of new synthetic fibers. The industry, however, has been staging a comeback, due to the increase in mechanization, with the development of the mechanical pickers and strippers. The dominant crop in western Kansas is winter wheat; spring wheat is found in North Dakota.

Herds of range livestock roam the plains from Mexico to Canada and from the Rockies to the Mississippi River. Here are the great cattle ranches, the homes of America's colorful cowboys, and their world-famous rodeos. From the plains states, the great Chicago stockyards receive beef cattle to supply the meat-packing industry. (See *Food Products*)

Most of America's large dairy farms are found in the East and in the Great Lakes regions. Usually, they are located close to large cities where milk and cheese processing plants are operated, and where large markets exist for dairy products. (See *Food Products*)

Specialty crops are common in the far West. There we find America's largest vineyards. Apricots, almonds, alfalfa, asparagus, cherries, prunes, lemons, oranges, and peaches are grown in abundance on the West Coast. The greatest region for citrus fruit farms is Florida, source of grapefruit, oranges, lemons, limes, and tangerines. Hawaii's principal crops are pineapples and sugar cane.

The types of farming found in various sections of the North American continent are largely governed by climate. Yet the farmer still must contend with unusual weather conditions, storms, and severe changes of temperature. Weather is either the farmer's best friend or his worst enemy. Though human ingenuity has yet to devise a means of controlling the weather, farmers do attempt to modify growing conditions by irrigation, various protective coverings for plants at certain seasons, and by wise planning based on improved weather forecasting. Space technology, which is expected to make important advances in meteorology, can therefore have practical value for the farmer.

SCIENCE ON THE FARM

As this is a scientific age, it would be surprising if science had not entered the farming industry. There are several areas of agriculture where the laboratory plays a vital role. Studies of soil chemistry, fertilizers, plant and animal diseases, insect control, and hybridization of plants, represent only a few of the many scientific programs being conducted by chemical firms, oil companies, seed growers, canners,

dairy and meat products companies, and a host of related industries. (See *Food Products, Chemicals, Petroleum*)

To assist farmers, there are a number of agencies and organizations, including agricultural schools, the United States Department of Agriculture, and county agents. One of the most active farm organizations is the Farmers Union, or Farmers Educational and Cooperative Union of America, whose chief function is to promote legislation that will be beneficial to agriculture. The Union has some three hundred thousand members in forty states. Most young people in the farm areas belong to the 4-H Club. Working under the guidance of Cooperative Extension workers or local volunteer leaders, boys and girls from 10 to 21 years of age are encouraged in farming and home-making activities. The four H's are *head, heart, hands, and health*. With over two million members and some ninety-one thousand local Clubs spread throughout every state of the Union and Puerto Rico, 4-H is one of the world's greatest young people's associations. Projects fostered by the Club include raising livestock, developing improved crops, canning fruit. Frequent 4-H competitions are held at county fairs where America's future farmers exhibit their handiwork or their prize animals and produce.

Another important aspect of the farm industry is the Cooperative. In many parts of the country, farmers have joined cooperatives for the purpose of marketing their crops at better prices without employing the services of middlemen.

CONTRACT FARMING

With the growth of America's huge canning industry (See *Food Products*), many farmers plant crops which are sold before the seeds are in the ground. Canning companies contract to purchase tremendous quantities of fruits and vegetables of all kinds, and their support of farmers has helped to stabilize the industry by providing a sure,

Most amazing of modern farm machines, the cotton picker is a compact unit which can be driven by a single operator. This two-row picker can do in an hour what formerly required two men working a ten-hour day.

The tractor is the workhorse of modern farming. This farmer is using an Allis-Chalmers forage blower, powered by a tractor. A second tractor provides the operating power for a self-unloading forage wagon.

steady market for perishable foods. Some farmers turn over their entire production to canning firms; others enter into contracts only for certain crops or for specified portions of their crops.

In sugar beet farming, the practice is for the sugar mills to pay for the crop on the basis of the amount of sugar yield, rather than on the weight or bulk of the beets delivered by the farmer. (See *Sugar, Salt*)

FARMING IS BIG BUSINESS

Although a great many small farms still exist in America, and although many of these have remained virtually untouched by modern mechanization, their number is steadily decreasing. Farming in the past 50 years has been so transformed by science and technology that it has become an industry in the true sense of the word. It is joining the ranks of big business.

The modern farm requires large capital outlays for up-to-date machinery. At the same time, the speed and efficiency of mechanized farming is such that it becomes practicable only on large farms with high rates of production. As in any other business, expensive, high-speed machinery pays for itself only when it can be operated at full or nearly full capacity. As a result, the number of large, well-managed farms is increasing while the old-fashioned family farms are slowly disappearing from the American scene.

Today, the farmer is likely to be well acquainted with modern business methods. Usually he has an up-to-date bookkeeping and filing system. Large farms may have cost accounting procedures in which the amortization of ma-

Cattle are served by a McCormick power forage feeder, powered by a tractor.

chines and other property is calculated, along with operating costs, in making up profit and loss figures.

According to the Department of Agriculture statistics the size of the average American farm in 1960 was 315 acres. Despite a great increase in food production and consumption, modern mechanization of farms has reduced annual man-hours in agriculture from twenty-three billion in 1920 to twelve billion in the 60's.

There is little doubt that the next few years will show equally significant progress. Farming in America scarcely can be said to offer a leisurely, easy way of life; still, it no longer involves either the backbreaking drudgery or the fear of ruinous crop failures that were commonplace a century ago. The future of farming points to the same realms as do so many other industries—to its science and technology. Today, we see airplanes dusting crops and sowing the seed for vast wheat or rice fields. Giant combines bring in the harvest efficiently and with astonishing speed. New fertilizers and hybridized seeds are producing larger and better crops. Vitamin enriched feed gives us improved strains of poultry and cattle. Nowadays, it is almost unheard of to have a "tough bird" at a Thanksgiving or a Christmas dinner. Steaks are literally tenderized "on the hoof."

These and many other advances which benefit both the farmer and the consumer are keeping career-minded young people down on the farm, not merely as tillers of the soil, but as accountants, marketing experts, technicians, mechanics, veterinarians, scientists, and agricultural engineers. In this second half of the twentieth century, farming is, indeed, big business.

American farm machinery is extremely versatile and is made so that a number of units can be linked up in tandem. Here a combination of units forms an eight-row planter pulled by a Farmall tractor.

11 Sugar and Salt

Sugar cane is still harvested by machete-wielding workers in countries where labor costs are low. This wagon is being loaded with cane in Puerto Rico.

Although sugar and salt are not foods in themselves, they are essential elements in human diet, and few foods are prepared without the addition of one or the other. In many instances, both sugar and salt must be added to make foods palatable. Of the two, salt is probably the more important, because natural sugars in fruits, milk, and certain vegetables might suffice if no other sugar were available. But a certain amount of table salt is an absolute requirement for the health of normal people.

SUGAR

Sugar is a popular food additive, regardless of its nutritive value. Throughout modern history it has been enjoyed in all sorts of confections, beverages, and desserts. Among the earliest writings to mention cane sugar are the accounts of Alexander the Great's Indus River expedition in 325 B.C. The chronicler referred to "honey bearing reeds." There is Biblical mention of "sweet cane from a far country." Beet sugar, on the other hand, was not known until a German chemist named Marggraf discovered a way to extract it from the beets in 1747.

Despite its long history, cane sugar was considered a luxury for many centuries. In 1742, it sold in London for the equivalent of nearly three dollars a pound.

The sugar industry now produces millions of pounds of fine, granulated cane sugar every day. One large American company's daily output is some seventeen million pounds. From the growing of cane in tropical countries to the packaging and distributing of the finished product, a host of complex operations is involved.

Large sugar cane plantations are found in Cuba, Puerto

Rico, the Philippines, Hawaii, India, Java, most South and Central American countries, Egypt, South Africa, Formosa, and Australia. The plant, which grows in clumps of canes eight to twenty feet in height, is started from foot-long cuttings, each having two or three seed buds. Harvesting occurs once every 12 to 14 months. Though mechanical harvesters are coming into use, most of the cutting is still done by field workers wielding machetes. The machines have serious competition in countries with low-cost labor where a good worker can cut and load several tons of cane a day.

Harvested cane is received at the raw sugar mills or "centrals." There, crushing rollers shred the canes, then steel rollers press out the juice. The fuel, used to generate power for the mill, consists often of waste cane fibers called "bagasse."

The cane juice is heated and filtered. In steam-heated evaporators, the juice is converted to syrup and finally boiled in large tanks. Properly controlled heating causes the syrup to crystallize, and a mass of molasses and sugar crystals is then pumped into centrifugal machines. These basket-like drums revolve at 1,000 to 2,000 rpm, whirling off the liquid molasses while sugar crystals remain trapped inside the screen. This crystalline residue is the raw sugar, not usable as food, which is shipped in burlap bags from the cane-growing country to overseas refineries. Some modern ships are built to take the raw sugar in bulk into their holds, to be unloaded later on automatic conveyors.

Large sugar refineries are located in New Orleans, Philadelphia, Baltimore, Boston, and New York. Refining operations begin with crushing raw sugar lumps and mixing the charge with syrup to form a thick fluid known as "magma." Next, centrifugal washers remove a molasses film from the crystals; warm water dissolves them. To this solution is added diatomaceous earth, a porous substance which absorbs impurities. Cloth filters are used to separate the amber-colored liquid sugar from the diatomaceous earth. Finally, the last vestiges of color are removed by passing the liquid through granular bone char in huge tanks about 20 ft. high. When the clear sugar solution is conveyed to steam-heated vacuum pans, it boils at low temperature. Water content evaporates, and the remaining sugar forms into crystals. Still, the refining process is not complete. Further mixing with magma syrup, and centrifugal separation are required to produce the pure, snow-white grains suitable for packaging and delivery to the markets.

BEET SUGAR

Pure sugar, or sucrose, may be extracted from many plants and fruits, though some plants contain more of this carbohydrate than others. While cane sugar is still the principal source, more beet sugar is being used every year. Actually, refined beet sugar cannot be distinguished from the cane product, as each type is 99.9% sucrose.

In the United States, the growing of sugar beets and refining of beet sugar has spread to 22 states. Though the processing is basically the same as for cane sugar, it is more often accomplished by a continuous operation, in a single factory, from raw sugar through the various stages to the refined product. Since sugar beets grow well in arid regions wherever irrigation water is available, a large part of the industry is located west of the Mississippi. Beet sugar factories, close to the growing areas, are located in California, Washington State, Montana, Idaho, Utah, Kansas, Nebraska, and Minnesota, as well as in Canada, where sugar beets thrive. In all, there are some seventy beet sugar factories in the United States and six in Canada.

Today, beet harvesting is almost completely mechanized. As there are several operations involved, complex machines had to be perfected; most of them have been developed since World War II. Beets have very long taproots, often extending six or seven feet into the ground. A beet lifter loosens the plants, pulls up the long, sugar-bearing roots, cuts off leafy tops. Automatic loaders fill trucks which carry the crop to refineries, while beet tops are loaded separately as feed for livestock. There are machines to pulverize the leaves used for fertilizer; others perform the whole series of operations in one continuous cycle.

Recent giant strides in beet sugar production are due largely to laboratory research, which has given American farmers a superior strain of beets especially adapted to American soil and climate. Until recently, nearly all sugar beet seed came from European producers. But U.S. researchers discovered a method of planting in fall months to raise seed-bearing stalks early the following spring. The result was a quicker and easier way of seed harvesting, known as "overwintering."

Since growers raise sugar beets under contract with the sugar companies, there is close cooperation between the two. Sugar-company field men help the farmer to improve his crops. A unique feature of this industry is the practice of paying the farmer on the basis of the amount of sugar extracted per ton of beets. Thus the farmer's income is related directly to the net return achieved by the processor, rather than to the gross weight regardless of quality of the crop. The arrangement has the advantage of giving farmer and processor a mutual interest in improved technology and in efficient operations.

SUGAR PRODUCTS AND BY-PRODUCTS

In addition to refined crystallized sugar, there are several familiar sugar products available in the markets. These include brown sugar, containing a percentage of cane syrup;

Hundreds of cane varieties are crossbred at the Experiment Station of the Hawaiian Sugar Planters Association. Each year, half a million sugar cane seedlings are developed from crosses of the world's best commercial canes.

A modern 12-roller mill in one of Hawaii's 26 sugar mills. These mechanized plants represent some of America's finest skill and know-how. Over a million tons of sugar are processed annually in Hawaiian sugar mills.

invert sugar, an acid-produced mixture of dextrose and levulose. Invert sugar, having greater moisture retention than other types of sugar, is valuable for the preservation of certain foods. Liquid sugars, or syrups, include the invert sugars as well as other colorless solutions. Refiners' syrups are the strong-flavored dark liquid by-products of the cane sugar refining process. Molasses, a still thicker syrup, sometimes known as the "mother liquor" is drawn off during the production of raw cane sugar. The third and final boiling in the processing of raw sugar produces the very dark "blackstrap" molasses which is used mostly in making industrial alcohol. Beet blackstrap, the comparable product of beet sugar production, is valuable as cattle feed and for the manufacture of yeast and citric acid.

Powdered, confectioners' sugars, widely employed in candy and pastry manufacture, are ground to varying degrees of fineness and are usually packed with small amounts of cornstarch which prevents caking.

Dextrose, or corn sugar, results from the inversion of sucrose, but it is generally produced from starch by means of heat and acids. Half as sweet as sucrose, it is used by food industries where a sweetening less soluble than ordinary sugar is desired.

Another well-known and popular sugar is made from the sap of the sugar maple tree. Production of maple sugar and maple syrup is largely a New England and Canadian industry since the sugar maple is a native of those colder regions. The sap is tapped when it begins to run in early spring, and after being collected in pails, it is taken to mills—often small, privately operated boilers. There it is crystallized or converted to maple syrup. As its production is slow and as sources of supply are limited, maple sugar products are expensive. They are used largely in the candy and confectionery industries and are valued for their distinctive flavor.

USES OF SUGAR

America's immensely sweet tooth is not the only demand made upon the sugar industry. In addition to the millions of pounds of candy, tons of ice cream, the cakes, pies, cookies, desserts, canned food products, and just plain table sugar used in millions of cups of coffee and tea, there are a number of important industrial operations requiring sugar. These include the manufacture of synthetic rubber, acetone, histamine, certain plastics, textiles, paper, soap, cement, and cosmetics. Annual world consumption of sugar is about fifty million tons, of which the United States uses close to ten million.

SALT

An essential, life-giving substance, salt (sodium chloride) has been mined from the earth and extracted from seawater for thousands of years. So important is salt to human existence that ancient tribal wars were fought over salt deposits and over sources of brine, while many religious rites grew up based on the belief in the divine properties of salt. In the Hebrew "covenant of salt," the sacred mineral was a symbol of perpetuity. Christ referred to His disciples as "salt of the earth," thus emphasizing their spiritual role in the world.

An automatic filling machine in operation at Morton Salt Company. Operator watches as four lines of filled cans converge and leave the filler in single file.

Even before the time of Alexander the Great, huge salt mines were being worked in northern India. There is reference to the production of salt from seawater almost 4,800 years ago by Peng-Tzao-Kan-Mu, a Chinese chronicler. Probably the belief, that spilling salt is unlucky, grew from Leonardo da Vinci's painting of "The Last Supper," which shows an overturned salt cellar in front of Judas Iscariot.

SOURCES

Fortunately for mankind, the sources of salt are virtually inexhaustible. Estimates state that the seas contain four and one-half million cubic miles of salt, since most seawater holds about three-eighths of a pound of salt per gallon of water. There is still considerable production of ocean salt by evaporation being carried on in France, Portugal, the San Francisco Bay area, and at Great Salt Lake, Utah; however, most of the world's supply comes from mined rock salt. The most important North American deposits are in Michigan, New York, Ohio, Kansas, California, Louisiana, and in Ontario, Canada. Smaller quantities are found in many other states. America's largest salt deposits are at Retsof, N.Y. and the deep shaft mine near Detroit, Mich. The supply seems to be unlimited. In Nevada there is a saline bluff extending along the Virgin River for 25 miles.

SALT MINING

The mining of rock salt is accomplished in much the same manner as the mining of coal. (See *Mining*) Shafts are sunk, often deep into the ground, until the salt deposit is reached. Nowadays, automatic cutting and breaking machines are used to loosen the salt, load it into cars or onto conveyors which transport it to the surface.

So pure is most rock salt that it needs no refining, but may simply be crushed into fine, natural crystals which are then ready for packaging.

Occasionally, where natural brine is found, salt wells are

dug. The brine is pumped to the surface, and the salt is extracted by evaporation of the water in steam-heated pans.

USES AND BY-PRODUCTS OF SALT

Salt companies offer several grades of salt for a variety of uses. These include finely ground table salt, dairy salt, and packer's salt, which is used in the preservation of meat and fish.

In addition to its importance in food industries, salt is used in a large number of manufacturing operations. For example, the manufacture of chemicals requires more salt than any other basic industry. It is an ingredient in the production of soda ash, sodium carbonate, and caustic soda. It is used to harden soaps, glaze pottery, cure hides in leather manufacturing, and to increase the clarity of glass. As a fertilizer, it serves to hold moisture and to free inert plant food in the soil.

Recently, there has been an increasing use of rock salt in the building of gravel roads and in supplementing gravel along the shoulders of highways. Salt stabilization in road building has proved to be both effective and economical. It is also an excellent melting agent to keep roads and sidewalks free from ice and snow in the winter time.

SALT AND HEALTH

In every organ in the human body, and in every microscopic cell, a small percentage of salt is required for the maintenance of life. About .6% sodium chloride is found in blood plasma as well as in the fluid surrounding the cells. If a person loses too much salt, he becomes easily tired, suffers from cramps and dizziness. If the condition becomes extreme, the patient may languish and die. When Napoleon's army retreated from Moscow, hundreds of his soldiers died because slight wounds failed to heal due to salt deficiency.

It is particularly important for people to have extra salt in their diet during hot weather when perspiration robs them of salt.

Salt production is an essential and fairly stabilized industry whose future growth will doubtless be in proportion to the increase in population.

In the room-and-pillar method of salt mining, salt is removed in checkerboard pattern and leaves permanent solid pillars of salt standing for roof support. A shuttle car is seen on its way to get a new load of salt after delivering a load to the crusher.

Aluminum six-ounce cans are filled with citrus juice concentrate prior to freezing in a Florida processing plant.

12 Food Products

For centuries one of the most pressing problems of mankind was the preservation, storage, and transportation of food. It is amazing that men were able to explore the earth as they did without adequate methods of food preservation. Imagine the conditions aboard Columbus' ship when, after several weeks at sea, the only food available was bad salt pork infested with maggots, and perhaps some mouldy bread! The prevalence of scurvy among seamen, due entirely to dietary deficiency, plagued sailing vessels as late as the nineteenth century. In 1795, when France was at war with most of the nations of Europe, the problem of feeding the armies became so acute that the French Government offered a 12,000-franc prize to anyone who could perfect a way of preserving food in the field.

Nicolas Appert, a French chef, pickler, brewer, and confectioner, worked at the problem for 14 years. At last, in 1809, he was awarded the government prize by Napoleon when he demonstrated that food which he had boiled in sealed bottles remained wholesome after many weeks at sea.

In his journal, Appert wrote, "I prepared these articles as if for common use, but only three-fourths dressed, the young partridges being roasted. When they were grown cold, I put these articles into bottles of a sufficient size, having well corked, luted, and dropped them all into the water bath which was kept on the boil for half an hour. They were . . . sent to sea for four months and ten days, together with some vegetables and gravy. . . . When opened, 18 different kinds of preserved food were tasted, every one of which had retained its freshness, and not a single substance had undergone the least change at sea."

Nicolas Appert, using his prize money as capital, established his own canning factory which his descendants are still operating. Recognized as the father of the canning industry, Appert has been humorously immortalized by canners who claim that canned food is "appertising."

Today, with so many varieties of canned, bottled, and packaged foods available to us, it is hard to imagine how people existed without them.

69

CANNING INDUSTRY

Canning is big business in the United States. There are about 2,700 canneries in 49 of the 50 states (Nevada is the exception), and in all the territories. Annual production is more than twenty-two billion pounds representing nearly 9% of the total U.S. supply of food. Retail sale of canned foods amounts to about four and three-fourths billion dollars a year. Americans can buy at least 1,000 different canned food items which include fruits, vegetables, juices, fish, seafoods, meats, soups, baby foods, milk, jams, and jellies. The industry employs some three hundred fifty thousand workers.

HISTORY OF CANNING

Since Nicolas Appert's discovery, the canning of foods has developed at an accelerated pace throughout the world. Strangely, Appert learned how to preserve foods without understanding why his process worked. Not until Louis Pasteur discovered that food spoiled because of the presence of bacteria, was the answer found; even then the importance of destroying bacteria was not fully appreciated. In the late nineteenth century, H. L. Russell in Wisconsin, Samuel C. Prescott and W. L. Underwood in Massachusetts demonstrated that bacteria were the offending agent in food fermentation.

Canning is a word which embraces all cooking of food in airtight containers. It came into use after 1810 when Peter Durand patented a tin canister in England. His container was made of tin-coated iron. A good tinsmith could produce 10 of these cans per day!

The U.S. canning industry was started by an Englishman, William Underwood, who arrived in New Orleans in 1817 with the express purpose of setting up a canning plant. Unfortunately, no one could be found to back his enterprise. His limited funds exhausted, he walked the entire distance from New Orleans to Boston, and there, in 1820, he at last succeeded in setting up a small plant for the canning of fruits and pickles.

At the same time, the canning of salmon, lobsters, and oysters was being carried out by Thomas Kensett and Ezra Dagget in New York. Kensett was granted the first American patent for a tin canister in 1825. Soon the abbreviated word "can" came into common use, and to this day the lowly tin can plays a vital role in everyday living.

THE TIN CAN GOES TO WAR

No sooner had the guns begun to thunder in Virginia in 1861, than the federal armies clamored for more and more canned food. Fortunately by this time, canners had discovered that, by adding calcium chloride to the water in which cans were cooked, higher temperatures were achieved and the processing time could be shortened. Both the Union and the Confederate forces used tremendous quantities of canned foods during the Civil War.

After the War, in 1874, A. K. Shriver of Baltimore invented the retort, or pressure cooker, which made it possible to control accurately the cooking temperature of canned foods. The retort replaced the calcium chloride processing method.

By the time of World War II, two-thirds of the food supply used by the Armed Forces was in cans. However, when Japan seized major tin sources in Malaya, American canning factories faced a serious shortage of metal. New types of packaging were introduced, and the use of glass became more prevalent.

Although glass jars were employed in the earliest days of the canning industry, the original methods of sealing were far from satisfactory. Modern science and machinery have overcome this difficulty. The greatest advance in this area was the creation of machinery for vacuum packing in the 1930's. Meanwhile new types of glass have been introduced with lighter weight, greater tensile strength, higher heat resistance, and improved design. In recent years, glass containers have become almost as common as cans for vegetables, fruits, and other popular canned foods.

RESEARCH AND DEVELOPMENT

Improvements in canning methods and materials never cease. As in most other American industries, there are tremendous opportunities for scientists and technicians in the field of food technology. This comparatively new science now boasts a professional organization, The Institute of Food Technologists. Since it was founded in 1939, its membership has grown to several thousand.

What do food technologists, working for large canning concerns, hope to accomplish?

Research carries the scientist into the field, to the farms and to the farmers themselves, for the canning industry depends entirely upon sound growing practices. Canners generally contract for huge quantities of produce even in advance of planting; they pay farmers more than a billion dollars a year for top-grade crops. Thus they share the farmer's risk and aid him in every possible way. Canners' research seeks improvement of farm machinery, fertilizers, pest and weed controls, and strains of fruits and vegetables. Their laboratories are working on such projects as improved processing, prevention of spoilage, disposal of factory waste, quality controls, better containers.

Among the improved processes recently perfected are high temperature sterilizing, agitating cooks, and "aseptic canning." In the latter process, the food product is sterilized and cooled prior to being put into sterilized containers. Food technicians are currently studying methods of sterilization by radiation. Experiments with the radiation of atomic fission materials show great promise for the future.

HOW CANS ARE MADE

Machine-made cans, are a far cry from Peter Durand's tin canisters. Not only are they produced at higher speed, but they are safer and more efficient food containers. The modern open-top cylindrical can, known as the "sanitary can," was introduced around the turn of the century. Before that time, cans were constructed with small openings, caps for which had to be soldered in place.

Bodies and ends of cylindrical cans are cut from sheets of tin plate. This plate is in reality about 99% sheet steel, with a thin 1% coating of tin. The tin is applied to the steel by a process of electrolysis.

The body blanks are fed into a machine called the body

maker. This notches corners and turns back each edge, forming hooks which will lock the cylinder together. A flanger curls the rims outward. Meanwhile, the circular ends are punched from sheets of "tin." When the rims are curled, a thin film of rubber composition is applied to them. Finally the flanges of the bodies and the rims of the ends are folded together so tightly that the layer of rubber renders the end seams absolutely airtight. The side seam is made airtight by applying solder to the outside of the can.

Some years ago, unfavorable publicity about poisonous effects of tin on certain foods caused many people to avoid canned products. But scientific studies have conclusively proved that tin is perfectly harmless. It is true that most foods, particularly fruits, have a slight solvent action on tin. This chemical reaction is a safeguard, however, since it prevents attack on the steel under the tin coating. Some colored foods, such as small red fruits, are slowly bleached by ordinary tin plate, while certain food proteins release sulphur when heated, causing reaction with the tin that discolors the food. These harmless but unpleasant chemical reactions are prevented by baking special lacquers on the inside surfaces of the cans.

MECHANIZED OPERATIONS

Canning is one of the most highly mechanized of all industries. The phrase "untouched by human hands" is its byword, the only exception being in the initial trimming of some fresh foods.

Inside the canning factory, we follow a whole series of amazing automatic operations. In flumes of running water, we watch veritable rivers of tempting fruit or vegetables flowing rapidly toward the canning line. Moving mesh screens with different mesh openings sort the crop according to size. Chaff and other unwanted matter is removed in a flotation washer where food is floated free of dirt.

There are special machines for almost every type of food and for each phase of the canning operation. For example, the pea cutter-loader cuts entire pea vines from the roots and loads them onto trucks. At the canning plant, pea viners shake peas from the pods, then discard the vines and empty pods.

Corn ears are husked, trimmed, and washed, and the kernels are cut from the ears. All this is accomplished by machinery. Specially designed knives are adjusted to cut close to the cob for whole-kernel corn, whereas only the tops of the kernels are sliced off for the creamed variety.

Pits of peaches and apricots are cut out mechanically as are the cores of apples. Machines cut, slice, chop, and peel various foods. In the huge Hawaiian pineapple canneries, everything is done by machinery from the time the fruit reaches the factory.

In the case of fish and shellfish the initial scaling, boning, or shelling is often done by hand, although in West Coast salmon canneries a machine called the Iron Chink cleans the fish, removes heads, tails, fins, and entrails. The name Iron Chink derives from the fact that these chores were formerly performed by Chinese workers.

Along the entire line, raw food is carefully inspected, yet a final inspection is conducted by experienced workers who

Preparation of canned foods is carried out in gleaming kitchens where modern equipment processes great quantities of ingredients. Here steam jacketed kettles are being used in the preparation of soups prior to canning.

In recent years there has been increasing use of glass in canning operations. This merry-go-round rig at the H. J. Heinz Company in Pittsburgh, Pa. fills 225 pint bottles of vinegar per minute.

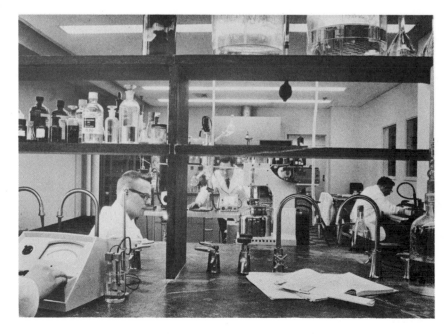

Scientists at work in one of 20 laboratories of the Campbell Soup Company. Among investigations are the search for new sources of food and attempts to learn how the human body can use food more efficiently.

pick out crushed or broken pieces of food, or any foreign matter that managed to get through earlier cleaning operations.

At this stage most foods are blanched. This is done by scalding them with hot water or steam at scientifically controlled temperatures. The temperature varies for different food products. Blanching serves to expel air and gases, to wilt leafy products, such as spinach; thus greater quantities can be packed in containers.

At last the raw foods are ready to be inserted in the cans or jars. The conveyors carry the food to the canning line where the open cans, like an endless parade of tin soldiers, are marched on other automatic runways from steam sterilizers. At rates up to 1,200 cans per minute, the containers

which subject the containers to spraying or immersion in cold water.

Finally, labels are automatically applied and the cans are packed in shipping cartons.

MARKETING PRACTICES

Because of the seasonal nature of many raw foods, special marketing procedures have been devised. The marketing year for each seasonal product begins after packing is completed and continues to the beginning of the next packing season. Annual conventions are held in January or February when 12,000 to 15,000 canners, canned food brokers, wholesale and retail grocers, and manufacturers of canning machinery gather to plan their marketing for the

These cans of orange juice concentrate, like a huge army on parade, are moving on a conveyor through a freezing tunnel at the Birds Eye plant of General Foods Corporation at Florence Villa, Florida.

are automatically filled with the exact amount of food. The line moves rapidly on to another machine which may deposit proper quantities of sugar, salt, or water in the filled cans. Now the clattering, closing machines expel air from containers, often by forcing steam into the headspace, and seal on the tops at a rate of speed which is almost impossible for the eye to follow. Foods are subjected to heat processing after being hermetically sealed in the containers. The heat treatment destroys bacteria and other microorganisms which would otherwise spoil the food.

The sterilizing, and cooking processes vary with different foods. After cooking, the cans move to cooling devices

next season. A common sales practice is termed S.A.P. orders, or orders "subject to approval of prices." This helps to minimize speculative losses for buyers and sellers. The orders are tentative and do not become binding until the marketing season begins and prices, based upon the size of the crop and current farm prices, may be finally negotiated.

The distribution of seven hundred million cases containing some twenty-two billion tins and glass jars each year is a highly complex business requiring experts in a number of different fields. The operations include warehousing, financing, advertising and sales promoting, transporting, and retailing. Few canners have their own sales forces to carry out these complicated procedures. Canned-food brokers are employed to find markets for the products. Brokers arrange for sales to wholesalers and chain stores within certain territories. They are generally paid their commissions by the canning firms whose lines they handle.

With new and improved manufacturing, marketing and distributing techniques, the canning industry must inevitably expand. Canning is a fundamental market for the American farmer, assuring him of stabilized prices, long-range income and a broad, national market for his perishable crops. The industry is a great boon to the general public, and it strives constantly to achieve higher and better food production at lower cost.

Among the future prospects for canned foods are methods of achieving improved taste, more closely approximating that of fresh-cooked vegetables and other foods; increased nutrition; new varieties of canned goods. Large canneries, such as Campbell's Soups, have entered the field of frozen foods, making possible the production of such canned items as oyster and clam stew and other delicacies with "cooked to order" flavor.

FROZEN FOODS

The most modern of packaged food products are the quick-frozen foods, whose history dates back only to the 1920's. That was when Clarence Birdseye was experimenting with cold storage methods in his General Seafoods Corporation plant at Gloucester, Mass.

Birdseye's company had been preparing and distributing chilled fish for some time when he developed the "belt froster." This idea was first put into commercial operation in 1927. It consisted of a pair of endless monel metal belts, between which either whole fish or sealed packages of fillets were squeezed firmly in place. As the belts were rotated they were sprayed from above and from below with a calcium brine solution at minus 40° F. Although the machine was comparatively crude and bulky by present-day standards, it proved the practicability of continuous quick-freezing, and from that time forward a new industry developed at an amazing pace.

The freezing of foods, as a method of preserving them, had been demonstrated by nature as well as by many human experimenters before Birdseye. When a Russian hunter in northern Asia discovered the complete, perfectly preserved remains of a mammoth in 1900, he had uncovered a natural demonstration of deep-freeze preservation. But the problem was to develop artificial refrigeration methods that could be both economical and rapid. Cold storage meats were often edible but of inferior flavor. This, Birdseye explained in a technical paper written in 1929:

"Cold storage flesh products are inferior not so much because they have been held in cold storage as because their physical and chemical structure has been damaged in the freezing process."

He then pointed out that the microscopic cells in muscle and tissues contain a protoplasmic jelly made up of water and other substances. Slow freezing causes the water to form ice crystals which tend to rupture the cell walls. When the meat is thawed, much of the moisture is lost, carrying

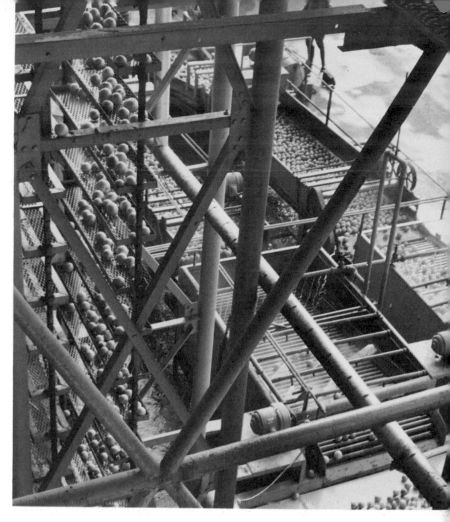

In a fruit elevator at a Florida Birds Eye processing plant, oranges are washed, sorted, and moved into the plant on these elaborate conveyors.

During the peak season more than 500 tons of sweet corn are delivered to the Birds Eye plant at Avon, New York. The corn is dumped onto a concrete slab, then is pushed by tractors into the conveyor feeding the plant.

away considerable food value and flavor. At the same time, the broken cell walls allow bacteria to enter and to multiply, causing spoilage soon after thawing.

"But if the flesh is frozen with extreme rapidity," he continued, "there is no time for the formation of large ice crystals, and therefore no apparent damage to the cell structure. Thus a quick-frozen product may be entirely fresh, even though frozen hard as marble."

The principle of quick-freezing had been understood by scientists for years; yet no one had invented a good commercial freezing system until Birdseye perfected his methods.

BIRTH OF AN INDUSTRY

Frozen foods as an industry came into being when the Postum Company and Goldman-Sachs Trading Corporation purchased Birdseye's patents and trade marks for twenty-two million dollars. This was in 1929, and the sum was reputed to be the largest ever paid for a single process. The company name was changed to General Foods Corporation, and its new subsidiary was set up as Birds Eye Frosted Foods, Inc.

Despite public skepticism, due to people's dislike of "cold storage foods," and despite the merchandising and handling problems of the new deep-freeze product, General Foods created a successful local market for frozen foods within nine months. Through intensive advertising and promotion in a 40-week campaign, 27 frozen products were offered in 18 stores in Springfield, Mass. These

products included such diversified foods as strawberries, chicken, sirloin steaks, haddock, and spinach.

The establishment of such a revolutionary food concept required education of the buying public, new merchandising methods and equipment, better freezing machinery. Frigidaire designed the first frozen food retail store unit. Its price was $1,500; since no grocery store or food market would invest that much money merely to offer a new, untried product, General Foods bought and installed the units, without charge, in selected outlets. Meanwhile, super-insulated railroad refrigeration cars had to be built to transport the products. In a deepening depression, Birds Eye Frosted Foods plunged into the red. To build sales volume, Birds Eye cut its prices in a daring move to win public acceptance. The plan worked, and by 1937, the mammoth gamble began to show a profit. Sales reached ten million dollars in that year.

Only ten years later, annual frozen food processing exceeded a billion pounds of merchandise valued at two hundred fifty million dollars. Now it is an industry of close to two thousand processors who pack four and one-half to five billion pounds of quick-frozen foods, valued at two and one-half to three billion dollars, each year.

RESEARCH FOR THE FUTURE

As in other food industries, frozen foods are being constantly studied and improved in the laboratories. New items are being added to an already lengthy list. Frozen fish sticks, artichoke hearts, clam chowder, tangerine juice, haddock in white wine sauce are just a few of the tempting foods available in the markets. Each new frozen dish is carefully pretested to determine whether it can be successfully quick-frozen at 0° F. Research centers use latest equipment for their studies: spectrophotometers to measure colors of foods; refractometers for determining the degree of sweetness of syrups. Meanwhile, horticulturists and other researchers are learning how to improve specialized crops to meet the requirements of quick-freezing. Ordinary squash, for example, lost its texture in the freezing process. A variety of squash cultivated in a special manner solved the problem.

Birds Eye has been joined by numerous other companies in the building of this newest of the packaged food industries. Housewives across the United States are familiar with such brand names as Dulaney, Seabrook Farms, Minute Maid, Morton, Swanson, and many other local and national processing firms. Frozen dinners, completely cooked and cleverly packaged in compartmented aluminum foil dish-type containers are made up ready to heat in the oven for a few minutes, then serve.

Of course the key to this modern industry is another industry—refrigeration. (See *Refrigeration and Air Conditioning*) Without the great strides in electric and gas refrigeration that have been made in the past two or three decades, frozen foods would be a limited field. Today, most American homes are equipped either with separate deep freeze units or with spacious freezer compartments in their regular refrigerators. It is the rare home refrigerator that is not well stocked with a wide assortment of inviting frozen food packages.

At St. Joseph Stockyards a shipment of hogs is loaded onto a truck. Meatmen boast that they "use everything in the pig but the squeal."

74

MEAT-PACKING AND MEAT PRODUCTS

Americans are first in many things, and being the world's best-fed nation it is not surprising that the United States leads the world in meat consumption. The average American eats 165 lb. of meat each year. Since meat is highly nutritious, this has contributed measurably to the superior general health of Americans.

Meat-packing is one of the largest U.S. industries, involving billions of dollars in capital and the labor of more than six million people including ranchers, farmers, truck drivers, packers, and a tremendous army of wholesalers and retailers. The total annual output of beef, pork, and lamb exceeds twenty-seven billion pounds.

Little more than a century ago, only the wealthy could afford fresh meat except on special occasions. Men had to hunt or raise their own meat supply. Even then they endured long, seasonal meatless periods. What cuts they did manage to preserve were put down or packed into salt barrels, hence the term "meat-packing." Mass slaughtering and distribution of fresh meats became practical only with the development of modern transportation and refrigeration.

In the early days of salt pork production, the center of the industry was Cincinnati, which still bears the facetious nickname of "Porkopolis." But the meat industry moved west with the settlement of the plains states, and Chicago became the natural receiving point for livestock. Late in the 1860's the first refrigerator car was patented. This opened the way for a giant meat industry. Gustavus Swift built improved refrigerator cars which were capable of transporting fresh meat. The name of Swift still looms large among wholesale meat-packers.

The industry embraces wholesale slaughtering, dressing, meat-packing, curing, and preparation of meat by-products. Not too many years ago, only edible flesh was utilized. Today, special food products include brains, livers, kidneys, hearts, and tongues. Certain intestines are used for sausage skins. After trimming and cleaning, pig's feet are

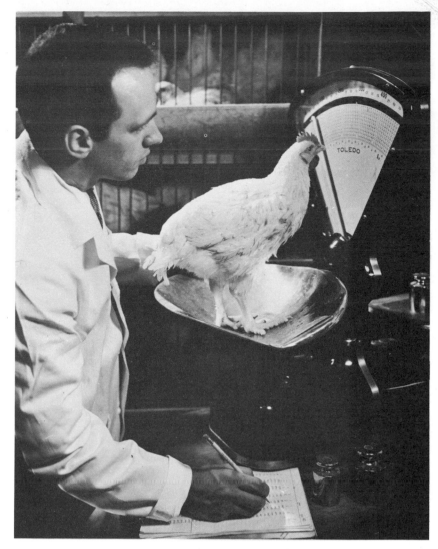

Nutritional values of by-products for use in feeds are determined by animal- and poultry-feeding tests. Oscar Rasmussen of the American Meat Institute Foundation checks the weight of a healthy and well-fed chicken.

After being sold at a Kansas auction, 3,000 head of cattle are ready for shipment to meat-packing firms, many of which are in the Chicago area.

Using a rotary-branding device, workers stamp sides of beef with the company trademark in a Swift and Company meat-packing plant.

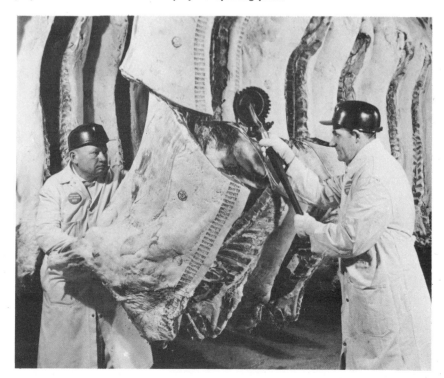

The vast Union Stockyards in Chicago, world's largest livestock market, extend for many acres. Thousands of cattle are inspected and bought here daily as the buyers from meat-packing concerns bargain with farmers' agents, or commission men.

served as delicacies. Important medicines are derived from various organs, for example ACTH, which is made from the pituitary gland. Other gland extracts are insulin, cortisone, and trypsin. Bones and hides yield gelatin, glue, leather, and fertilizer. Annual production of lard is estimated to be about three billion pounds.

Swift is quoted as having remarked, "In the meat business you don't make money, you save it."

When Philip Danforth Armour began slaughtering hogs in Chicago, he revolutionized a rapidly expanding industry. A true business genius, Armour had already made his first fortune in California, not by panning gold, but by selling sluiceways to prospectors. As a meat-packer, he built the first chill room in 1872, making possible year-round slaughtering. He also installed a mechanical device to de-hair hogs and worked out production line methods which are basically the same as those used today.

The Union Stockyards in Chicago are the world's largest. Here, crowded into pens which extend for many acres, thousands of cattle await the buyers who enact a fascinating drama. In the early morning, the buyers for meat-packing companies ride on horseback into the yards. Farmers' agents, known as commission men are on hand to handle sales.

"What are you saying?" asks the agent.

"Twenty-three seventy-five," is the reply.

"Over the hill."

The buyer shrugs, turns his horse, and asks the agent to "open the gate."

This dialogue, simply translated, means that the buyer has offered $23.75 per hundred weight. The agent has demanded that he go to $24 or over, but the buyer has refused and moved on to the next pen.

When a sale is made, it is confirmed simply by the buyer's saying, "Weigh 'em."

ASSEMBLY LINE IN REVERSE

Unlike other mass production industries, meat-packing requires dismembering instead of assembling. With amazing speed and razor-keen knives, master meat cutters con-

vert the animal carcasses into choice cuts. Suspended, dehided sides of beef move quickly down the line to be expertly halved, quartered, or divided into "primal cuts," such as rounds, loins, and flanks. Hogs are dismembered so skillfully and so thoroughly, that it is a byword of the industry that meat men "use everything in the pig but the squeal." Some claim that even this is used for taxicab brakes. Hams are prepared for the curing rooms where they are subjected to carefully controlled smoking. Even in this industry modern electronics are being used in exploring ways of speeding up the curing processes. In other departments of a pork packing plant, meat is ground and blended with seasoning to make sausages (there are some 200 varieties). On a long conveyor table, which might be termed a "dis-assembly line," sides of bacon are carved by skilled workers, each of whom slices a specific cut from the slabs as they move down the line. Bacon is finally sliced and wrapped by machinery at the speed of one pound per second.

One of the newest meat processing advances is a method of tenderizing which goes under the trade name of ProTen. Perfected by Swift and Company's laboratories, this patented process involves the introduction of enzymes into the circulatory systems of cattle prior to dressing. The result is increased tenderness of all beef cuts.

Because ordinary meat-packing is basically a simple procedure, unprotected by patents and not requiring huge capital, there are more than 3,500 meat-packing companies in the United States and several thousand commercial slaughter houses. The firms vary greatly in size. Actually the size of a meat-packing operation is no criterion for success. Small firms often turn in as good a profit as their large competitors.

The market is gigantic. Meat is sold through more than two hundred eighty thousand grocery stores, one hundred eighty thousand restaurants and ten thousand locker plants.

MEAT CANNING

Among his earliest canning experiments, Nicolas Appert concocted some amazing products. One memorable delicacy was "matelote of eels, carp, and pike with an addition of mushrooms, onions, butter, and anchovies all dressed in white wine."

With the most modern equipment, meat is prepared for market rapidly and efficiently. Cattle hides are removed by special machinery as an operator manipulates the controls.

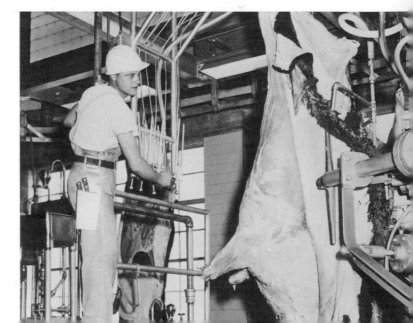

Although American meat-packers have not been as imaginative as Appert, they have created some well-known meat specialties.

In 1872, Arthur Libby, a Chicago meat-packer, began marketing canned corned beef. He was a great promoter, and some of his advertising pieces were classics. He published a series of 2½-in. by 4-in. cards, colorfully illustrated and bearing such literary masterpieces as:

JULIET: "How come'st thou hither, Romeo, and wherefore? If any of my kinsmen find thee, they'll·murder thee!"

ROMEO: "I have night's cloak to hide me from their sight, and I would adventure much to bring thee, Love, such merchandise as Libby, McNeill & Libby's cooked corned beef."

The American hot dog is a pork product that has attained international fame. The first meat man to put the hot dog in cans was Louis Meyer, a New York packer, who introduced canned frankfurters in 1928.

Meanwhile Jay Hormel was popularizing canned ham, but he discovered that many giant hogs produced hams too large for practical packaging. He hit upon a variety of spiced-ham spreads and luncheon meats, and finally concocted Spam. This ham product became the butt of jokes during World War II, since millions of cans were used as military rations. Yet sales of Spam have continued to rise, and a host of imitations have appeared on the grocery shelves.

FLOUR AND BREAD

No one knows how long ago people discovered that wheat is an important and highly nourishing food. Records show that men were using wheat ten to fifteen thousand years before Christ. It was a major crop in ancient Egypt, Greece, and China. As a source of flour for breadmaking, wheat is used in tremendous quantities by nations and peoples throughout the world.

Flour milling also goes back to the misty beginnings of man's recorded history. It began crudely when the wheat kernels were crushed between stones, producing a coarse meal. Next, the rotary mill, called a "quern," was developed about 300 B.C. Two flat stones were fitted together, the top one being drilled so that wheat could be poured into the opening. By means of a wooden handle, the upper stone was rotated, grinding the grain as it trickled down through the hole. From this basic rotary mill, various types of power mills were evolved. Water wheels, so familiar in the Colonial period, were employed to turn large millstones which operated on the principle of the quern. In Holland, windmills were built to achieve the same results.

One of the best flour mills in early America was in the Allegheny Mountains. It was owned by George Washington, and his flour was of such excellent quality that it was in great demand.

By the late 1800's, roller mills, operated by steam power and utilizing steel rollers, largely replaced the wind and water mills of the early days.

Refinement of white flour made a significant stride in 1870 when Edmund La Croix invented the "middlings

Baking pies in a modern bakery is done on a mass production basis. Bakers at the Tasty Baking Company in Philadelphia stack hundreds of oven-fresh pies.

purifier." This machine separates the outer covering, or bran, from the white endosperm by means of strong blasts of air and a sieve of bolting cloth.

FLOUR MILLING TODAY

Modern flour mills are large factories which are fully automated to produce some twenty-five billion pounds of flour in the United States each year. Raw wheat is fed continuously into a mill. Within half an hour the grain has undergone more than a hundred processing steps and is converted to the fine, white flour that fills the sacks at the end of the production line.

Different types of wheat are carefully blended for flours of varied characteristics. The blend is then cleaned, sifted, and tempered. Tempering consists of subjecting the grain to exactly the right amount of moisture at a certain temperature. Next the wheat goes through steel rollers. This is the "first break," and it is followed by a sifting operation. The sifters, large receptacles containing a series of vibrating sieves, remove the coarse particles of bran and allow only the powdery white endosperm and minute amounts of bran to pass through. The middlings purifier eliminates the last vestiges of bran.

Now further sifters and rollers mill the flour to its desired fineness.

Flour is aged to improve its baking quality. Formerly, this was done by exposure to oxygen, for several days. Now, the flour is aged by means of special maturing agents, so that the product is ready for use the day it goes through the mill.

BY-PRODUCTS AND GRADES

The by-products of white flour manufacture are bran, the outer covering of wheat; feed middlings or "shorts," consisting of coarse particles of endosperm with fine bran and germ flakes (used as cattle feed); farina, purified middlings of hard wheat after the germ is removed. In addition, there are whole wheat flour containing parts of the wheat kernel, "straight flour," which is ungraded, and several grades of patent or clear flour containing varying amounts of bran particles. Finally, there is the pure, white

FOOD PRODUCTS

patent flour containing only the finest portion of the endosperm.

The various grades of flour are laboratory tested to determine their moisture, protein, and mineral content; baking qualities; nutritional value. Large flour mills have test kitchens where breads, cakes, and other flour products are prepared, tasted, and analysed.

BREAD MANUFACTURE

The fact that most people in all periods of history have made some sort of bread is proof that the so-called "staff of life" is one of the fundamental foods. Yet its production is not a simple process.

To the flour, shortening and some type of liquid must be added. This liquid may be milk, water, potato water, fruit or vegetable juices. When the flour, shortening, and liquid are combined, the mixture is called dough. Next a leavening agent is added to the dough to make it rise and become light. Leavening is accomplished by air, steam, or carbon dioxide gas; the latter being produced when yeast, soda, or baking powders are combined with moisture.

Yeast is actually a plant which grows and multiplies rapidly under the influence of warmth and moisture. As it grows, it gives off carbon dioxide gas, causing dough to fill with tiny bubbles and to rise. This is a type of fermentation and imparts delicious flavor and aroma to yeast breads.

To modern bread doughs, eggs, sugar, salt, and various flavorings may be added. Many breads are enriched with thiamine, niacin, riboflavin, calcium, and iron. Approximately 80% of bakery bread is enriched with these important nutrients.

Bread doughs must be punched, kneaded, rolled, cut into various shapes for loaves, then baked in ovens. Large commercial bakeries have machinery to perform all of these operations. They can produce several thousand loaves per hour.

The baking industry provides Americans with many wheat and flour products in addition to a variety of breads. Rolls, crackers, cakes, cookies, doughnuts, buns, and pies are among the ready-made bakery items available. Added to these familiar products are new frozen ones, such as brown-and-serve rolls, breads, and pies which need only a few minutes in the oven before serving. Canned breads include Boston brown, date and nut bread. Packaged cake, waffle and biscuit mixes make modern home baking a comparatively simple procedure.

CEREALS

By popularizing breakfast cereals as energy builders, the large producers of grain products have made Wheaties, corn flakes, Cheerios, Grape Nuts, Rice Chex, and dozens of other cereal brands an essential part of the American diet. Such catchy slogans as "Breakfast of Champions," and the inclusion in the packages of toys for youngsters help to keep young Americans devouring enormous quantities of these important and tasty foods.

One of the greatest manufacturers of cereals, General Mills, was organized in 1928 on the principle of joining together, into a single company, milling operations near all

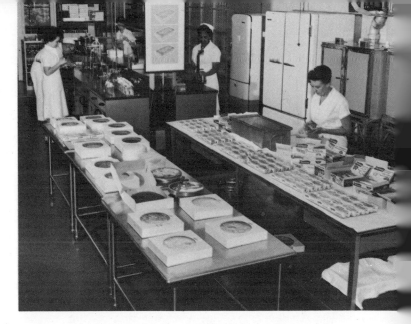

Quality control is maintained in the gleaming kitchens and laboratories of modern bakeries where sample products are tested and analysed.

of the various wheat-producing areas. This meant that if a crop failed in one or two areas, the wheat supply in other sections would take up the slack for the entire system. Thus the risk of failure due to underproduction or overproduction of grain was largely eliminated.

More important than its advertising and promotion, is the cereal industry's development of varied grain processing. The flakes, puffed kernels, shredded varieties, oats in the shape of tiny doughnuts, and crunchy rice or corn pellets are rendered tempting and delicious by ingenious techniques of cooking and processing.

Professor Alexander Pierce Anderson, a graduate of the University of Minnesota, had studied cereals for many years. It was he who found that, when the starch in grains is submitted to intense heat, it expands rapidly. He shot raw grain kernels from a contraption resembling a small cannon to produce puffed varieties of wheat and corn. After he was granted patents, a number of improvements on the process were devised. Dr. F. A. Collatz, working in General Foods' Products Control Laboratory, prepared a mixture of cooked and seasoned grain. The dough was forced through a die to give it a specific shape, then exploded in a puffing gun.

Today, cereal production by General Mills, Kellogg, Post, Quaker Oats, Ralston Purina, and others constitutes a major segment of the packaged food industry. Through modern chemistry, American mills are seeking and finding ways of enriching grain products, contributing greatly to human health. The laboratories are also working on new by-products. Cornstarch has recently been joined by "wheat starch," which has many important industrial applications, including sizing of the warp in textile finishing. Glutamic acid, a vital ingredient in many pharmaceutical products, is made from wheat gluten.

As in so many industries, the future of grain products is closely linked to chemistry—the most promising of scientific frontiers.

DAIRY PRODUCTS

If you had strolled past Boston Common on a summer day in early Colonial times, you would probably have seen a herd of cows grazing peacefully. The center city park was then a community pasture. In 1624 the Pilgrims' first cows arrived, and the colony averted the tragedy of starvation. Throughout American history, the cow has accompanied men on their westward advance, for milk and dairy products have been vital to human survival.

Today, dairy products constitutes one of America's major industries.

Historians believe that the first use of milk from domesticated animals was around 9,000 years before Christ. People have used many animals for milk production, including goats, camels, reindeer, yaks, and water buffaloes, but the domesticated cow produced nine or ten times more milk than any other animal. In the course of thousands of years, dairy farmers have developed strains of milk-producing cows: the best known being Holstein-Friesians from Holland; Guernseys and Jerseys from the English Channel islands of those names; Ayrshires from Scotland; Brown Swiss from Switzerland. The raising of cows requires special care, since most dairy cows need protection from extreme heat and cold. (See *Farming*) The largest dairies are found therefore in the temperate zones.

Modern dairy business is big business. There are more than twenty million cows producing about sixty billion quarts of milk annually for U.S. dairy products. So great is American milk consumption that the large dairy plants are automated factories, designed and equipped for mass production. A striking feature of such plants is their gleaming cleanliness. Tanks, pasteurizers, homogenizers are made of polished stainless steel. Glass and tile on walls, partitions, and floors are kept spotlessly clean.

The cows in all except the smallest local dairies are milked by machines. Warm milk is pumped directly from the milking machines into refrigerated tanks. Here the chilled milk is sampled before it is pumped into waiting tank trucks to be transported to a processing plant.

Milk processing includes pasteurizing, homogenizing, and packaging. At all stages, the milk is under constant laboratory control, being tested for bacteria, fat content, Vitamin A, and so on. First the milk is put into huge refrigerated storage tanks. From these tanks it flows through a centrifuge, called a "clarifier." Next it is pumped into the pasteurizer. Louis Pasteur invented the process for destroying bacteria in milk without impairing flavor or nutrition. Two principal methods of pasteurization are employed. The one most used by large dairy plants is known as HTST (high-temperature, short-time). By this method, milk is heated to 161° F. for a minimum of 15 seconds and is then rapidly cooled to 35° F. In a slower process, the milk is heated to 145° F. for a full 30 minutes before being cooled. Pasteurization of all milk is required by law.

Just prior to pasteurization, some of the milk is homogenized in a machine which breaks up the fat into minute particles. Heated milk is forced through tiny apertures so small that the sieved fat particles remain suspended in the milk and no longer rise to the top as cream. Next, the homogenized milk is pasteurized, and as is the regular milk, it is automatically packaged in sterile glass bottles or paper cartons.

Throughout the entire processing the milk flows through pipes, tanks and processing machines without exposure to hands or outside air.

Large national dairies such as Sealtest, The Borden Company, and Foremost Dairies manufacture a variety of milk products which include cultured buttermilk, skim milk, evaporated milk, powdered milk, butter, cottage cheese, various cheeses, chocolate-flavored milk, and ice cream.

CHEESE MAKING

Cheese is an important food with a record as old as man's recorded history. According to legend, an Arabian merchant named Kanana carried some milk on a journey, using a container made from the lining of a sheep's stomach. After walking many miles he discovered that the milk had disappeared. In its place was a curious white food which tasted delicious. Though he was mystified, the explanation is simple enough. Kanana's "canteen" contained a substance known as rennin, a digestive chemical present in the stomachs of all mammals. The rennin, acting upon the milk, had curded it and turned it to cheese.

Today there are dozens of kinds of cheeses. Every country in the world has native cheeses, many of which were developed centuries ago. Basically, the cheese-making process consists of heating milk, adding a "starter" which contains certain useful bacteria, and then a liquid rennet. The resulting curd is cubed, heated, and drained of its juices, called "whey." After turning and stacking

An overall view of a milk-processing plant shows the piping and equipment required to prepare milk for market. Pasteurizers, homogenizers, flavor standardizers, bottle and carton fillers, and caser-stackers are all integrated in the system.

A caser-stacker is the final stage in the automatic milk processing. This machine accepts the cartons from a filler, cases them, then nests the cases for movement via a floor level conveyor into a low temperature storage room.

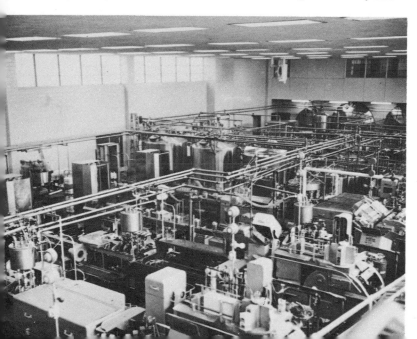

strips of the curd in a process known as "cheddaring," a machine chops the cheddared cheese into small pieces, stirs them, and removes the last vestiges of whey. Salt is added and the soft pieces of curd are pressed into blocks or large lumps of cheese. Finally the cheese must be aged in a cool, dry storage space to be ripened. Ripening may require periods from several weeks to more than a year.

Endless variations in the cheese-making processes have produced such types as roquefort, camembert, blue cheese, stilton, cheddar and gorgonzola.

BUTTER

Until the beginning of the twentieth century most butter was made on farms, but since 1900, factory production of butter has grown to an industry comprising over 5,000 creameries which process about 75% of America's butter. One of the important butter-producing areas is the Great Lakes region where there is a heavy concentration of large dairy farms.

Rich cream, separated from milk by centrifugal cream separators, is warmed and then subjected to high temperature in a pasteurizer. After pasteurization and subsequent rapid cooling, the cream is churned. Buttermilk is drained off; the churned butter is washed, salted, and churned again. The resulting mass of butter is solidified by refrigeration, molded, or cut into convenient blocks for packaging—all by means of automatic equipment.

U.S. butter production amounts to more than one billion pounds per year, although in recent years it has decreased somewhat due to growing use of oleomargarine and other substitutes.

ICE CREAM

The glamor product of the dairy industry is America's favorite dessert, ice cream. Contrary to what many people

Stacking ten-quart containers of ice cream, these men are dressed to withstand the 20 degrees below zero temperature of the ice-cream plant's freezing room.

believe, ice cream is not a modern invention but had its origin in ices and frozen dishes as long ago as the days of ancient Rome. Roman emperors are known to have had snow and ice transported into Rome for freezing fruit drinks. Centuries later, a French chef named De Mirco, or DeMirro, employed by Charles I of England, served a frozen milk dessert which so delighted the king that the Frenchman was awarded a pension of £500 a year, to keep the secret.

Marco Polo obtained an oriental recipe for water ices which had been made in Asia for thousands of years. Thereupon iced juices and iced milk desserts soon became the rage of Venice and other Renaissance Italian cities.

Ice cream came to America from Europe in the early 1700's, and in 1774 a New York caterer, Philip Lenzi, advertised in a newspaper that he could supply ice cream at banquets and for special occasions. At his home in Mount Vernon, George Washington served ice cream, as did Mrs. Alexander Hamilton, wife of the first Secretary of the Treasury.

However this highly prized dessert remained an expensive delicacy until modern mechanization made large scale production possible. The first step in the direction of mechanical ice-cream making was taken by a woman, Nancy Johnson, who invented in 1846 the ice-cream freezer operated by hand. The same type of home freezer can be found in use today.

Wholesale ice-cream business began in America when Jacob Fussell, a Baltimore milk distributor, began to manufacture ice cream in 1851. So successful was this enterprise that he soon opened other ice-cream plants in Boston, New York, and Washington. With the development of steam and electric power as well as modern refrigeration, (See *Refrigeration and Air Conditioning*) ice-cream manufacture really came into its own. Today it is a major industry, employing thousands of people in some 33,000 manufacturing, wholesale, and retail firms. According to the industry's 1960 figures total production of ice creams and sherbets in that year amounted to more than nine hundred million gallons. Undoubtedly later figures will show an excess of a billion gallons annually.

HOW ICE CREAM IS MADE

The basic mix of cream, milk solids, and sugar is prepared in a mixing tank. A minute amount of a harmless chemical stabilizer is added to prevent formation of ice crystals. Next the mix is pumped into a pasteurizer, a homogenizer, a cooler and finally a freezer. Most large ice-cream plants have continuous freezers which keep up a constant production flow, rather than turn out the ice cream in batches. In the freezer, blades or "dashers" churn and aerate the mix, thus preventing its solidifying into a hard, frozen chunk. A mechanical feeder adds nuts, liquid flavoring, and fruits. Finally the ice cream is forced into various types of containers and packages for shipment to wholesale and retail outlets.

AN INDUSTRY FOR HEALTH AND PLEASURE

The vast dairy industry which encompasses so many healthful and enjoyable foods is remarkably profitable.

(Left) This machine is molding chocolate kisses by the thousands at the Hershey Chocolate Corporation plant in Hershey, Pa., world's largest maker of chocolate products. (Right) At the Whitman Chocolate plant, a starch-casting machine deposits liquid material into starch impressions that will become firm enough for chocolate coating of creams, jellies, fudges, and caramel.

For an annual outlay of some five hundred million dollars in supplies and equipment, dairy industries turn out more than ten billion dollars' worth of products. These products run to billions of pounds of milk, butter, cheese, and ice cream. Improvements in mechanical production, in vitamin and nutrient content, and in packaging and marketing methods are being made constantly. Even the cows are improving! Through laboratory studies, better feeds and the reduction of cattle diseases are increasing milk production at a greater rate every year.

CANDY

If you wished to describe the typical child's dream of paradise in two words, the words would undoubtedly be *toys* and *candy*. Candy suggests a world of magic and pleasure. Fairy tales abound with candy villages and candy castles, while most holidays and festivals are celebrated with special candy treats. In Moore's famous *Night Before Christmas*, one of the best remembered lines is, "The children were nestled, all snug in their beds, while visions of sugarplums danced in their heads."

References to confections are found in the earliest writings of man. In ancient Egypt, sweetmeats were in great demand. Greek and Roman physicians tempted patients to swallow bitter doses of medicine by offering various types of sweets. At the time when Venice was trading with the Far East, during the fifteenth century, sugarcoated pills were introduced to Europeans, and as early as 1535, the first North American sugar mill was built by Cortez in Mexico. This mill is still in operation.

An important U.S. center of candy manufacturing today is New England. This area boasts a long tradition of candy making, for the first American chocolate mill was established in Dorchester, Mass., by John Hannon in 1765. At the present time the New England States produce about three hundred seventy million pounds of candy annually—approximately one-eighth of the total national output.

Although candy making is still something of an art, it is big business and has become increasingly automated. In one New England candy factory, a machine operated by six people produces over twenty-five million pieces of candy every day. The industry ranges from small confectioners who make hand-dipped candies for sale in their own local shops, to modern plants which are air conditioned and fully automated with electronically controlled machinery. In the larger factories, batches of candy weighing several hundred pounds are blended, homogenized, cooked, cooled, molded, decorated, and packaged automatically.

The making of candy involves the use of mouthwatering ingredients from every part of the globe. In addition to its sugar content, a single pound of candy may contain choice food products from two dozen countries scattered over five continents. Among these products may be Mexican vanilla; cacao from the African Gold Coast or from the West and East Indies; ginger root from China; pineapple from Hawaii; cashew nuts from India; figs and dates from Turkey. From every corner of the United States come cane, beet, and maple sugars; honey; corn syrup, dextrose, starch; soya, cottonseed and peanut oils; dates, strawberries, peaches, cherries, apricots, oranges, limes, and lemons; eggs, butter, milk, cream; walnuts, pecans, and almonds.

Egg whites, sugar, and corn syrup are whipped together, forming a light, aerated confection called "frappé." This mixture is used to give texture to fudges and creams and is the basic ingredient in nougats.

Candies are classified as hard, soft, or chewy. Hard candies contain little moisture and are cooked under vacuum. The various nut brittles are prepared with about 25% nut meats in the mixture, so that the nuts are roasted as the candy cooks. The chewy candies—caramels, peanut chews, nougats and taffies—contain between 50% and 70% corn syrup, 20% to 40% sugar, and 4% to 7% fat, as well as salt, flavoring, and coloring. The taffies are pulled to produce desired texture. Special pulling machines have been designed for this purpose, mechanically performing the task of guests at the old-fashioned taffy pulls. Soft candies are generally made with creamed sugar (fondant), marshmallow, or jelly.

Though some candy manufacturers coat the centers by hand, more and more "enrobing" machines and revolving pans are being installed. Enrobing consists of covering various centers with chocolate or with a special icing. First, cream centers are poured into starch molds and allowed to stiffen. Next, they pass through the enrobing machine which is a highly complex mechanism. By means of a pump, a constant flow of liquid chocolate, kept at the proper temperature by steam jackets, is poured over the centers. Blowers remove excess chocolate while a wire conveyor carries the centers through the step-by-step processing. The final step is the decoration, called "stringing." To identify each type of center, a variety of designs, or "strings" have been devised. These curlicues are applied either by hand or by decorating machines; then the candies move on through a refrigerated passage where they cool and solidify.

Revolving pans have been built to carry out the entire process in a single unit. While the centers revolve in a large copper or stainless steel drum, a fine spray of chocolate or other coating material covers them. Another jet of cool air serves to solidify the candy.

CHOCOLATE—THE UNIVERSAL CANDY

Almost as valuable as the gold they were seeking, and certainly more pleasurable, was the Spaniards' acquisition of an Aztec Indian secret in 1519. When Hernando Cortez first tasted a delicious Aztec chocolate beverage, he insisted on learning the method of its preparation. The Indians showed him how they made the drink from seeds of the *cacahuatl* tree, and the Spaniards contracted the strange name to cacao. For many years, members of the Spanish court withheld the secret of making chocolate; only royalty and wealthy Spaniards were privileged to enjoy the delicious beverage. But by the early eighteenth century, knowledge of chocolate had spread to the rest of Europe.

As the cacao tree grows only in the tropics, it is widely cultivated in South and Central America, the West and East Indies, Ghana and West Africa. This delicate tree bears large pods about the size and shape of eggplants. Each pod yields about two ounces of dried beans, and a tree produces twenty to thirty pods per year. The beans acquire their fine flavor through fermentation. They are then dried in the sun.

The U.S. candy industry consumes tremendous quantities of chocolate, the basic ingredient in hundreds of candy variations, as well as the most popular of all candies in its own right. The world's largest chocolate plant is located at Hershey, Pa., the chocolate city founded by Milton Snavely Hershey in 1903. Here, cocoa beans from many tropical countries are roasted in huge, revolving drums at temperatures above 400° F. At exactly the right moment, the beans must be removed from the roaster and

cooled. This timing is critical, as too much heat will destroy the flavor.

After being roasted, the beans are ground into small pieces called "nibs," while their shells are blown off like chaff. As the nibs are crushed through a series of grinding stones, cocoa butter emerges as a dark brown liquid. This is the fundamental ingredient of all chocolate products, which include baking chocolate, cocoa, sweet chocolate, and milk chocolate.

In moderate amounts, candy is an important food as well as an enjoyable confection, for sugar is recognized as a great energy builder. Since the industry is perpetually studying and improving the nutritional qualities of its product, there is a need for technologists and scientists, as well as for skilled workers in the many candy-making operations. Research is being done for improvement in the growth and production of basic raw materials and in the various manufacturing processes.

COFFEE AND TEA

Without the morning coffee break, American industry might have a general strike on its hands. This custom of workers taking a few minutes each morning to relax over a cup of coffee has become widely accepted. In business offices and plants many large companies have established rules governing coffee breaks, installed automatic coffee machines, and have found it necessary to calculate man-hours by taking into account the cumulative effect of coffee-time lost in production. Some companies have mobile coffee units which make the rounds of various departments and serve coffee, buns, and small cakes in midmorning. Despite all the jokes and cartoons whose barbs have been directed at the coffee break, two things can be said in its favor: first, it definitely is a morale booster; second, by pouring millions of cups of coffee down American throats, it has consequently poured millions of dollars into the coffee industry.

Coffee was first used in Abyssinia and Arabia, and until about 1700 most of the world's coffee came from Arabia. In the eighteenth century, coffee houses were common in most European cities. It was in one famous coffee house—Lloyd's of London—that modern insurance and underwriting became a significant factor in the financial world. (See *Finance*)

Today, coffee trees grow in the West Indies, in Cuba, Puerto Rico, and in South America. Brazil is the largest producer of coffee, with Colombia running second. When Arabian coffee trees were cultivated in Java (now Indonesia), Javan coffee became so popular that the American nickname "Java" is still applied to the beverage.

By far the world's greatest importer of coffee, the United States uses about 83% of the Latin American production. Most American coffee is a blend of the strong sun-grown Brazilian coffee with the milder shade-grown coffees of Colombia and the Caribbean islands.

An evergreen tree that grows to a maximum height of about 30 ft., the coffee plant has glossy oval leaves, pure white blossoms, and dark red berries about the size of small cherries. Inside each berry are twin seeds from which coffee is made. The coffee beans are dried, washed, and

A cup taster with an "educated palate" passes on samples representing 50,000 bags of coffee at the world's largest coffee plant — Maxwell House in Hoboken, N. J.

vertical tank structure five or six stories high. When the extract is pumped into an upper drying chamber, it is atomized. At the same time a flow of hot air dehydrates the extract, which is discharged at the bottom into a conical "settling chamber." The resulting dry, finely powdered coffee is drawn off and packaged by machinery.

COFFEE AND STILL MORE COFFEE

In coffee-vending machines alone, U.S. consumption of coffee is averaging between two and three million cups per day at an annual value of close to two hundred million dollars. Total coffee consumption is estimated to be nearly four hundred million cups daily.

Many of the country's coffee processing plants are near ports of entry. New Orleans, Houston, San Francisco, Philadelphia, and New York are all major importing and processing centers, and millions of pounds of green coffee enter these ports from coffee-growing countries in all parts of the world. In the 1960's, annual consumption of roasted coffee was estimated to be nearly three billion pounds, which represented a daily 2.7 to 3.2 cups for every person in the nation over 10 years of age. With an ever increasing population it would appear that even greater demands will be made on the coffee industry in the future. To meet this demand, many technical improvements are being developed, including electronic machines for sorting and grading the green coffee, as well as greatly improved methods of making soluble coffees.

dried again in the sun. They are then hulled by a machine which removes the pulp and parchment covering. Finally the beans are roasted.

Proper roasting brings out the coffee bean's oil, "caffeol," enhancing the rich flavor and aroma. Most of this processing is done in U.S. plants where the imported green beans are roasted in large electric ovens. The roasted beans are then ground and packaged in airtight containers to preserve the flavor.

INSTANT COFFEE

As the pace of modern living has increased, various types of quick-preparation foods have become popular. Probably the most notable of these is instant, or soluble coffee. Its production requires a skillfully engineered plant and some highly complex machinery. A modern soluble coffee plant can process as much as 1,000 lb. per hour.

First, green coffee is cleaned and roasted. It then passes through a stoner, and moves to an automatic blender which weighs the exact proportions of different batches to produce the desired blend. The ingredients pass to a mixer, a granulator, an extractor, and then into a spray dryer.

The extractor is made up of a bank of six large vessels which are operated on a carefully established time cycle. Temperatures in each vessel are set to gain the best possible extract from the coffee. At one end of the extractor, hot water is introduced. As it passes through the grounds, a certain amount of extract is drawn off. This process is repeated through the series of six tanks. Steam pressure expels spent coffee grounds while the usable extract is cooled, tested for blend, moved through a centrifuge, and into the spray dryer. This dryer is a huge,

To be sure of uniform high quality a continuous roaster operator compares a roasted coffee sample to beans being roasted. Proper roasting enhances the flavor and aroma.

From this "regular mixer," roasters are supplied with green coffee beans after they arrive from the blending department at a modern, mechanized coffee plant.

TEA

Although coffee is the most popular American beverage, tea leads all other drinks for world popularity. A legend relates that the Chinese drank tea 4,000 years ago, but no one is certain exactly when the use of tea began in the Orient. Europeans imported tea from China during their earliest trade with that country, and due to her extensive oriental trade, England became a major tea-consuming country. Today, although the British are the world's greatest tea drinkers, tea consumption in the United States has reached a substantial figure. In 1960, for example, Americans used one hundred eight million pounds of tea as compared with Britain's five hundred seventy-nine million pounds.

The tea industry in the United States is largely an importing business—India, Ceylon, China, Japan, and Indonesia being the largest producers. Although China grows about 50% of the world supply, her own population consumes the greater portion of it.

The two principal varieties are black tea and green tea; the difference results from the method of processing the tea leaves. Black tea is fermented by crushing the leaves and spreading them in rooms that are kept cool, moist, and free from sunlight. After the fermentation period, the leaves are placed in an oven and fired at temperatures of 220° to 250° F. Rolling, cutting, and further firing to remove all moisture completes the process.

Green tea, which is also known as China tea because it is favored by the Chinese, is placed immediately in the firing ovens to prevent fermentation.

There is an intermediate variety, partially fermented, known as oolong tea. Produced in Formosa, it is popular in the United States.

American tea business is showing signs of increasing with the introduction of instant tea and tea-vending machines. Machines are being introduced to furnish both hot and iced tea. Probably, the development of soluble tea will be largely an American phase of the tea industry, for tea-drinking traditions are more firmly implanted in other countries. At the same time, American preference for convenience and automation may result in an upsurge of tea drinking in the United States as the use of vending machines becomes more widespread.

Green coffee from a dozen countries arrives at the world's largest coffee plant. Quality appraisal, testing, and final selection of green coffees is a highly developed art. Green coffee buyers must be familiar with coffee-growing technology, preferred sources of supply, and even the political climate in coffee-growing countries.

13 Fishing

Purse seining for salmon in Yes Bay, Southeast Alaska. The gear used by a seiner consists of a large net, held in position with weights and cork floats. After a set has been made, the net is pursed and the fish are brailed. Purse seining is the most common method of capturing fish.

From time immemorial, fishing fleets have gone out from coastal villages. While the women and children anxiously await their return, the fishermen risk the hazards of treacherous seas and pray for the good fortune of a large catch. Fishing was a major industry of the Phoenicians, the ancient Egyptians, the Greeks, and the Romans. Medieval Germans fished for herring in the North Sea.

In the very beginning of America's settlement, fishing was an important source of food, particularly along the New England coast where it was the foundation of Colonial commerce. An important section of the 1783 Treaty of Paris gave America fishing rights to the whole Atlantic coast. However, these rights remained a source of international conflict for many years. For the most part, modern fishing rights are clearly defined and strictly enforced.

FISHING TODAY

Methods of fishing have not changed greatly over the years. Except for the use of modern power-driven vessels and motor winches, the various techniques for catching quantities of fish have remained basically the same for centuries

Trawling is done with nets extended from beams 40 to 50 ft. long. Dragged along the sea bottom by large and powerful fishing vessels, the nets scoop up fish caught in their path. This method is sometimes known as "beam trawling."

Another way of netting fish is called *seining*. A circular net, suspended from a series of floats, is depressed in the center by means of lead weights. After the seine is towed to sea by one boat, it is attached to a second. Then the ends of the net are drawn together in a semicircle. Entire surface schools of fish are trapped in this manner, and as large congregations of herring and mackerel are easily spotted from a distance, rival fishing crews frequently engage in exciting races to reach the catch first.

Drifting consists of stringing out a series of nets, 50 to 60 yards long, joined together by surface rope several miles in length. Supported by floats along the upper edge, the nets hang vertically in the water, forming a wall across tidal currents. Such nets are referred to as "gill nets" because fish are caught by their gills in the meshes.

For catching whales and very large fish, *harpooning* is used. Most harpoons, today, are fired from guns with great accuracy and force.

NORTH AMERICAN FISHING GROUNDS

Some of the best fishing areas in the world are off the coast of Newfoundland, along the famous Green Banks and Grand Banks, where cod is caught in great numbers. Until recently most cod was packed in salt, but quick-freezing is the preferred method of preservation today. (See *Frozen Foods*) Off the New England coast the fishing fleets bring in haddock, flounder, hake, sole, halibut, clams, tuna, and whiting; of course, the Maine coast is noted for lobster. Although Maine lobsters faced extermination in the 1920's, restocking by Government hatcheries and strict regulations have helped this tasty crustacean to stage a comeback. Lobstermen set out crate-like traps, called lobster pots, or they drag the ocean bottom with grapplers.

Along the Atlantic coast, especially the Chesapeake Bay area, and Long Island are large oyster beds. Some are artificially cultivated "farms." The old practice of catching oysters and clams with huge iron rakes is being abandoned, since raking caused large numbers of the shellfish to be buried and destroyed.

Some of America's richest fishing grounds are off Alaska and the West Coast. There salmon is king. The most important segment of the U.S. fishing industry, salmon canning, employs 50,000 people in Alaska, Washington, and Oregon; there, 82% of America's seafood canning is done. In Alaska alone, salmon canning represents an investment of over one hundred million dollars. Each year the West Coast States produce some seven million cases, or three hundred fifty million cans of high-grade salmon.

SALMON FISHING THROUGH THE AGES

Proof that the salmon was known and esteemed by cavemen 12,000 years ago was uncovered when an accurate cave drawing of the fish was discovered recently in France. Conquering Romans found salmon in Gaul about 56 B.C., and both the British Isles and Northern Europe had plentiful supplies of this highly prized fish. Long before the arrival of Europeans, American Indians smoked and dried salmon to provide food for the winter months.

There are several varieties of Pacific salmon. The largest is the chinook, king, or spring salmon which averages 25 lb. and has been known to weigh up to 100 lb. It is caught primarily on the Columbia and Cooper Rivers as well as at Cook Inlet in central Alaska. The entire pack of Yukon River canning operations is made up of chinook salmon.

The sockeye, red, or blueback salmon is distinguished by its bright red color at spawning time as well as by its red meat. It is one of the world's most important commercial fish. The largest canning operations are in the Bristol Bay area of northwestern Alaska where more than half of the entire North American pack is produced. The red is also abundant along the Alaska Peninsula, around Kodiak Island, Cook Inlet, Cooper River, the Fraser River of British Columbia, and in Puget Sound.

Pink salmon, found in large numbers in southeast Alaska, British Columbia, Kodiak Island, Prince William Sound, and Puget Sound, is the smallest of the species. For some unexplained reason, pinks make their appearance only in odd-numbered years.

Because of its pale color, chum is less marketable and therefore commands lower prices than other varieties of salmon. It is, nevertheless, good eating and as nourishing as other species. Distribution of chum salmon covers a wide area, though the largest canning operations are found in southeast Alaska.

Much of the quick-frozen salmon is coho or silver which is caught and packed in nearly all of the Pacific coastal fishing grounds except western Alaska. Silvers average about nine pounds in weight; their flesh has a rich coral-red color, which fades with cooking.

Salmon are caught by gillnetting, or drifting; the nets are

SILVER SALMON (Oncorhynchus kisutch)

CHINOOK SALMON (Oncorhynchus tschawytscha)

HUMPBACK SALMON (Oncorhynchus gorbuscha)

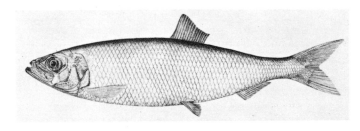

COMMON HERRING (Clupea harengus)

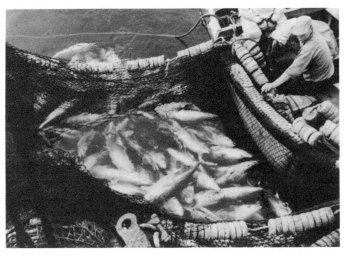

A large catch of tuna is pursed and ready to be brailed off the New England coast. This photo was made during exploratory fishing operations of the Fish and Wildlife Service.

Fishermen in the racks on the "Hugh M. Smith" are catching one-pole yellow-fin tuna from a surface school in the central Pacific. Tuna, attracted by live bait, are pulled in with heavy poles, short lines, and barbless hooks.

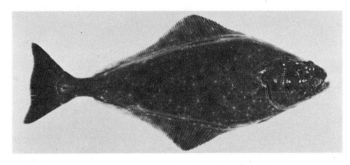

PACIFIC HALIBUT (Hippoglossus stenolepis)

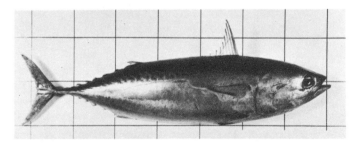

PACIFIC FRIGATE MACKEREL (Auxis thazard)

BIG EYED TUNA (Thunnus obesus)

made generally of nylon or linen twine, double knotted to prevent slippage. Sometimes salmon traps are constructed with nets forming a maze leading into a final compartment known as the "spiller." Fish are removed in huge quantities from the trap by scooping, or "brailing." Another specialty of West Coast fishermen is "purse seining." This is worked on the same principle as other seining with certain refinements. The operation is carried out by a single vessel which moves in a circle about a school of fish while the seine (net), which may be as much as 1,800 ft. long, is dropped from the stern. A power winch then draws in a "purse line," run through rings attached to the edge of the net. As soon as the rings are bunched together aboard the boat, the encircling net is completely "pursed," and the trapped fish can be drawn in and brailed.

TUNA FISHING

A somewhat mysterious, but extremely important commercial fish is the tuna, whose migration and spawning habits are not completely known. Tuna are widely distributed in nearly all Pacific waters, and the bluefin variety is found both in the Atlantic and Pacific Oceans. Four distinct species are caught for American packers: the albacore, most highly regarded because of its fine light-colored meat; yellowfin, a large and abundant tuna, often weighing 150 to 400 lb.; bluefin, also large, found in warm seas in all parts of the world; and skipjack, smallest tuna, usually no more than 25 in. long.

A large proportion of tuna fishing is done with live bait from boats called tuna clippers. Distinguished by large bait tanks in the sterns, tuna clippers are equipped with refrigeration systems to freeze the catch. Standing on iron platforms suspended from the vessel's stern, tuna fishermen work almost at a level with the water to facilitate swinging the big fish aboard with their poles. When a school of tuna is spotted, live sardines and anchovies are tossed from the bait tank into the sea. This attracts the tuna to the vessel, and with heavy bamboo poles, short lines, and barbless hooks, fishermen pull in the excited fish in rapid succession.

Purse seining and trawling or "jig fishing" are also employed in tuna fishing; the latter method is used more for albacore than for other species of tuna.

Operating a tuna clipper or seiner is a major business venture. These vessels may be 150 ft. long and are driven by three or more diesel engines which can provide up to 2,000 horsepower. Auxiliary engines are used for pumps and refrigeration. Such a vessel represents an investment of $400,000, while purse seining nets may cost as much as $40,000 each. Brine chilling of the tuna permits a vessel to accumulate several hundred tons of fish and to remain at sea three or four months before bringing in the cargo.

Between nine and ten million cases of canned tuna are produced annually. Such large-scale production has been made possible solely by modern brine-chilling refrigeration methods. (See *Refrigeration and Air Conditioning*)

OTHER IMPORTANT COMMERCIAL FISH

The bonito is a relative of the tuna, similar to it in appearance and flavor. It is caught off the southwestern coast of the United States and the west coast of South America.

Yellowtail is another tuna-like fish, but it belongs to a separate family.

Mackerel is caught in huge quantities both in the Atlantic and the Pacific and is one of the most important of commercial fishes. On the West Coast, two varieties are packed at California canning factories—Pacific mackerel and jack mackerel. Well over a million 48-lb. cases are packed each year. Mackerel is generally caught in purse seines.

American sardines make up a large portion of the Maine and California fishing industries. Contrary to popular notion, sardines are not a species of fish but are usually small fish of the herring family. The name sardine is used to designate a method of packing several different varieties of fish which include sild, brislings, and pilchards. Most sardines are precooked and then packed in olive oil or in some type of sauce. Sardine catches on the West Coast are largest in the summer and fall months in an area extending from San Francisco south to San Diego. Although many sardines used to be taken in Canadian and northern New England waters, these areas have suffered from dwindling supplies in recent years.

Because Pacific sardines glow with phosphorescence in dark waters, most of the fishing is done at night and is suspended whenever there is a full moon. However, with the development of echo-sounding equipment, fishermen are able to locate schools of fish in daylight as easily as at night. Various types of purse seining are employed for these small fish. Some of the smaller nets are called lampara or half-ring nets.

A true variety of anchovy is found in Pacific waters and is being caught in ever larger numbers. Due to a falling off of the sardine catch, canning of Pacific anchovies has been on the increase. Some are packed in the manner of sardines but may not be so labeled under U.S. food regulations. Because it is costly to make up the European style of rolled fillets, American canners have not been able to compete with the imported product but have limited their operations to sardine-style packing of anchovies.

These fishermen are preparing to hoist purse rings on a fishing boat off the New England coast.

Steamed in open cans for about 45 minutes the anchovies are then drained of natural oil and moisture. Before the cans are sealed, tomato or other special sauces are added.

A potential threat to the West Coast fishing industry is the high-seas fishing of salmon by the Japanese. Although Japanese fishing vessels have strictly observed the North Pacific Treaty and have limited their activities to an area bounded on the east by the 175th meridian of west longitude, experts believe that their catch of red salmon may well consist of Alaskan fish during their period of growth.

BY-PRODUCTS OF THE FISHING INDUSTRY

As in many other industries today, modern fishing is finding new and expanded uses for its products. Certain seaweeds, which used to be discarded from the nets, are valuable sources of iodine, potash, and proteins. Studies are being made of edible algae which are found in the seas in great volume. From codfish come not only meat but liver oil—a product used in the tanning of leather, manufacture of soap, and tempering of steel. Cod-liver oil is also a medicinal source of vitamins A and D. Bones of the cod are finely ground to make a bone meal rich in phosphorus for animal feed and plant fertilizer, while a strong glue is derived from the skin. In medicine and bacteriology, a spongy sea plant called agar-agar is used as a culture medium.

Fishing industries provide the jewelry trade with a number of items, including pearls, corals, tortoise shell, and abalone shell.

Sponge fishing is active in the West Indies and off the coast of Florida.

FISH CONSERVATION

Government agencies, working in cooperation with canning and fishing industries, are engaged in extensive programs of restocking streams and ocean fishing grounds. The building of power dams has tended to obstruct the natural spawning habits of salmon. Fisheries, together with the Army Corps of Engineers, are studying ways of opening passages for fish runs where hydroelectric dams have been constructed. Some success has been achieved, although it is estimated that a 15% to 50% mortality occurs as the fish battle the turbulent spillway currents. There is also the problem of getting young fish back over the dams when they migrate to sea.

Experiments have included putting electrical charges into the water to guide fish into specially designed channels. On the basis of studies, construction of new dams will take into consideration salmon and other fish migrations.

The future of this industry lies in the direction of improved conservation methods which will serve to preserve or increase the supply of fish. Linked to the efforts of fisheries are studies of stream and ocean pollution by other industries. One of the unsolved problems in this direction is how to dispose of radioactive atomic waste resulting from the development of nuclear power. Large numbers of sealed drums containing this lethal material have been sunk in the deepest parts of the ocean. Some scientists warn that there is serious danger of fish contamination resulting from using the ocean as an atomic dumping ground.

14 Stone, Concrete, and Brick

In a large marble quarry, huge slabs are cut from sheer rock walls. Solid blocks of marble are cut into thin slabs with "gang saws." Water, sand, and other abrasives run over the blades, taking the place of teeth. Sometimes diamond-toothed saws are used for rapid cutting.

Ever since man began to construct permanent shelters for himself, stone has been his most important building material. Even the primitive natural shelters were stone caves. Probably, people began building with loose stones from their earliest days on earth. They must have seen, too, that they needed something to hold the stones together. While sticky clay furnished a crude, natural cement, it washed away in the rain. For thousands of years, human shelters remained little better than animal dens.

As late in human history as the Assyrian and Babylonian civilizations, clay was used to bind stone structures. The Egyptians discovered that a mixture of lime and gypsum was an improvement upon ordinary clay, and they used this form of cement in the building of the pyramids. Hydraulic mortar, which hardened under water, was made by mixing slaked lime with volcanic ash from Mount Vesuvius. However, the technique was lost during the Middle Ages and it was many centuries before the secret was rediscovered. The Romans used concrete not only as mortar, but also as an independent building material. Many examples of their masonry including the Colosseum and the great Roman baths are still intact today.

STONE QUARRYING

The story of both stone and concrete is centered around the stone quarry. From quarries come building stones as well as the material for making the mortar which binds

them together. These raw materials are chiefly limestone, sand, and gravel. Limestone is the main ingredient of modern portland cement. The sand and gravel deposits along the Delaware River are among the world's richest. They supply about five million tons annually for Pennsylvania's cement and concrete industry.

When the Erie Canal was being built, the demand for mortar stimulated a search for natural cement. In Madison County, N.Y., an engineer by the name of Canvass White discovered large rock deposits which produced a natural hydraulic cement requiring a minimum of processing. Other important deposits were uncovered in Indiana, Kentucky, and the Lehigh Valley in Pennsylvania. Today, some of the largest limestone quarries in the world are in east-central Pennsylvania where the Warner Company's quarry and plant facilities turn out some three hundred thousand tons of high-magnesium and high-calcium lime in the course of a year.

Small fieldstone quarries, found near many communities around the country, supply most of the stone used in home and stone wall construction. Most quarries are open-pit excavations. To break up the rock formations, two methods are used. By the first, entire cliffs may be blown to rubble with explosives (a single blast breaking up sometimes as much as half a million tons of stone). By the second, the "plug and feather" method, uniform pressure is exerted on a rock mass along a cleavage line or fault. Wedges, called plugs, and thin pieces of steel, called feathers, are used. Workmen insert two feathers into each of a series of drilled holes and drive a wedge between them to split the rock.

DISTRIBUTION OF ROCK

Four major stones make up the bulk of quarrying in the United States: granite, limestone, sandstone, and marble. Granite is found in quantity in California, Connecticut, Georgia, Louisiana, Massachusetts, New Hampshire, Vermont, Pennsylvania, Minnesota, and North Carolina. Limestone is very widely distributed, with many quarries in Illinois, Indiana, Kansas, Ohio, Wisconsin, Pennsylvania, and other states. Sandstone is found in most of these states as well as in Colorado, West Virginia, and Wisconsin.

The largest marble-producing states are Vermont, Pennsylvania, California, Tennessee, Georgia, Alabama, and New York. Marble is actually a limestone which has been subjected to great heat and has become crystallized. It ranges in color, due to the presence of various minerals, from the white of pure marble through greens, reds, and browns to coal black. Some limestones, made up of the shells and bones of fossilized animals, are called *fossiliferous* marble. Marble quarries at Rutland, Vermont have been excavated to depths of 500 ft. or more and are still producing high-grade marble.

PORTLAND CEMENT

Without the broad ribbons of concrete that connect every town and city in America, the automobile and trucking industries would have been seriously retarded. Bridges,

Cement and concrete are primary building materials of the modern world. Highways, bridges, and towering buildings all require portland cement, as may be seen in this view of Central Philadelphia.

towering skyscrapers, giant dams for hydroelectric power, churches, and schools are built with concrete, the end product of portland cement. The term "portland cement" does not refer to the cities in Maine or Oregon, nor is it the brand name of a single manufacturer. It was the name given to modern hydraulic cement by its inventor, an English bricklayer and stonemason named Joseph Aspdin, who considered his product similar in color to stone quarried on the Isle of Portland off the British mainland. In 1824, Aspdin patented his cement, which he made by pulverizing limestone and clay, burning the mixture in a kiln, then grinding the resulting clinker into a fine powder. Part of his secret was in the careful apportionment of lime, silica, iron oxide, and alumina. Although the new patented mortar was slow to be accepted in place of natural cement, 98% of U.S. production today is portland cement. Natural cement is still quarried but, because the proportions of lime and clay vary greatly in nature, the quality of the end product is unpredictable.

For many years portland cement was exported to the United States from Europe. But after 1895 American production began to satisfy domestic demand. Now U.S. companies manufacture two to three times more portland cement than any other country—approximately three hundred million barrels per year. Canadian annual production has been between twenty-two and thirty million barrels over the past several years.

HOW PORTLAND CEMENT IS MADE

There are some 80 separate operations involved in the manufacture of portland cement. Most of it is made in very large plants which are designed, almost literally, to pulverize mountains. Tremendous amounts of heat and electrical power are consumed in the process. (See *Power*)

The first step is the crushing operation. Tons of rock, in chunks as large as barrels, are reduced by giant crushers to small stones about four to six inches in diameter. Mammoth steel-crunching jaws at the bottoms of hoppers chew up whole truckloads of rock in less than two minutes. In order to prevent clogging, workmen tend the crushers and occasionally pry loose the jammed rocks by means of long rods. To protect the workmen from being swallowed whole in the maws of these awesome crushing machines, the men wear safety belts with heavy chains attached overhead.

From these primary crushers, the rock mass enters a second set of crushers or hammer mills where it is reduced to small, pebble-sized pieces.

The next stage of manufacture is the addition of certain raw materials (shells, chalk or marl, shale, clay, slate or blast-furnace slag, silica sand, and iron ore) to the pulverized limestone, and the grinding and blending of this mixture. Two principal methods are used. In one process, (wet), water is mixed with the raw materials and the grinding forms "slurry" of a thick fluid consistency, which is then fed to the kiln. In the other process, (dry), the ingredients are ground, blended, and put into the kiln dry.

When the finely ground mixture, either wet or dry, is ready to be "burned," it enters the kilns. In modern cement factories, kilns are cylindrical steel structures as much as 12 ft. in diameter and 400 to 500 ft. long. Lined with firebrick and mounted on slightly tilted axes, they revolve slowly while roaring jets of flame 30 or 40 ft. long heat the slurry or dry mixture to 2,700° F. This burning releases some elements in the form of gases, while the remaining charge forms a substance known as "clinker." Through observation slits, workmen, wearing dark glasses, can see a magnificent display of color as the clinker mass forms. Purples, reds, orange, and weirdly incandescent lights glow from the chemically changing mass. This is discharged, red-hot, through the lower end of the kiln, in the form of hard, small pieces about the size of pebbles or marbles.

Next, the clinker enters a series of new grinding machines where gypsum is added. This is the ingredient which controls the hardening time of concrete. In the "finishing mills," the clinker is ground into a powder so fine that most of it will pass through a sieve containing a hundred thousand openings per square inch. This is portland cement.

After being poured automatically into strong paper sacks or into specially constructed railroad hopper cars, trucks, or barges, the cement is ready for market.

Exclusive of fuels and explosives, which are used in huge quantities, it has been estimated that some 643 lb. of raw materials are used to produce a single barrel of portland cement weighing 376 lb. Weight loss is due to the elimination of waste gases in the kilns.

In a recent survey, figures show that one year's production of the U.S. cement industry consumed well over eight million tons of coal (See *Mining*), two hundred seventy-six million gallons of oil, and one hundred twenty-six million cubic feet of gas.

In all of its operations, the modern cement factory maintains strict chemical control through laboratory testing. Hourly samples are examined at all stages of production, so that absolute uniformity of the finished product will result.

CONCRETE

Portland cement alone does not become sufficiently hard to be used as a building material. It serves as the binder for other materials which, in various combinations, produce concrete. Nowadays, most concrete is ready-mixed. It is made in "batching plants" where sand, coarse aggregates (gravel, crushed stone, or slag), and portland cement are scientifically mixed with the proper amount of water. The resulting plastic mixtures are loaded into special agitator trucks which transport the concrete to building sites. Sometimes the dry ingredients are loaded into the mixer trucks. Separate water tanks, mounted on a truck, can feed the correct amount of water into the slowly rotating mixer drum while the load is in transit.

Each order received by the batching plant is prepared to satisfy the specifications of the job. A batch operator, working controls to weigh the required amounts of cement, sand, gravel, etc., prepares the mixture by releasing each ingredient from its separate bin into the weighing hopper and thence into the mixer. Every batch is tailor-made to the customer's requirements. Delivery is made at the exact day and time it is needed. This must be precisely established when the order is given to the ready-mix plant, since careful planning of amounts of concrete needed, prepara-

Many bridges today are constructed with prestressed concrete beams like those shown here. Reinforcing steel is stretched either before concrete has been poured or after it has hardened, superimposing compressive stresses in the concrete.

Riding over miles of conveyor belts, graded crushed rock is transported to the building site of the Hungry Horse Dam, where it is stockpiled so that huge quantities of concrete may be mixed and poured.

tion of forms, number of workmen on hand to handle the spading and troweling, must be worked out in advance by the builder. Delays can be costly; hence many ready-mix concrete trucks are equipped with two-way radios to expedite service.

There are more than 4,100 companies producing ready-mix concrete in the United States and Canada. These firms in the early 1960's were producing over one hundred thirty million cubic yards of concrete annually with a value of almost two billion dollars.

USES OF CONCRETE

With three and one-half million miles of roads in the United States, highway building is still using tremendous quantities of concrete as programs of replacing, rebuilding, improving, and adding new roads continue. Traffic is expanding at such a rate that highway engineers can scarcely keep pace with the problem. (See *Automobiles*) Nearly all superhighways and freeways are constructed with concrete. Along with the building of roads goes the erection of many reinforced concrete bridges. Some of these structures are spectacular in their modern beauty. Airport runways, sidewalks, foundations of buildings, frameworks of large skyscrapers or factories, floors, footings, basements, concrete pipes, and building blocks are among the many uses of this versatile material.

Concrete shell roofs, which make possible unusual designs in modern architecture, are being used for aircraft hangars, industrial buildings, gymnasiums, and auditoriums. Generally such roofs are only three inches thick; yet they can span broad areas without beams, trusses, or

crete and thus eliminating the tearing-apart tensile stresses to which bridges and buildings are subjected. Steel reinforcements may be stretched either before concrete has been poured or after it has hardened. In posttensioning, the stretched steel is fastened usually at the ends of concrete blocks by anchors. As a result, when tension on the steel is increased, there is a corresponding compressive squeeze against the concrete. The first prestressed concrete bridge to be undertaken in the United States was the Walnut Lane Bridge in Fairmount Park, Philadelphia, completed in 1951, with a center span 160 ft. long.

RESEARCH FOR THE FUTURE

In the world's largest and best equipped cement and concrete laboratories, technicians of the Portland Cement Association in Chicago are studying the chemical proper-

Concrete being poured on a bridge in the construction of a modern metropolitan expressway. Buildings are also constructed with reinforced concrete.

interior columns. If properly engineered, concrete shell roofs or domes are exceptionally strong.

Because concrete can be molded virtually into any shape, it can be used for arches, decorative masonry (railings and balustrades), pillars, and pipe sections of various sizes.

NEW PRODUCTS AND METHODS

A fast, economical method of erecting concrete structures is called "tiltup." This system, which has come into wide use since World War II, consists of preforming concrete wall panels in a horizontal position; then the hardened slabs are tilted vertically into place by means of lifting devices.

Improving upon the strength of conventional reinforced concrete is the newer "prestressed" concrete. It is accomplished by stretching the reinforcing steel. This has the effect of superimposing compressive stresses in the con-

ties of concrete and its various ingredients. Tests of the tensile strengths of different mixtures are carried on endlessly. High-frequency, sonic testing machines are used to determine the internal properties of solid concrete blocks. Such research established the fact that the ratio of cement and water has an important bearing on the durability of concrete. Other studies have made cement frost resistant or impervious to a variety of climatic conditions. Several thousand concrete specimens are exposed to many different weather and soil conditions at two test plots in Georgia and Illinois. Concrete pilings, driven into the ocean bottom off Cape Cod and in the Pacific near Los Angeles, are being observed for erosion and chemical changes. Scientists also make frequent checks of the concrete in large dams, bridges, and other concrete structures throughout the country.

Research is creating new cement and concrete products

which are bringing about a revolution in building methods and architectural design. Asbestos-cement building products, for example, are now being manufactured with improved methods by more than a dozen companies. Asbestos cement combining portland cement with asbestos fibers is used for roofing shingles, wallboard, and sidings in many attractive colors and textures.

BRICKMAKING

A well-known British expression, used to describe a person of good character and integrity, is "he's a regular brick." The phrase is significant for through history the lowly brick has been a symbol of strength, reliability, and permanence. Along with the development of early clay mortar came the molding of clay blocks as building materials. Sun-dried, "adobe" bricks were in use thousands of years before history was recorded on clay tablets. Probably the earliest bricks were naturally formed blocks of sun-baked clay which people found along the banks of rivers, such as the Euphrates and the Tigris.

At Ur, the ancient Old Testament city of Abraham, excavations have uncovered a structure known as the Ziggurat. This is a sort of pyramid, built in steps, on which ancient priests studied the heavens. Its lowest stage, built about 2300 B.C., is made of crude brick foundation and is faced with an outer layer of fine burned brick which remains in a state of excellent preservation to this day.

Historians are in disagreement as to whether bricks or pottery were the first clay products. (See *Ceramics*) In any case, brickmaking is a very ancient craft which has been highly respected by the peoples of many lands and eras. Among the wonders of Babylon were the huge walls, magnificent temples, and the hanging gardens of Nebuchadnezzar, all built of brick.

Clay bricks were made in all of the ancient civilizations of Persia, India, China, Egypt, Asia Minor, Greece, and Rome. From the remarkable Roman brickwork, Europeans learned the craft, and the first brick structures in England were built by the Romans during more than three centuries of their occupation. But modern English brickmaking, from which the American industry was derived, did not really develop until the sixteenth century. Finally, the great London fire of 1666 spurred the use of brick rather than wood for most dwellings. The famous Georgian architecture of the eighteenth century depends almost exclusively upon designs with brick exteriors.

BRICKMAKING IN AMERICA

Probably the earliest appearance of the industry in America was adobe brick made by the natives of Peru and Mexico. Modern brickmaking came largely with the English settlement of the North American colonies; brick houses were first constructed with materials transported from the old country, then with domestically produced bricks. Early brick kilns were operated in Virginia in 1611 and in Massachusetts about 1629.

From that time to the 1880's, most American production consisted of common brick for wall construction. After that began a growing interest in using brick for decorative and artistic effect in architecture. Today, a great

This 5,000-year-old molded brick from the ancient Mesopotamian city of Ur was unearthed by an archaeological expedition. The brick bears the royal stamp of King Shulgi of the Third Dynasty of Ur.

variety of color tones and textures is available for both interior and exterior construction.

Although the number of brickmaking plants in America has declined from about 6,000 in 1890 to some 500 or 600 in the 1960's, the total volume of production has steadily increased. Except for the lean depression years of the 1930's, U.S. brick production has gone forward in quantity and quality.

MANUFACTURING METHODS

Basically all brick plants have three main manufacturing units: preparation, molding, and burning. Within these general areas of processing are a number of special processes, such as glazing and model making.

Clay as it is brought from a pit or mine must be refined by removing stones and other foreign matter. By means of crushers, the clay is reduced to a fine consistency. This

A new clay masonry facing material is applied to a wall by driving a nail into a metal clip attached to the brick veneer. Mortar is spread in the joints by a special pressure gun, then tooled in the conventional manner.

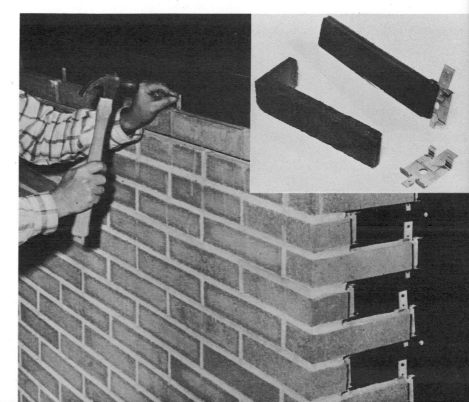

In landscaping, brick is an ideal building material. This brick charcoal grill built into a garden wall provides an attractive cooking area for the outdoor chef.

Brick is by no means limited to outdoor construction. Many modern interior walls are masonry. Here, the rugged texture of the brick is tastefully combined with wood.

Clay products include decorative tile and architectural terra-cotta ornaments which can achieve a high degree of artistry. Here is an outstanding example of modern custom-made architectural terra-cotta, an 18-foot-high sculpture by Victor Schreckengost above the entrance to the Lakewood, Ohio, High School. Color glazes, baked into the clay surfaces under intense heat will retain original richness indefinitely.

is done in two stages. First or preliminary grinding is accomplished by one of three types of machines descriptively known as roll, gyratory, or jaw grinders. A secondary grinding by a dry pan consists of placing the clay in a large rotating metal pan, within which two heavy milling wheels revolve, and crushing the material as it is fed to the machine in batches. Secondary grinding may also be carried out in a granulator, an open trough in which a series of spirally arranged steel knives on a revolving shaft cut through the clay mass. Ground clay is next passed over a series of screens which sift out oversized particles. These are returned to the crushing apparatus for regrinding.

Now the refined clay moves to the molding operation, which may be one of three processes. By the STIFF-MUD process, heavy clay is forced through a die, whereas SOFT-MUD molding consists of forming a fluid clay in separate molds. The third method, called the DRY-PRESS process, subjects dry clay to extreme pressure and forces it into individual molds. Generally speaking, brick is made by the stiff- and soft-mud processes; tile and terra-cotta pipe are usually formed by stiff-mud molding. The dry-press method produces almost perfect face brick. Special shapes are hand molded.

The refined clay is mixed with the proper amount of water in a machine called a pug mill which kneads the clay to uniform consistency with rotating knives. A "de-airing" machine, which compacts the material, eliminating air bubbles, makes it ready for molding. Three processes are used according to the amount of water added by the pug mill.

For stiff-mud molding, the clay is extruded through the molding die by means of a revolving screw or auger. A cutting machine then slices the continuous ribbon of formed clay into sections of predetermined size. In making terra-cotta pipe, a crew of five or six men is needed to operate the pipe press which extrudes lengths of large sewer pipe. The pipe-molding mechanism operates vertically, a piston forcing out a length of pipe with each down stroke.

94

Brick construction may have a rustic appearance or be laid in formal patterns as shown above. Made from natural clay, brick adds color and interest to garden settings.

Modern clay masonry is made in a great variety of shapes for indoor and outdoor construction. These homes are enhanced by porch screens made of structural clay tile.

The clay is then pressed against a forming head to shape the flared end of the pipe section; the section is then cut and lifted by hand from the forming head.

In the soft-mud operation, clay goes from the pug mill into the top of a vertical press and is forced by a piston into sand-lined molds accommodating nine or ten bricks. As each clay-filled mold is ejected from the machine it is inverted, leaving the soft bricks on a pallet. Special shapes are sometimes formed on hydraulic die presses in which two-piece dies are forced together to mold the clay.

Before burning, wet clay must be partially dried and hardened. Most driers are built in the form of heated tunnels, through which pallets of soft bricks move on conveyors. At the receiving end of the drier, temperature is about 120° F. This increases to 300° F. at the discharge end.

For glazed finishes, a liquid glaze is applied to unburned clay by means of manual or mechanical spray guns.

Finally, the dried bricks, pipes or other products are set in piles for burning. This "setting" operation is often accomplished by manual labor, although some modern brick plants have mechanical cranes or loading forks to do the job. Setting must be done in such a way that maximum surface area of the materials is exposed to heat. Bricks are piled on edge, with open spaces around each unit. They are then moved to the kilns.

Two types of kilns are used for burning clay products: periodic and continuous. After bricks are loaded in a periodic kiln, fires are started and the clay is baked at the required temperature for a number of hours. At a predetermined time, the kiln is allowed to cool, and the burned products are removed. Continuous kilns, held at a constant burning temperature, are built usually in the form of tunnels with maximum heat at the center and diminishing temperatures at each end. They may be gas- or oil-fired. Loaded kiln cars are rolled into the tunnel entrance and pushed through the kiln as new cars are added to the line.

Workmen are easing into place a prefabricated brick wall section four feet wide and nineteen feet high on a Chicago store construction job. The reinforced wall section has just been lifted into place by a crane. This type of wall section, called a "plate girder," one of the most recent developments in the structural clay industry, is two and one-half inches thick.

GROWTH OF AUTOMATION

This is one of the few industries still in the process of being mechanized.

Much of the loading, setting, and packing of structural clay products is still done by manual labor. The Structural Clay Products Research Foundation in Geneva, Illinois is making studies to develop machinery for the various operations. Pilot machines are operated and thoroughly tested before they are recommended to brickmaking plants.

Products are also subjected to exhaustive tests by the Foundation. After tests of strength and resistance to weather conditions have been carried out, new products may be installed in actual building operations, where men from the Foundation's Field Division work directly with building contractors on better construction techniques.

NEW PRODUCTS

Bricks and clay products are, today, being made in dozens of new styles and colors for use in modern architecture. Along with special glazes, bricks in new shapes and forms are being designed. For example, "acoustile"

is a structural clay unit punched with small holes and lined in the center with a fibrous glass pad. Such acoustical brick has an average sound absorption of 65%. One of the newest of building materials is the ceramic panel which consists of a prefabricated brick wall section one to two feet wide and up to thirteen feet in length.

Lightweight brick, made of low density, fused clay aggregate is being produced with structural strength equal to standard bricks, yet weighing 17% to 40% less than conventional materials. Experiments are being conducted to produce lightweight brick by a new method, forming them directly from hot aggregate which will fuse into virtually any size and shape desired.

The future of structural clay products holds the promise of whole new concepts in building methods and materials. Walls, which are now laboriously put together, brick by brick, in tiny units, may soon be formed in complete elements. Sheer walls, plate girders, floor panels, and roof sections, with built-in sound and thermal insulation, may be formed of structural clay and joined by new "high bond" mortars possessing greater strength than ever.

Bricklaying, an ancient and honorable craft, is today being revolutionized by the introduction of many new and improved types of structural clay products. While the skilled handwork of building walls brick by brick is still widely practiced, prefabricated terra-cotta panels and roof sections may soon change many building concepts.

15 Building

The building of skyscrapers is a distinctively American development, epitomized by some of the amazing structures found in midtown Manhattan. This is the famed Rockefeller Center, a 16-building complex of soaring office towers. The central structure is the 70-story RCA Building, largest privately owned office building in the world.

Man is a builder. Since his entrance upon the stage of earth's history he has been putting clay, stones, and other materials together, forming monuments to his energy and ingenuity, monuments that have endured through centuries. Egyptian pyramids, Greek temples, the Roman Colosseum, the Chinese Wall, and the mysterious, weirdly beautiful Angkor Wat in Cambodia all testify in different ways and in widely separated times and places that the restless human spirit is impelled to build something permanent.

Only a part of this impulse is brought about by the practical need for shelter, or for means of crossing chasms and streams. Were this not so, almost no ancient buildings would remain on earth, for human dwellings are usually small and comparatively frail structures. Where homes or the palaces of kings have been built for permanence, more than necessity has prompted the effort. There is something satisfying to the soul in a great and enduring structure, perhaps because it gives us a sense of the continuity of humankind.

ARCHITECTURE

Building graduated from mere piles of stones when men began to plan and design their structures in advance. This is the art known as architecture. Throughout history, architectural styles have been influenced by several factors: climate, and consequently the need for certain types of walls, roofs, and other practical features; discoveries of new structural methods; availability and use of certain building materials; expression of religious concepts; per-

97

sonal tastes of the architects and builders. Certain basic structural features are common to almost all styles of architecture but are designed and ornamented in endless variations. Pillars, cornices, railings, arches, and windows are subject to individual design treatments.

Today, architecture is big business. Large architectural firms, employing staffs of draftsmen and engineers, are engaged by building contractors to design and make the blueprints for factories, office buildings, schools, churches, and other public buildings. Private homes, on the other hand, are often planned by individual architects who work as professional free-lance artists.

AMERICAN BUILDING INDUSTRY

Taken as a whole, building is America's largest manufacturing industry. Including the construction of homes, apartment buildings, churches, schools, commercial and public buildings, bridges and roads, it has, in peak years, amounted to more than forty billion dollars. In addition, Americans spend some twenty billions each year for modernization and renovation of existing structures. Light construction (homes and small commercial buildings) employs between five and six million workers for actual construction and supply services.

At the same time, building is not an industry of concentrated, giant corporations, but is spread throughout the nation in every community and among thousands of building contractors, large and small. During the decade between 1950 and 1960, American builders constructed more new homes and private dwellings than can be found in any other country. A staggering total of fifteen million housing units at a cost of one hundred seventy billion dollars were built.

To gain some idea of the scope of the so-called light construction industry, it is interesting to note that for one hundred thousand housing starts, nearly two hundred fifty thousand workers are required, and more than six hundred million dollars' worth of building materials. Total amount of money expended will be about one and three-quarters billion dollars. There are approximately one hundred twenty-five thousand U.S. building contractors in this field.

Meanwhile, America's greatest boom in school building began in the 1950's and is likely to continue for years to come. In a 15-year period from 1945 to 1960, U.S. school enrollment doubled from twenty-four to forty-eight million pupils.

Commercial buildings, including drive-in banks, bowling alleys, retail stores, and offices, have been increasing year by year; dollar volume in this field is expected, according to experts, to reach six and one-half billion by 1970. The trend is toward small suburban office buildings and light manufacturing units as business and industry become more decentralized and diversified.

With its advantages of eliminating overcrowding, of offering lower rentals and taxes, and pleasant surroundings, the move to the suburbs has created problems. Builders have been forced to undertake new road paving and sewer construction. One of the problems facing the light construction industry is to determine a dividing line between municipal governments' and builders' responsibilities. Outdated zoning laws, which local officials are reluctant to change, are preventing needed construction in many localities. Intelligent, long-range planning by municipal officials, with provision for suburban expansion, is necessary. Good municipal planning is advantageous, not only to the building industry but to the community itself. Because of various legal restrictions, building costs are often greater than they need to be. Due to zoning ordinances the home buyer may, for example, be forced to purchase a house which reflects a waste of both materials and land. Sometimes such restrictions as minimum half-acre lots and excessive minimum sizes for houses in a given community prevent any building at all. On the other hand, a nearby section, with almost no restrictions but with a limited amount of land available, may quickly be overcrowded with small, closely packed houses that have few of the amenities average home owners desire.

It is clear that a fresh, modern approach to community planning and building codes is needed for the developing building boom in America.

HOW IS A HOUSE BUILT?

Most American homes are "operation" built, which means that a contractor builds a number of identical or very similar houses on a large tract of land that has been subdivided into smaller, individual lots. A "custom" built home is, as the term implies, constructed to the individual customer's specifications. Because the operative builder

Still the largest of all American industries, home and commercial building amounts to some forty billion dollars a year, with another twenty billions spent on renovation of existing structures. Each of these new homes in Columbus, Ohio provides three man years of work to construct the house and to make the materials from which it is built.

is able to work from a single set of blueprints and is in a position to order materials in wholesale quantities, he can offer houses at generally lower prices than is possible in custom building.

In either case, the steps in construction are fundamentally the same, but there are dozens of variations in methods of assembly. Although some houses, particularly in the southwestern part of the United States, are built without basements, most American home building begins with an excavation for the cellar or basement. After the excavation has been dug, generally with a power shovel, foundation walls of stone, cinder block, or poured concrete are constructed. The basis of every foundation is the footings, usually concrete, width and thickness of which are determined by the type of soil. When the foundation walls have been built to a height several inches above ground and after a cement basement floor has been laid, one or

other type is post-and-beam framing. This provides a gabled roof without interior supports or obstructions. A heavy ridge beam, attached to a post at each end of the house, supports transverse beams which form the main skeleton of the roof.

There are a number of other roof construction methods: trussed-roof framing, in which a series of triangular frames are placed transversely from wall to wall without any load-bearing interior partitions; rafters with ridge support, in which a central load-bearing partition, topped by a heavy ridge beam, provides the main support for the rafters.

To the skeleton or framework, various exterior walls may be added. Brick, stone, stucco, concrete block, clapboard and shingle are the most familiar exteriors used. Generally speaking, most masonry is a veneer, or shell, surrounding the basic wood framework. However, a modern trend is toward "through-the-wall" masonry, in which

Walls of this Chicago store incorporate 27 preassembled "plate girders," made of structural clay, each 4 feet wide and 19 feet high. These panels are steel reinforced and are fabricated with ceramic glazed 'brick' units measuring 12 inches by 2¼ inches on the face and 2½ inches thick. Prefabrication is making slow but significant progress in the building industry, with increased use of preassembled parts, precut joists, studs, beams, rafters, and lintels.

more steel I-beams are placed in position, spanning the crawl space (shallow excavation) or basement. Lally columns, usually steel posts filled with concrete, are used as vertical supports for the I-beam. Next, joists are laid to form the main structural members for the first floor. These 2 x 8 or 2 x 10 wooden beams are placed 16 in. apart, with small cross members nailed between them for rigidity. These angled supports are known as "bridging."

The walls of the house now begin to take form as a framework of 2 x 4 vertical studding at 16-in. intervals is erected. Often the framework is built up as a "box sill," which is a prefabricated platform of joists and subflooring, to which the stud-wall skeletons are attached.

Ceiling joists for a second floor or attic must be set across the wall and partition frames and nailed into place. They are also nailed to the roof rafters at the eaves. At the peak of the roof, the ridgeboard serves as an anchor for the rafters. This type of construction, called joist-and-rafter framing, is the most common in average homes. An-

brick or stone forms at least a part of the interior trim. For the framework itself, structural steel is being used to some extent for studs, joists, and rafters.

PREFABRICATION

Shortly after World War II, with the tremendous demand for housing, many experts expected a rapid development of prefabricating methods. Prefabrication has grown, but more slowly than was anticipated, due largely to entrenched traditions, labor union rules, and outmoded zoning ordinances.

Nevertheless, some houses today are almost completely prefabricated in factories where wall sections, floors, and roofs are made and are rapidly erected by specialists in the contracting field who use power equipment and special tools. While the ready-built house is still somewhat of a rarity in America, builders are using more and more preassembled parts and precut joists, studs, beams, rafters, and lintels.

Despite these modern methods and their obvious advantages in speed and economy, most cutting and assembling are still done on the individual building site, with the result that home building is far more costly than it would have to be if current technology were fully utilized. Even masonry wall panels of brick or concrete are coming into use (See *Stone, Concrete and Brick*) and builders are trying molded plastics, metal, hardboard, and new types of plywood for wall and ceiling construction.

Within the shell of a house or other building go the electrical systems, plumbing, wall finishes, tiling, trim, and various fixtures. Each job is done by specialized craftsmen employed by the builder, who must include their charges in his overall estimate for the construction. Carpenters, plasterers, painters, electricians, plumbers, bricklayers, stone masons, roofers, telephone men, and cement and concrete contractors all may work at different times on a single house.

HEAVY CONSTRUCTION

Contractors for heavy construction jobs submit bids to the government agency, company, or syndicate that will order the building. When several sets of estimates have been received, committees of experts analyze them and award the contract to the builder who, in their opinion, can do the best job at a fair price and in the required time.

The building of a large apartment house, office building, or factory is not unlike building a home, but it is on a much larger scale and consequently requires special engineering knowledge and equipment. A modern skyscraper's framework is made usually of reinforced concrete. Floors of poured concrete are formed on beams and girders, while a great variety of outer facings are used. These include brick, structural clay panels, aluminum facing, precast stone or concrete panels, coupled with prefabricated window units. Some modern window units for large buildings consist of two panes of glass, four or five inches apart with built-in blinds between the glass layers. Within precast stone mullions, heat ducts and pipes are likewise provided as built-in units.

Supplying the materials for any building, large or small, are a host of industries, whose activities are described in other sections of this book. (See *Primary Metals; Lumbering; Stone, Concrete, and Brick; Mining; Paints and Varnishes; Refrigeration and Air Conditioning; Glass; Plastics*)

BRIDGE BUILDING

In the realm of heavy construction no project is more spectacular than the building of a bridge. From the crude wood, rope, and pontoon bridges of early times, bridge building has become one of mankind's greatest engineering accomplishments. One of the first developments to

Steel bridges on concrete supports carry highways and railroads across streams and valleys in all parts of the United States. This turnpike bridge at Bristol, Pa. connects the Pennsylvania and New Jersey Turnpikes.

To erect a suspension bridge, a slender wire is first suspended from the top of each tower, then a device called a "spider" weaves the heavy cable. Above is a view of the Delaware Memorial Bridge under construction.

make possible long bridges was the invention of the arch. A 600-foot-long brick arch bridge is believed to have spanned the Euphrates River in Babylon about 200 B.C. Then, with the perfection of steel, longer spans became possible. By means of cantilever and suspension construction, some of the world's mightiest spans have been built.

The steel cantilever bridge is built on piers, each of which has two balancing cantilevers. Long steel girders connect cantilevers to form the spans.

Roadways of suspension bridges are hung from a system of cables which are, in turn, tied to lofty towers at each end of the span. The world's longest bridges have been built in this manner. San Francisco's famous Golden Gate Bridge has towers the height of a 65-story building and a center span 4,200 ft. long. To erect such a bridge is an engineering feat of vast proportions. After the giant steel or masonry towers have been built, a slender wire thread is first suspended from the top of each tower and is fastened at the solid masonry anchorages at each end of the bridge. A device called a "spider" moves back and forth on the wire, weaving the heavy cable. The cable for a large suspension bridge may consist of 20,000 or more galvanized wires. From the main cables on each side of the bridge, vertical cables or steel rods are dropped at intervals. Steel girders, attached horizontally to the suspension cables, form the support for the roadway. Construction workers must have nerves as tough as the steel on which they work. They ride giant girders being hoisted into position by derricks, set rivets hundreds of feet above the river or chasm being spanned, walk along the swaying cables, and paint massive beams in the towers. It is

hazardous, exciting work requiring patience, skill, and strength. A completed suspension bridge is not only a miracle of planning and engineering; it is one of the most graceful and beautiful structures made by man.

THE FUTURE

The highly complex and diversified building industry in America is beginning to undergo significant, technological changes. As has been pointed out, prefabrication has already revolutionized the building of skyscrapers and large commercial structures. It is logical to assume that it will have an increasingly important role in home building as time goes on.

All estimates of the future indicate that there will be a steady increase in U.S. construction of all types with housing leading the way. Along with greater use of prefabrication will come a slow shift in labor from on-site to off-site employment; by 1970, it is anticipated that there will be a greater dollar volume increase of subcontracting, supply, and service than in on-site building itself. Builders, who specialize in remodeling, may look for the largest increase of all the major types of construction because there will be many more houses and other structures to remodel.

As in other industries, important opportunities exist for engineers and technicians who can find new and better materials and methods of construction. However, the application of new ideas is made more difficult than in some industries, due to the existence of restrictive building codes and union rules. It remains for imaginative builders, architects, workers, manufacturers, and government officials to remove these roadblocks to progress.

The Golden Gate Bridge, linking San Francisco with Marin County, has six traffic lanes and two walkways; it is 6,400 feet long and the towers supporting the span are 191 feet taller than the Washington Monument.

16 Paints and Varnishes

To mix the raw materials for paint, oils, resins, varnish, and dry pigments are put through "grinding mills" and giant mixing tanks. The grinding operation shown above mixes ingredients to a smooth, pasty consistency.

Consider the magic of a coat of new paint. An old, shabby looking house is transformed by fresh paint into gleaming newness, while its owner experiences renewed pride in his possession. At the same time, the paint provides a preservative coating for wood and metal. Inside, by means of a few dollars' worth of paint, a brush, a roller, and a little old-fashioned "elbow grease," the dingy walls are soon made to sparkle with sample-home brilliance. A coat of well-chosen color can make a room gay or restful, according to its occupant's preference. The chipped or rusty bicycles and toys that have been gathering dust and grime in the garage can be made as exciting as Christmas morning by means of skillfully applied paint and varnish.

WHO INVENTED PAINT?

As in so many industries, the making of paints and varnishes began thousands of years ago. Yet since the time of ancient Egypt few significant advances in paint manufacture were made until the past 50 years. About 20,000 years ago, men contrived to paint pictorial records on the stone ceilings of their caves, using yellow and red ocher made from clays, and a green derived from an earth known as glauconite. Egyptians were painting decorations as long ago as 6000 B.C. At a later period, they worked with slate palettes and crude brushes. Meanwhile they were developing preservative coatings to encase mummies in a form

of asphalt. By 1500 B.C., paint making was an active industry in Greece and Crete as well as in Egypt. The number of available colors had increased with the importation of madder, a red, and indigo, a blue, from India. Various "lakes," such as crimson lake, shades of red, violet, and brown, were derived from the madder root.

Probably the ancient Egyptians were the first to make varnish. They had at least two types. One was made from the resin of certain trees in the Libyan forests; another, a glossy varnish paint, was produced by mixing beeswax with dyes. From the sap of the acacia tree the Egyptians derived gum arabic which was also used as a protective coating.

During the Renaissance, the great Italian painters developed some paint-making techniques which have survived to this day. As a medium, they used linseed oil, still considered one of the best of paint binders. Master craftsmen, working in their own shops, developed secret formulas known only to themselves and their apprentices. While many of these formulas were preserved, undoubtedly others were buried with their inventors.

PAINT INDUSTRY IN AMERICA

In the early years of North America's colonization, there were comparatively few paint makers. Most houses were built of rough, unpainted logs, and in those days, even

102

in Europe, a painted house was a sign of the owner's affluence. But around 1700, several paint craftsmen had established businesses in America. One of the first of these was Thomas Child who operated a paint mill in Boston from 1692 to 1706. He and his contemporaries ground their colors on stone tables, using granite balls as the grinders.

Modern American paint manufacturing may be said to have started about 1852, when the American zinc oxide process was developed and when sulphate of lead and lithopone came into use. Up to this time, paints were sold as unmixed pigments and oils; customers did their own mixing. But in 1867, "prepared paints" were introduced to the American market.

As in the case of the dye and chemical industries, World War I served as the impetus to American paint manufacturing. With imported materials in short supply, American firms began to rely almost entirely upon domestic raw materials. From that point on, U.S. paint manufacturing began to assume world leadership.

HOW PAINT IS MADE

Basically all paints are made up of three classes of ingredients: pigments, binders, and thinners.

PIGMENTS: White hiding pigments are employed for opacity. For centuries, white lead was the principal white pigment, but today titanium dioxide is more widely used. Colored pigments, providing both color and opacity, are made either from various earth substances or from chemicals, while "reinforcing" or "extending" pigments are mined from the earth. (See *Chemicals, Mining*)

BINDERS: Binders consist of oils and resins. Their function is to dry and to form a tough film which binds the pigment particles together. Thanks to modern chemistry, many new oils and synthetic resins are being developed for the production of a great variety of paint textures and finishes.

THINNERS: Solvents or reducers, whose names are descriptive of their function, are generally made from turpentine, petroleum, coal tar, or alcohol. They act as vehicles for the solid pigments so that the paint will flow on various surfaces. They are constituted to evaporate, rapidly at first, then more slowly, until they leave only the permanent paint film.

Paint factories receive hundreds of tons of liquid raw materials which are transported by railroad tank cars and trailer tank trucks. They are stored temporarily in a "tank farm" outside the plant and pumped into the mill as they are needed. Varnish is made by a separate operation, from hard resins and from various oils, which are placed in huge kettles, cooked, thinned, filtered, and finally put in storage. Meanwhile, dry ingredients in sacks, barrels, or metal containers are stockpiled in another section of the plant.

To mix the raw materials, a tank is placed on a scale; as oils, resins, and varnish are poured in, each ingredient is precisely weighed. From the weighing operation, the tank is moved to a ball mill where dry pigments are mixed into the batch and are ground with the liquid constituents to a smooth paste. Other grinding mills with giant mixing tanks are used to produce a variety of finishes. The main

types of mills, each designed for making a different kind of paint, are buhrstone, three-roll, five-roll, Bramley, pebble, steel ball, and high speed.

After milling, the batch goes through a thinning operation where special oils, varnish, resins, or thinners are added. Large 500- or 600-gallon tanks are mechanically agitated to mix the ingredients.

"Tinting" the batch consists of adding a carefully measured amount of colored pigment. As in most modern manufacturing processes, laboratory samples are taken at every stage of production. These samples are analysed and tested to check color standards, flowing properties, drying, brushing, and many other qualities. When the batch has been approved- as meeting standard specifications, it is emptied out of the mixing tanks, forced through strainers, and into hoppers which feed the filling machinery. In the filling operation, cans of various sizes move on conveyors, passing under spouts which automatically discharge the exact amount of paint needed to fill each can. Cans are then capped and conveyed to a shipping department to be loaded on trains and trucks.

Dry pigment is being added to a dispenser as paint ingredients are put through an initial mixing.

Tinting the batch is an art requiring skill and experience. It consists of adding a carefully measured amount of colored pigment. Color standards are carefully and scientifically checked at all stages of production.

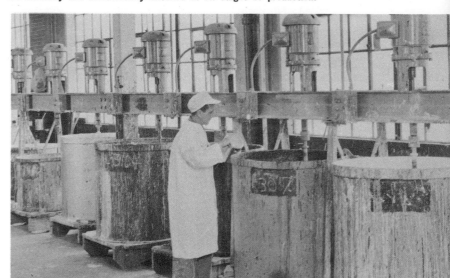

In some types of paint manufacturing, the liquids, called vehicles, and the pigments are placed in mixing tanks for preliminary mixing. The batch is then conveyed to grinding mills.

Lacquers, also known as spirit varnishes, are natural or synthetic resin solutions which evaporate rapidly. They are made by churning and dissolving the ingredients in large tanks without "cooking." Both lacquer and shellac derive their names from their basic raw material, lac, a natural resin produced by the lac bug in India. This tiny insect, no larger than the head of a pin, feeds on tree bark and secretes the sticky resin until it covers him like a tent. On a single tree, millions of lac bugs secrete enough resin in six months to produce an inch-thick layer which is removed by native laborers, dried over slow fires, and then stretched into thin sheets for shipment to U.S. paint and varnish manufacturers. Lac is a valuable material used in the making of phonograph records, TV tubes, shoe polish, and light bulbs.

CHEMICAL PROPERTIES OF PAINT

During World War I, a Du Pont chemist, working on a project to create a type of new photographic film, examined the contents of a drum of liquid cellulose which had been standing for several days under a corrugated iron shed roof. The hot July sun had been beating down on the roof, and the shed was as hot as an oven. When the chemist examined the cellulose, he noticed at once a change since it had been placed in the storage shed. He dipped a brush handle into the liquid and saw with increasing excitement that it became coated with a clear, colorless film which rapidly dried to a hard, brilliant finish.

The discovery led to the development of a new lacquer-finish paint which could be sprayed on metal or other surfaces, and which dried so rapidly that several coats could be applied in a matter of hours. This was the famous Duco pyroxylin lacquer. It revolutionized the automobile industry, making it possible to give cars a lustrous, weatherproof coating in one day where slow-drying paints formerly required several days and special baking processes to produce a good finish.

More than this, the Du Pont discovery radically changed the entire paint industry. Quick to realize that chemistry was the key to their future, paint manufacturers established chemical laboratories and hired chemists to develop new products. Today there are over 2,000 paint research chemists in the United States. Through their studies and experiments, during the past decade the industry has made phenomenal strides. They have created fireproof paints, paints that can withstand sub-zero or high temperatures, special acid-, gas-, and weather-resistant finishes. Some coatings are designed to be impervious to fungi, mildew, or sunlight. There are luminous paints, paints which fluoresce under black light, and infrared-reflecting paints.

In another field of scientific study, color specialists are engaged not only to learn the chemistry of pigments and to develop light-fast paints, but to evaluate people's emotional reactions to various colors. Millions of dollars are spent on scientifically graded color charts and on the selection of pleasing hues for exterior and interior decorative purposes.

BRUSHES AND BRISTLES

From the time the ancient Egyptians began to use animal-hair brushes to apply their paints, people have been cursed by the loose bristle and by brushes that shed their

BALL MILL PROCESS

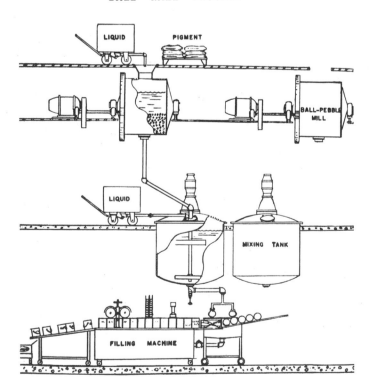

In this scientifically controlled varnish cooker, hard resins and oils are heated to the proper temperature. After cooking, the varnish is thinned, put through filters, and stored in tanks until needed for the paint-making process. The varnishes used for various paints are generally made in the paint factory.

hair as do bald-headed men. Paints have been made to smooth themselves as they dry, thus eliminating brush strokes. Many types of brushes and rollers have been devised to make the job of painting easier and less messy.

As in the paint industry itself, brush manufacturers have been experimenting with synthetic or plastic bristles. Camel's hair and red sable hair have long been used for artists' brushes; the latter is considered one of the best quality bristles available. Hogs' hair, horsehair, and many other natural bristles are in wide use for various types of brushes. An important phase of research is now devoted to producing texturized synthetic bristles and to improving the cross-sectional shape and uniformity of such bristles.

RETAIL OPERATIONS

Hardware and paint stores throughout the United States dispense millions of gallons of paints and varnishes every year, with a retail value of nearly two billion dollars. In addition, the sale of brushes, rollers, oils, thinners, and other painting supplies is big business. A specialized segment of the paint industry is devoted to artists' paints and brushes. Many art supply stores specialize in handling the water color, oil, and tempera colors for commercial artists and fine arts painters.

Most of the major paint manufacturers have their own dealers who sell their products exclusively, while general hardware stores will often offer several brand names and lines of paint products. Among the familiar American brands are Duco, Sherwin-Williams, Dutch Boy, Felton Sibley, Benjamin Moore Paints, Pittsburgh Paints, M. A. Bruder (MAB), Buten's, and Glidden Paints. There are in all, over 1,500 paint, varnish, and lacquer manufacturers in America, employing about 80,000 people.

Today, paints are not only decorative but are durable, protective coatings for all sorts of materials which would otherwise deteriorate. With the advancement of organic polymer chemistry, the paint industry's products are multiplying rapidly to include hundreds of coatings for every conceivable purpose. Among the more spectacular developments are the latex paints which use water solvent, vinyl plastisols, reactive polyester resins, and fluid epoxy resins. The water soluble paints have revolutionized interior decoration. Although they are known as "latex" paints, the term is a misnomer. Actually they are emulsions of resinous polymer in water. They are made in a pressure reactor with 60 to 70 parts styrene and 30 to 40 parts butadiene. In the reactor, the normally gaseous butadiene liquifies and both monomers are emulsified in an aqueous medium. Other vinyl monomers and a variety of acrylates are similarly emulsified, thus yielding a whole new category of paint vehicles.

The industry looks to a promising future when an expanding population will require tremendous volume of paints for new houses, furniture, and thousands of other products and uses. Job opportunities will increase for production workers with technical and chemical knowledge. Material-control management requires ability in mathematics.

Above all, the paint and varnish industry needs forward-looking, imaginative personnel who will help to develop the finishes and colorful protective coatings of tomorrow's technological world. For paint is no longer limited to the traditonal earth pigments mixed with oil; now it embraces a host of new liquid plastics and organic chemicals, each made to endure under conditions which would have driven the old-time paint makers to despair.

At a Chicago wood furniture plant, cabinets go through the preparation line for final packing and shipping. Every piece must be considered perfect before it can be released and sent to the retailer and the ultimate consumer.

17 Furniture

Although the making of furniture dates far back in human history, it did not begin with primitive man, who squatted and slept on the ground with little regard for comfort. Probably, he occasionally found a convenient stone or log on which to sit, and he may even have used flat stones as tables inside his cave dwellings. But the conception of furniture in the modern sense is a highly refined product of civilization. Among the first peoples to create furniture were the Assyrians, the ancient Egyptians, and the Chinese. In Egypt, chairs, stools, thrones, and couches have been found dating back earlier than 3500 B.C. The Egyptian furniture was often richly decorated and highly polished, whereas the early Assyrians built their chairs and tables along more severe lines, indicating a martial character of the people.

A study of furniture design through the ages among various races and nationalities provides fascinating insight into human temperaments and customs. Greek furniture was simple, exquisitely proportioned; Romans built heavier, more solid pieces; the Italian Renaissance produced complex and highly ornate furniture. In each civilization, furniture reflected the nature of its creators and the conditions under which they lived.

FURNITURE IN AMERICA

Until about 100 years ago, furniture was made either by skilled craftsmen and cabinetmakers, or by the householder for his own use. American colonists found little time at first for decorating their homemade furniture. They built simply and economically from materials at hand. As a result, Colonial period furniture has the natural beauty of functional simplicity. The first, rough-hewn styles were gradually refined until, in the hands of expert craftsmen, a genuine American furniture developed. Colonial-style furniture today is second only in popularity to American modern.

As a major industry, U.S. furniture manufacturing began around the Civil War period. At that time, Cincinnati and Louisville became important centers of commercial furniture making, and their products were shipped by steamboat to cities located along the Ohio and Mississippi Rivers. By 1870, the nation's furniture shipments amounted to seventy-six million dollars, a figure which grew at a rapid rate topping two hundred million dollars by the turn of the century. Currently, United States furniture production exceeds five billion dollars annually.

In spite of its size and importance, the industry has produced no giant corporations comparable to General Motors or Du Pont. It is composed of some 4,000 comparatively small firms, only 300 or 400 of which do more than a million dollars' worth of business a year. They sell most of their merchandise directly to retail outlets; furniture stores handle about 70% of the total output while the remaining 30% is sold in department stores and large mail-order concerns.

CENTRAL MARKETING

An important factor in the growth of this industry was the development of a central marketing system. In 1924, the American Furniture Mart was established in Chicago so that the nation's furniture manufacturers could display their wares to retailers from all parts of the country. The huge Merchandise Mart, erected in 1930, further strengthened Chicago's position as the furniture center of the United States, although there are now about 25 markets in other parts of the country where furniture is exhibited to dealers at certain seasons of the year.

For custom-built furniture of high quality, Grand Rapids, Mich. is considered America's number one marketplace. Other major markets are New York; Los Angeles; Dallas; San Francisco; Jamestown, N.Y.; Atlanta; High Point, N.C., an important furniture manufacturing center.

MANUFACTURING PROCEDURES

There are, of course, many types of furniture, and manufacturers have a tendency to specialize. The most complex in construction is the upholstered living room furniture which requires the utmost skill and quality control to produce good pieces. Frames are generally made of high-grade hardwoods that have been air seasoned and kiln dried to prevent warping. Joints of quality pieces are doweled and glued, while important "stress" points may be double doweled and reinforced with corner blocks.

Before the assembled frame is upholstered, springs are installed for seats and backs. Coil springs may be mounted on tempered spring wires which are fastened to the wood frame and suspended by helical springs from the two ends. Stabilizing wires are added to prevent side sway. Other types of spring construction include "sinuous wire," and double level springing (combination of deep coil and sinuous wire springs). Sinuous wire is a stiff wire bent in a snake-like form and joined to the frame at the ends.

An insulating layer of tough rubberized material or a resin bonded pad made from crushed wood fibers is used to cover the springs. Finally the upholstering, or padding, is fastened over the spring sections of seat, back, and cushions. Upholstery materials include cotton felt, rubberized hair pads, and sisal pads which are made of a tough vegetable fiber from plants of the amaryllis family and imported from the East Indies, West Indies, Mexico, South America, and Africa. In recent years there has been increasing use of modern plastic foams and foamed latex. (See *Rubber, Plastics*)

A new type of chair is being made by a mass production process whereby pure liquid foam is poured over a steel frame. When the foam has solidified, it is covered with various fabrics or plastic coverings. The result is a lightweight, durable chair of modern design and unusual comfort.

Foams used in chair construction and cushions are generally from the family of polyesters, or urethane foams, although foamed latex is still considered superior by many manufacturers for solid seat cushioning.

Finishing of upholstered chairs and sofas is done with a great variety of fabrics, leather, and plastics. As are many phases of furniture construction, this is a job for highly skilled craftsmen. In some plants, one man does the complete job; in others, the work may be divided among seat, arm, and back upholsterers.

There is a growing tendency for furniture to be produced by assembly line methods. Departmentalized factories employ machine room operators, assemblers, hand

Automatic ripsaws are used to cut lumber to specific lengths, widths, and thicknesses as the first step in the rough mill procedure of manufacturing furniture.

Profile shapers do the work of many hands. A workman at the Metz plant tends this profiler to see that it accurately and speedily routes and dovetails both ends, bores for drawer pulls and cuts guide slots.

In an upholstered furniture plant of Kroehler Manufacturing Company, machines are used to produce coil springs automatically. With 16 furniture plants in the United States and Canada, Kroehler is recognized as the world's largest furniture maker.

Through a new design principle, this elegant furniture achieves a softness never before possible in slim contemporary style. Instead of the usual spring under construction, the new technique uses all foam cushioning.

sanders, finishers, springers, cutters, cushion makers, upholsterers, and trimmers, who perform their specialties as the furniture pieces move along the assembly line.

Most furniture workers learn their trade on the job, starting as general helpers and gradually acquiring a specialty. Generally speaking, from four to six years are required to become a furniture specialist.

A medium sized, modern furniture plant occupies about two hundred thousand square feet of floor space. If its products are all or partially made of wood, it will include among its specialized equipment dry kilns for preparing properly seasoned lumber. It must also carry a large stock of materials, such as high-grade foreign and domestic woods especially selected for furniture making. For large, flat surfaces, fine plywood is prepared by joining thin veneers into laminated panels by means of waterproof glues and high-pressure bonding.

Finishing of woods is done with stains, lacquer, sealing, glazing, and wood shading, accomplished mostly in a modern factory with spray gun techniques, and is followed by hand padding and shading by highly trained specialists. Finally, mar acid and special lacquer coats are applied to provide durable and beautiful finishes. (See *Paints and Varnishes*) After the finish is allowed to age properly, it is rubbed by hand to a soft, permanent luster. For this purpose, craftsmen are using newly developed compounds which represent an improvement over old-time oil rubbing and waxing. These compounds are abrasive wax mixtures of such permanence that they never need to be vigorously rubbed or polished to retain a high gloss finish.

Casual or outdoor furniture is produced in ever increasing quantities as the popularity of outdoor living on terraces and beside home swimming pools has risen in America. For the most part this type of furniture is fabricated in highly mechanized plants where metal and plastic parts are mass produced. Sales in this field total about a quarter of a billion dollars a year.

Household furniture production includes upholstered living room pieces, dining room sets, metal dinettes, bedroom furniture, and juvenile furniture. There are many specialized manufacturers in each field, as well as producers of general household furniture.

In the field of office furniture, there are also a number of large manufacturers. Overall, this is one of the biggest segments of the industry with an annual volume exceeding one-half billion dollars.

One of the recent trends is toward prefabrication of parts. Suppliers to America's furniture industry now furnish legs, arms, bases, and cushioning to factories which in their turn specialize in assembling these parts. Each year the National Association of Furniture Manufacturers, located in Chicago, sponsors a supply fair where some 120 firms exhibit fabrics and cushioning, plastics, parts, and machinery. Such firms as Du Pont, U. S. Rubber, Dow Chemical, the Celanese Corporation and the Formica Corporation are represented at the fair, and they offer the benefit of their tremendous research facilities which smaller furniture fabricators could not afford.

With the development of modern design, new fabrics, and plastic materials, the furniture industry appears destined for exciting progress with increased production at substantial cost savings. As it is an industry only partially mechanized, there are great opportunities for imaginative designers, plant engineers, and mechanics to bring about revolutionary approaches to furniture making, particularly in the field of household furniture.

Kroehler, the manufacturer of this unusual modern chair, advertises that it is poured, not built. By a new process, pure foam is poured over an all-steel frame. Cutaway section shows the unique construction.

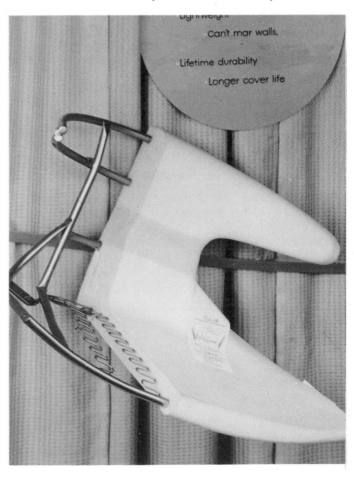

18 Refrigeration and Air Conditioning

This radically new type of furnace-air conditioner representing "residential heating and cooling of the future" was included in the United States display at the Brussels Universal and International Exhibition.

This essential industry has mushroomed in recent years, and while the refrigeration of food has taxed man's ingenuity for centuries, air conditioning of living and working space is a comparatively recent application of refrigeration principles. Even without a perfectly human desire to make life comfortable in hot weather, refrigeration technicians would have been challenged to develop air conditioning, since many of our modern scientific and technical activities depend upon reliable climate control.

So rapid has been the growth of public demand for air conditioning that in a brief span of 20 years after World War II it became difficult to rent stores or offices which were *not* air-conditioned. In the late 1950's, New York hotels alone spent some fifty million dollars on the installation of air conditioning. Comparable figures could be shown for every major city in the United States.

REFRIGERATION OF FOOD

Long before men dreamed of creating their own artificial climate, they were forced to find ways of chilling perishable foods. Throughout the history of mankind, preservation of food has been a major problem, particularly in warm regions. Salting, canning, and pickling methods have been devised, (See *Food Products*) but people have always sought a means of keeping food in its original, fresh state. Cold storage was practiced from earliest times, when men discovered that meat would keep longer if it were stored in the cool parts of their natural cave dwellings. In cold climates, snow and ice were readily available for food preservation. Egyptian rulers had their servants fill hundreds of shallow clay jars with water each evening; before dawn, a skim of ice would be gathered and put into containers out of the sun, for use during the day. Greek and Roman slaves were sent to the mountains to gather snow for cooling wine and keeping meats fresh. The packed snow was stored in deep pits, dug to depths of 50 ft. and covered with an insulation of straw. Porous clay vessels were kept wet. The rapid evaporation of water from the sides cooled the contents. During the Italian Renaissance, liquids were artificially cooled in long-necked bottles placed in solutions of water and saltpeter.

Yet for centuries, refrigeration methods remained so involved and so costly that only the wealthy could afford such luxuries as water ices or chilled drinks. (See *Dairy Products*) As late as the nineteenth century, so little was known about refrigeration that most fresh foods were considered delicacies, and fresh fruits and vegetables were virtually unobtainable in the winter.

COMMERCIAL SALE OF ICE

In France, dealers in ice and snow had created a profitable business as long ago as the seventeenth century. Frozen lemonade was popular in Paris 300 years ago. However, there is no record of active ice business in America until about 1800, when an enterprising merchant began cutting blocks of ice from a pond in New York City

109

and shipping it as far south as Charleston, S.C. Prior to that, most farms and some large city dwellings had their own icehouses for the storage of ice cut from ponds and streams during the winter months. Soon ice chests were built in the holds of sailing ships, not only to make possible the shipment of ice over long distances, but to provide a means of keeping food fresh during voyages.

By the early 1800's, large ice storehouses were built in the United States, where blocks of ice cut from streams and lakes in winter were covered with sawdust and straw and kept until summer. Meanwhile, with the development of railroads, attempts were made to refrigerate freight cars by means of ice cakes. These efforts met with little success as the melting ice damaged the cars as well as the produce. In the 1860's, the first refrigerator car was built with ice bunkers at each end. Perishable food was placed on floor racks which permitted circulation of the cool air around the freight.

For shipping fruit and delicate leafy vegetables, a system of blowing powdered ice over the produce was devised in 1925. Mechanical ice grinders pulverize the ice, while powerful blowers distribute as much as 2,000 lb. of "snow ice" through a refrigerator car within a few minutes. Snow icing is used for shipping lettuce, carrots, celery, and other green vegetables, as well as melons and corn. This method prevents loss of important vitamins A, B₂, and C.

The increasing demand for ice soon brought about a search for artificial means of making it. A number of ice-manufacturing machines had been built over the years, but none was too successful until a Frenchman, Ferdinand P. E. Carre, invented a method employing ammonia for evaporation. This made it possible to produce large quan-

tities of ice rapidly, and modern ice-manufacturing plants use processes based upon Carre's invention. Ice manufacturing is an important industry in the United States with production amounting to between fifty and sixty billion tons annually. Even home use of ice still consumes several million tons each year as there are millions of ice refrigerators in use, despite the development of the electric refrigerator. Hospitals, hotels, restaurants, produce markets, railroads, and trucking firms are large users of manufactured ice.

Dry ice, which is solidified carbon dioxide, is considerably colder than ordinary frozen water. It is widely used for packing ice cream and to produce snow ice for refrigerated truck trailers and railroad cars. Dry ice is made by washing carbon dioxide gas with water (thus removing alcohol and foreign matter), forcing the gas through charcoal to purify it and to remove unpleasant odors, cooling it, compressing it into a liquid and bottling it in steel cylinders. When this compressed liquid is permitted to expand suddenly, it forms flakes of "snow" which can be used for snow icing or can be pressed into cakes of dry ice.

DEVELOPMENT OF MECHANICAL REFRIGERATION

In the decade between 1920 and 1930, the introduction of mechanical home refrigerators revolutionized the food and refrigeration industries. Prior to this, some mechanical refrigeration plants had been built for meat-packers and food markets, but small, compact units were not available.

The modern home refrigerator works on a principle discovered by Michael Faraday in 1823. He found that condensation of certain gases into liquids could be ac-

Electronically controlled icing machines help speed perishable shipments from field to market. The machine illustrated here services two lines of refrigerator cars simultaneously, and it can ice a car in 90 seconds. "Snow icing" is used for shipping lettuce, carrots, celery, and other green vegetables, as well as melons and corn.

Ice cans are filled with treated water before being lowered into a dip tank for refrigeration. Each can freezes sufficient water to form a 300-pound ice block.

complished by pressure and that, if the pressure were suddenly reduced, very rapid evaporation of the liquid occurred. As a liquid turns to vapor it absorbs heat, and the more rapid the evaporation, the greater the cooling action.

In order to provide a continuous cooling process, liquified gas is circulated through a system which allows the pressure to drop suddenly at the point where it enters the tubes of the freezing unit. The result is a sudden boiling or "flash" as the liquid vaporizes and draws off heat from the air space of the freezing unit. The warmed vapor then enters a compression mechanism where it is condensed and once again becomes a cool liquid. When this flows back through the expansion valve into the freezer, the cycle begins again. Although ammonia is the gas most used in large cold storage plants, sulphur dioxide or freons are the coolants found in most household refrigerators because their fumes are less dangerous. Freons are chemical compounds sometimes known by their code names of F-12, F-21, F-114, etc.

Another type of mechanical refrigeration is achieved by an "absorption cycle." As with a compression system, the cooling is accomplished when the compressed liquid vaporizes, but at this point the vapor, usually ammonia gas, enters a tank of water where it is quickly dissolved. The solution of water and ammonia next passes into a generator tank where heat is supplied to bring the liquid to a boil and drive off the ammonia. The ammonia is compressed by the heat, re-enters the freezer as a liquid, vaporizes, and begins a new cycle.

REFRIGERATED WAREHOUSES AND TRANSPORTATION

An important segment of the food distribution industry in America is its great chain of cold storage warehouses. Throughout the United States are nearly 2,500 such refrigerated warehouses containing over eight hundred million cubic feet of storage space. Millions of tons of food, pharmaceutical products, herbs, hides, and even cut flowers, are held in cold storage warehouses awaiting shipment or commercial sale.

Warehouses are designed to accommodate many different foods and perishable products; their temperatures and moisture are controlled to meet specific requirements of various kinds of merchandise.

Frozen foods are kept at zero temperatures and, as this type of food product has increased in popularity, the growth of quick-freeze and deep-freeze units has been tremendous. (See *Frozen Foods*)

At the same time, some one hundred twenty-five thousand railroad refrigerator cars and two hundred thousand refrigerated trucks are in operation carrying perishable products from warehouses to the markets. (See *Railroading, Automobiles*)

There are also thousands of locker and freezer establishments where individuals may rent space to store meats and frozen foods. This enables the householder to buy in quantity at wholesale prices and to store foods for long periods.

REFRIGERATION IN INDUSTRY

As the age of chemicals and laboratory research advances, the need for maintaining exact temperatures for critical chemical processes increases in many segments of industry. Large refrigeration installations are built for laboratory use. Conditions in outer space can be simulated by creating a wide range of temperatures and humidity. Engines must be tested under the conditions of arctic cold. Pharmaceutical manufacturing requires perfect temperature controls at all times. (See *Pharmaceuticals*) Fractioning of human blood is accomplished in centrifuges where room temperature must be kept at 23° F. For making penicillin, temperature of 80° below zero must be produced at certain stages of the process.

Refrigeration is required in the making of dyes, in certain chemical processes, in the manufacture of plastics and synthetic rubber. When natural gas is moved through pipelines, large cooling systems are required to keep compressor stations at correct operational temperatures. Gasoline is cooled by refrigeration before it is put into the tanks of military and certain civilian aircraft; the purpose is to compress the fuel and thus permit extra gallons to fit into the tanks.

There are literally hundreds of important uses for refrigeration in industry, and with the great advances in temperature control has come the widespread use of air conditioning.

AIR CONDITIONING NOW AND IN THE FUTURE

It is surprising that air conditioning in homes, offices, factories, and public buildings was so long in coming, considering that the principles of refrigeration were known and highly developed early in the twentieth century. Possibly the lag was due to a failure of most people to recognize its importance. It was, and still is, looked upon as a luxury of soft living. The fact is, now that many places of business have climate control systems, we have learned that air conditioning is vital to the efficient operation of many industries. Not only is it essential for maintaining uniform results in many manufacturing processes, but the health benefits to millions of workers are incalculable. Doctors are beginning to recognize its value in combating

111

heart disease and various respiratory diseases. Those who suffer from such allergies as hay fever can work with complete relief in an air-conditioned office.

Some of the advances in our industrial capacity are directly related to the increased use of air conditioning. One excellent example is in the use of electronic calculators and other electronic machines. Unless they are artificially cooled, such devices heat up to extreme temperatures while they are in operation. Without air conditioning, it would be impossible to operate radar, missile-tracking instruments, electronic brains, accounting and business machines.

Since slight changes of temperature can cause metal to contract or expand, the making of precision machinery and parts requires absolutely uniform climate. So minute are the tolerances of some modern machines that a variance of .0001 in. can be ruinous. Only artificially controlled climate can provide the conditions necessary for such delicate tolerances. (See *Machinery*)

Wherever sensitive gauges and precision instruments are used, temperatures must be maintained usually with variations no greater than one-half degree.

Modern air conditioning involves a great deal more than simple air cooling. Humidity control, air filtering systems, and air circulation are essential for a complete operation. In atomic laboratories, for example, the ventilation pattern must be designed to carry radioactive dust away from workers at all times. To prevent explosions in chemical plants or in various types of laboratories, the correct level of humidity is needed; for example, a low level of humidity is conducive to static electricity and dangerous sparks. All atomic reactors are cooled by air-conditioning units.

One of the first industries to recognize the value of air conditioning for efficient production was textile manufacturing. To keep cotton threads moist and pliable requires high humidity and comparatively low temperature, and with the introduction of synthetc fibers, a variety of new climatic standards had to be set. Different temperature and humidity requirements apply to the various synthetics. Scientific application of air conditioning can dramatically increase the production capacity of a plant. For example, one Southern hosiery mill was producing 225 dozen pairs of nylon stockings per week. After air conditioning had been installed, production soared to 444 dozen pairs each week, while machine maintenance costs fell by about 80%.

Spectacular improvements in the printing industry have occurred with the use of air conditioning. It is particularly valuable in color printing, where the slightest increase in the moisture content of paper can cause misregister of multicolor pictures. (See *Printing*)

In optics, television, food processing, mining, and dozens of other industries, air conditioning has become essential. Along with its importance to chemical reactions and manufacturing processes, the comfort it provides for workers has cut absenteeism by large percentages.

WHAT IS THE REFRIGERATION INDUSTRY?

To furnish the refrigeration and air conditioning for millions of homes, factories, offices, and laboratories, a giant industry has come into being. Much of it has developed in the years since World War II.

With over 600 plants and factories, this industry employs more than one-half million people. Of these, at least one hundred thousand are directly engaged in the production of air conditioning and refrigeration equipment with an annual payroll in excess of five hundred seventy-five million dollars. Production in this field includes small, single-room units, automobile air conditioners, specially designed installations to cool huge plants, hotels, ships, trains, and entire office buildings. It is a billion-dollar-a-year industry which promises to grow to a multi-billion-dollar activity.

Such large electrical firms as Westinghouse, General Electric, Philco, General Motors, Radio Corporation of America, and Kelvinator are well known in the field of food refrigerators and freezers as well as air conditioners. There are also many firms which specialize in engineering and building air-conditioning units. Among these are Worthington Corporation in Harrison, N.J.; Lennox Industries, Inc., Marshalltown, Iowa; York Corporation, York, Pa.; Procter & Schwartz, Inc., Philadelphia; Dole Refrigerating Company, Chicago; American Plate Freezers Corp., Boston; Girdler Co., Louisville, Ky.

Refrigeration firms are called upon to engineer a great variety of applications from ice units for skating rinks and ice shows to specially designed, cold air, wind tunnels for testing aircraft.

Unlike many industries which began with small, comparatively crude products and gradually developed them for use on a large scale, refrigeration progressed to some extent in reverse order. First came refrigeration equipment for large ice-making plants and cold storage warehouses. Much later, the small, compact home refrigerators and air conditioners came into use. Now, the manufacture of compact units represents a major segment of the industry. One of the most recent developments in home air conditioning is a central unit which can be mounted on the outside walls of homes. Contained in 12-in. deep aluminum cabinets which can be painted to match the wall, it requires no interior floor space or window space. Such units may soon become standard items in the mass housing field.

Nearly two million room air conditioners were produced in 1960, along with three hundred fifteen thousand year-round central air-conditioning units. Exports of American made refrigeration and air-conditioning equipment amounted to approximately one hundred thirty-five million dollars.

The future for refrigeration engineers appears to be a brilliant one for many years to come. Not only is there a steady increase in home and office air conditioning, but with almost every new scientific breakthrough comes a need for better industrial climate control to fit the requirements of new products and new manufacturing processes.

Even ice-manufacturing firms, whose production has been falling off as the use of mechanically refrigerated trucks, railroad cars, ships, and warehouses has increased, are preparing for an expanding future by converting at least part of their operations to quick-freezing plants for the growing frozen food industry.

19 Wearing Apparel

In the design department of a dress pattern firm, the sewing primer layout is planned and illustrations are prepared. Accuracy is so important that all steps are checked four times before final approval.

Although the clothing industry, along with farming, food products, and the building trades, supplies one of the three basic requirements of humanity, it was one of the last important manufacturing operations to be mechanized. Even today, a considerable amount of manual labor is involved in the making of various types of garments.

Just before the turn of the twentieth century, garment making was carried on by thousands of workers in New York tenements, very much in the manner of eighteenth century home manufacturing, for although factory-made clothes began to appear in America about 1825, hand-sewing or home-operated sewing machines could be employed cheaply by contractors who gave out sewing assignments on a "team and task" basis. This meant that a number of workers, constituting a team, would divide up the work. Each worker would perform a specific job and would be paid a portion of the rate offered by the contractor to the entire team.

Contributing to the slow development of mechanization and to the low rates for labor in this industry was the great influx of foreign workers between 1880 and 1910. The contractors, called "sweaters," took every advantage of this overabundant cheap labor, hence the term sweat shop, which later came to mean almost any low-paid factory group. With the passage of the Tenement House Act

in 1892, the group piece rate practice began to disappear.

Some of the first factory-made clothing in the United States was designed for the use of sailors who wanted to acquire suits of civilian clothes cheaply and quickly while their ships were in port. Partly as a result of this, the leading garment centers evolved in the port cities of New York, Boston, Philadelphia and New Bedford, Mass. Meanwhile, inventors were busy seeking a way to sew by machine. Elias Howe's sewing machine, introduced in 1846, provided a superior type of stitch which could not be ripped apart as could the chain stitch. The power-driven needle of Howe's machine carried a strand of thread, drawn through an eye at the point end, through the cloth on each downstroke. On the opposite side of the cloth a hook moved up, caught the thread and pulled it into a loop. Next a bobbin drew a second strand of thread through the loop and, as the needle was withdrawn, its thread was caught on the strand on the cloth's under side. The result was a lock stitch. During the 1850's, Howe's machine was improved by Isaac Singer.

The Civil War created a demand for huge numbers of uniforms in all sizes; the result was a sudden boom in factory garments and, as a curious side benefit, the industry was provided with a mass of statistics concerning the sizes of men's clothing, making standardization possible.

113

Drawings and directions for newfashioned designs are checked against master patterns, muslin models, and with sewing information on pilot patterns.

To find proper placement for cutting material on grain, pattern pieces for each size are arranged on a measuring table.

After a series of major strikes in 1909 and 1910, collective bargaining was established for the clothing industry and working conditions underwent considerable improvement.

THE INDUSTRY TODAY

With more than a million production workers and annual sales amounting to well over five billion dollars, this is one of America's largest industries. While its national center is still the so-called garment district of New York City, concentrated within about one square mile of downtown Manhattan, it has been steadily expanding, so that its operations are now distributed through many sections of the United States. Certain cities seem to be characterized by special types of clothing manufacture. In men's wear, for example, Philadelphia plants are mostly of medium size, producing garments of intermediate quality. New York's specialty is cheap, high style suits and ability to increase production quickly to meet sudden or unexpected

Inside the modern, air-conditioned dye house of the Jantzen sweater plant, where garments are permanently mothproofed by treating the wool with a special chemical included in the dyeing process.

Approximately 42,000 miles of yarn are produced in this garment plant each day — enough to encircle the world more than one and one-half times.

demand. Chicago men's and boys' clothing establishments are mostly large firms producing high-quality products.

In recent years a great many garment factories have been moved out of city locations in an effort to escape high wages and taxes. This trend, fairly general throughout the clothing and textile industries (See *Textiles*) has brought an increasing number of factories into the South and Midwest.

Whereas the manufacturers of men's clothing are, gener-

ally speaking, concerns of medium size specializing in certain types of suits or furnishings, and are fairly widely distributed throughout the country, the women's clothing industry is more largely concentrated in New York City where several thousand small firms, the majority being the contractor type, supply more than 60% of the garments for American women. Because New York is the style center of the United States, and because women's fashions change rapidly, dress manufacturers must be in close

Skilled workers cut garments for exacting fit. Using power machines with a jigsaw type, razor-sharp blade, operators can cut precisely and quickly through 24 thicknesses of fabric at one time.

Department heads inspect muslin made from a master pattern as a model tries out a new dress design to test detail, comfort, wear, and style.

touch with style trends and must be ready to change patterns quickly. (See *Fashions*) As a result of this, New York's garment district is unique among industrial centers; its activities have the chaotic atmosphere of a carnival or a circus. During the noon lunch hour, workers and buyers jam the sidewalks. Representatives of retail stores bargain with manufacturers, while mobile racks carrying dresses on hangers are pushed along the streets, offering strange contrast to the streams of modern automobiles and taxis.

Inside the buildings, the sense of chaos is by no means diminished. Workrooms, storerooms, showrooms, and offices seem crowded, cramped, and cluttered. Hundreds of dresses of varied styles and sizes are hung on rows of racks. Workrooms are cluttered with patterns and scraps of material. The entire district seems to be in a constant state of feverish anxiety and nervous frenzy.

Behind this apparent chaos, the garment district is highly attuned to the pulse of fashion. The outpouring of buyers, managers, designers, patternmakers, and workers into the streets is a means of quick exchange of information to keep abreast of a rapidly changing market. The moment demand for a particular style drops off, production is stopped. Any new, popular trend in fashion is immediately picked up and imitated by hundreds of small entrepreneurs. The average number of employees in these shops is about 20 to 25. There is also a tendency to specialize in one or two types of garments, such as blouses, separate skirts, housedresses, and so forth. However, a recent trend is toward more diversification.

Again, because of constant style changes, a contractor system is still prevalent in women's clothing. It is easy to rent a small amount of floor space and a few sewing machines, and to pay pieceworkers the comparatively low wages of this industry. Nevertheless, the number of firms operating their own plants is increasing. Due to the fierce competition, the unstable market, and the conditions and processes peculiar to the industry, garment workers' labor unions are forced to fight an aggressive battle for increased wages. The contractor-jobber system, operating in hundreds of small shops, has the effect of putting the workers in competition with each other, since each contractor seeks to underbid the other shops and to keep his labor costs at the lowest possible level. Large chain stores, which buy many thousands of dresses at a time, have a huge number of small, competing shops and jobbers with whom they can place orders, with the result that they are in a strong bargaining position.

STEPS IN CLOTHING MANUFACTURE

The making of garments must, of course, begin with design. Many of the larger manufacturers have their own designers, although basic styles are generally set by the great fashion houses in New York City, Paris, London, and other major centers. (See *Fashions*)

After the material has been selected by the design department, the patternmaker cuts the shapes for body, sleeves, collar, cuffs, etc., out of stiff paper. Several sets of the same pattern are made for the various standard sizes, then the paper sections are pinned to cloth and the outlines are drawn on the material. One of the most important tasks at this stage is that of the cutter, who must arrange the patterns in such a way that there is a minimum of waste space between pieces. Although an extra inch of scrap material here and there is not important in the making of an individual garment, it is easy to see that in mass production, multiplying this waste by thousands can be a serious cost factor.

In the cutting operation we find some of the most highly mechanized equipment in the industry. There are a number of different types of cutting machines: high-speed, electrically operated, rotary disks and reciprocating knives which can cut through stacks of material nine or ten inches deep.

When the various pieces have been cut, the sewing operation begins. While there are more than 200 different types of sewing machines used for basting, hemstitching, spiral braiding, quilting, buttonholing, and so on, much of this phase still is not far removed from old-time handicrafts. Skilled workers specialize in certain operations. Some attach sleeves to bodices, other make cuffs or collars, and still others work on linings. Though it is true that more and better machine operations are being developed for pleating, tucking, and even embroidering, there are many finishing operations which require painstaking handwork.

The final pressing of assembled garments is generally done by pressing machines. A bed plate is shaped to fit a garment pattern or part of a garment, and a power-driven, steam-heated "head" is brought down to press the article of clothing on the bed.

Skill of human operators is a primary factor in the making of clothing. It has been estimated that between 65% and 75% of the manufacturing time consumed is in handling materials and garments, while only 25% to

35% is machine time. This does not take into consideration the hand-finishing operations after an article of clothing has been assembled.

SHOES AND LEATHER GOODS

Although the leather industry includes the manufacture of a number of products unrelated to shoes and clothing, 80% of the leather produced in America is used for shoes. Therefore, the shoe and leather industries are related closely enough to be considered as one.

Since prehistoric times, when men used animal skins as covering and rawhide thongs as bindings, the preparation of leather has been an important human activity. Much of the leather produced is actually one of the by-products of the meat-packing industry (See *Meat-Packing*), although in addition to the hides of such meat-producing animals as cattle, pigs, and sheep, those of deer, snakes, lizards, alligators, sharks, and seals are used for a variety of special leathers. Conversion of hides to leather is accomplished by the process of tanning which is carried out in several hundred tanneries throughout the United States.

In Colonial America, many people made their own leather from the hides of wild game or from cattle which they slaughtered for meat. But since the manufacture of really fine leather is a difficult and involved process, it was natural that tanning factories should be established in most communities. The Colonial tannery used vats, sunk in the ground near natural streams, to soak the hides. After they became pliable, layers of fat and blood vessels were removed, and the hair was scraped from the grain side. The scraped hides were then soaked in a solution containing oak or chestnut bark. Tannic acid in the bark served to preserve the fibers of the skins, but the process was extremely slow, requiring months to complete.

Little technical progress was made during most of the nineteenth century, though the number of tanneries in the United States had increased to 4,500 by 1870. But about 1875, the introduction of a tanning concentrate to replace bark brought about drastic changes in the industry. By cooking the bark, a distilled tannic acid was produced. A few years later, a mineral tannin was made from chrome.

Along with these developments came a movement of tanneries to the Middle Atlantic States, where special sheepskins and goatskins imported from Europe were readily obtainable, and to the great meat-packing regions in Illinois, Michigan, and Wisconsin. Gradually the number of U.S. tanneries decreased while the remaining individual factories greatly expanded in size.

PRESENT MANUFACTURING METHODS

Today, three principal methods are used in the tanning of leather: the vegetable process, employing tannin or tannic acid; the chrome process, using chrome or aluminum salts; and the chamois process, utilizing oils and fats.

Hides or skins arrive at the tannery in heavily salted bundles. They may be soft and moist, as in the case of hides from nearby slaughterhouses, or hard and stiff as are hides imported from distant countries. In either case they must first be soaked and cleaned. Hair is removed by a solution of lime, but it is not the lime itself that serves to

After liming, hides are soaked in solutions which neutralize the lime and open the pores of the skin so that they will absorb tanning liquid. Then they are placed in these revolving drums for actual tanning.

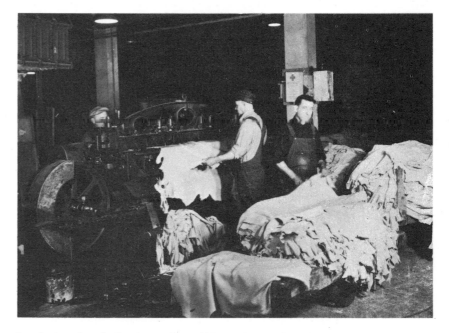

In order to reduce leather to a uniform thickness, it goes through a process known as "splitting." Actually, the term "shaving" would be more descriptive of this operation which is done on machines like the one shown.

loosen the bristles. First, the lime must be used to soak other skins. This allows bacteria to enter the solution, so that in later soakings, it is the action of bacteria, attacking the hair roots, which accomplishes the job. Discarded hair is a valuable by-product used as a binder in wall plaster, mattress stuffing, and rug cushions. As the hide softens and swells, its fat floats away and the epidermis is loosened. Now, by means of rapidly revolving knives, the epidermis layer, unwanted fat and tissue are easily scraped off. In modern tanneries, scraping operations are carried out largely by machinery. After a final acid bath to remove lime, dirt, and a few remaining bristles, the hides are ready to be tanned.

In a series of eight "rocker vats," or tanks, are tanning solutions of varying strengths, and in the vegetable process these are made by boiling oak, chestnut, willow, and other woods or bark in water. Some tanning materials are made from such exotic plants as myrobalans, algorobillia and divi-divi, the fruit and seeds of certain East Indian trees. Mimosa, larch, hemlock, quebracho (a wood from South America) and mangrove are also good sources of tannic acid. The different tannins are used for their coloring effect on leather, providing a range of colors from near white to reds and browns.

Hides are first treated with a weak tannin solution, also containing acids to neutralize any lime still clinging to the skin. In each succeeding tanning vat, the strength of the tannin solution is increased. This progressively stronger tanning action serves to prevent a "drawing of the grain" which would cause the skin surface to be permanently wrinkled. Emerging from the tanning pits, the hides are next stacked in piles and left for a week. Then they must be treated in still stronger liquors and stacked again for several weeks. During this seasoning period, a brownish deposit called "bloom" appears on the hides. This is removed by a scouring machine.

A last soaking in an extract of sumac or chestnut wood serves to bleach the leather. It is hung up to dry, and after a few days it is rubbed with cod oil on the hair, or grain, side. After being dried in a darkened room for several days, the leather is calendered between heavy steel rollers to impart a smooth finish to the grain side.

"Currying" is accomplished by working oils into the leather to make it flexible and strong. It is then stretched on a drying frame.

The lighter leathers from the skins of calf, sheep, and goat are made especially soft and pliable by soaking them in a bath of pancreatic enzymes, and by tanning in solutions of sumac, myrobalans, willow, mimosa bark, and birch bark, or by the chrome process. Sometimes hides are stitched in the form of bags, grain side out, and are then filled with sumac liquor. These bags are placed in tanks of heated sumac solution, and are allowed to soak for a few hours. After they are removed from the tanks, the bags are allowed to drain. Stitches are removed, the skins are stretched on frames, and dried.

Morocco graining of goatskin is embossed on the surface while the leather is still moist. The embossing machine imparts a pebbled texture to the grain side. To make a less expensive "French" morocco, sheepskins or calfskins are split to make them thin, then they are embossed with the pebbled texture.

Where vegetable tanning operations require many days, chrome tanning, used for treating light leathers, may be accomplished in hours. Hides are placed in rotating drums containing a solution of chrome alum and muriatic acid. The treatment requires about eight hours, after which the tanning liquor is drained off and the leather is soaked in borax and water to arrest the tanning action.

Chamoising, which is employed to produce suedes and chamois window cleaners, is an ancient method of oil tanning. By means of a special machine, the grain surfaces of lightweight skins are split from the under sides. The soft under part is then cleaned, dried, treated with cod oil and hung up to dry for two or three hours. After the process has been repeated several times, the hides are rinsed in warm water, dried in a wringing machine, soaked in warm, soda lye solution, and dried again. Following these steps is the bleaching process. Finally, the thin, soft leather is dried and the surface is roughened and fluffed against an emery wheel.

The U.S. leather industry comprises more than 500 firms which employ between 40,000 and 50,000 workers. Approximately 60% of its output is light leathers for the upper parts of shoes, gloves, garments, book covers, and leather accessories. Heavy leathers for shoe soles, bags, luggage and furniture make up the balance of production, and these leathers are derived from skins of the larger animals, such as cattle, horses, buffaloes, and oxen.

Despite the fact that leather tanning is essentially a chemical process, and in spite of the great strides in chemistry made during the past quarter century, the leather industry has only recently begun to seek improved chemical treatment and control. The greatest future progress will undoubtedly be made in reducing the time required for processing. Since leather manufacture still requires from three to six months, it is safe to predict that chemistry could revolutionize this important industry, particularly in its heavy leather segment where slow vegetable tanning processes prevail.

Such progress is sorely needed, as the independent tanning firms have been beset by difficulties. Not only has the market for leather been declining, partly due to a tremendous upsurge in the development and use of plastics (which see), but both large meat-packing firms and shoe manufacturers have established their own tanneries in direct competition with the independent companies. As a result of these factors, the leather industry's future does not appear as encouraging as it might. But aggressive and progressive sales promotion, coupled with modern chemical research, could go a long way toward rejuvenating an ancient and honorable trade.

SHOE MANUFACTURING

Along with their use of animal skins for clothing, prehistoric peoples very early devised ways of protecting their feet against cold, dampness, stones, and thorns. Probably, they first wrapped their feet in rawhide leather, then gradually evolved the sandal, which is the earliest form of shoe in human history. In its crudest application, the sandal was merely a roughly shaped piece of untanned skin strapped to the sole of the foot by means of rawhide thongs. As civilization advanced, designs of fitted sandals became refined and were even ornamented. Soles were made of tanned leather, wood, woven grass, and metal plates. For added warmth and protection, thongs were widened and eventually fitted and joined to produce a complete boot or shoe.

The craft of shoemaking came to America on the second voyage of the *Mayflower* in 1629, when Thomas Beard arrived with a supply of cowhides and the knowledge of his trade. From that time, Massachusetts became a major center of the American shoe industry, although for many years the Colonial people were served by itinerant shoemakers who would construct pairs of shoes out of hides provided by the farmers. However, as shoe manufacturing became mechanized, the demand for custom-built shoes died out, until today most small shoemaker shops are devoted to making repairs or putting new soles and heels on worn shoes.

LEASING MACHINERY

A unique feature of the modern shoe industry in America is its system of leasing machinery. This came about through a series of circumstances which began in 1858 when Lyman Blake invented a machine to sew soles to uppers. After demonstrating that the mechanism was practicable, he sold it to Gordon McKay who made a number of improvements, yet was unable to sell it to many manufacturers. Since most shoe firms were small and had limited capital, they were unwilling to invest in expensive equipment. Consequently McKay hit upon the idea of renting machines equipped with stitch counters. From the

each pair of shoes produced. In spite of this, and in spite of a 1954 Supreme Court ruling forcing United Shoe Machinery to sell as well as lease its machines, most shoe concerns still prefer to rent. Not only does USM replace worn out machines, but it has a staff of expert consultants who are available to advise customers, show them how to operate the machinery efficiently, and to solve special technical problems in individual plants.

Until the Supreme Court ruling, United Shoe Machinery Corporation would not sell its equipment to firms unless they agreed to purchase all their machines from the one source. Such a forcing policy was outlawed in the 1954 decision of the Court.

PATTERN ENGINEERING

As with other types of apparel, shoe manufacturing be-

In a shoe factory's "bottoming room," sole-stitching machines are used to lockstitch outsoles to the uppers of men's loafers. These intricate machines permanently fasten the outsole to the welt. A curved needle draws two waxed threads into each awl hole so that they loop tightly around each other, forming a series of individually locked stitches.

users, he could thus collect royalties based upon the number of shoes produced.

Meanwhile, Charles Goodyear introduced a new shoe-making process in 1875. This was the "welt" process, or "Goodyear welt" which is still in use today, and which is described later in this chapter. Goodyear's machines and a number of others faced the same resistance as had been met by Gordon McKay. Until a number of shoe machinery concerns merged to form the United Shoe Machinery Corporation in 1899, full mechanization of the industry was not accomplished. Then the new firm, controlling about 90% of the business, introduced an overall leasing arrangement which became a general practice throughout the industry, and which has certain advantages for the shoe manufacturer. Under this system, the lessee pays an installation fee, a monthly rental, and a royalty on

gins with design, and style is an important factor. Curiously, it was not until the nineteenth century that shoes were made with any regard for the differences of right and left feet. The first complete set of patterns for cutting shoe uppers was made in New England in 1832. Then, with the sudden demand for military footwear in the Civil War, shoe patternmaking and factory production of boots and shoes were given great impetus.

Although some shoe manufacturers maintain their own pattern departments, most patterns are made in specialized plants where skilled technicians work with special machines. Shoe patterns are made to fit precisely on the manufacturer's lasts. Once a basic pattern has been approved, all sizes and widths must be graded proportionately to maintain the same style features, whether for a 3B or a 9AAA shoe. It is the engineering of patterns to fit every

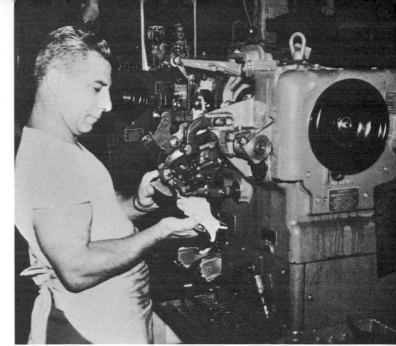

The flashing metal fingers of this machine lace thread through the eyelets and form an individually tied loop for each pair of eyelets.

The side-lasting operation serves to insure appearance, comfort, and fit for the life of the shoe. The upper is tightly stapled to the insole.

conceivable shape and size of foot that makes this an exacting and highly technical phase of the industry. The patterns are first formed by molding paper to a last. When the paper is flattened the patternmaker has the correct outlines of the basic shoe upper. To this, various pattern parts are added. These might include tip, foxing, vamp, straps, saddle, apron, and linings.

A shoe pattern model is reproduced in rigid metal, and the metal plates are then duplicated on a special type of cardboard, in various sizes, by means of a pantograph pattern-grading machine. Edges of the board patterns are reinforced with metal binding as a protection against cutting knives used in the shoe factory. For large volume production, cutting dies are shaped to conform with the pattern.

Because this is an industry affected by frequent style change, one of the shoe manufacturer's major investments is in lasts, which must be made in many sizes for each new design. After the designer, sales manager, and factory manager have conferred on the latest style trends, they decide upon a program of production for the coming season. Models of the new shoes are constructed, and custom-built samples are prepared for salesmen. Then the lasts must be made. These are wooden models, in the shape of human feet, over which the shoe uppers are formed.

MAKING THE LAST

When Thomas Beard opened America's first shoe-making shop in 1629, he made his own lasts which, according to early records, he "whittled from maple or hard wood with spoke shave and drawknife." Evidently last making did not become a specialty until William Young, a Philadelphian, obtained a patent for a minor last improvement in 1807. Then, in 1815 Thomas Blanchard of Sutton, Massachusetts, invented a lathe for turning irregular shapes such as axe handles, gunstocks and, finally, shoe lasts. A later variation of the Blanchard lathe, the Gilman lathe which provides for grading of sizes, is now used throughout the last-making industry.

The idea of standardized charts for last measurement was introduced by E. B. Stimpson of New York in 1881. A few years afterward, in 1887, a similar measurement chart was adopted by the Retail Boot and Shoe Dealers' National Association. This chart has provided a set of industry standards which with only minor changes is used today.

Shoe measurement began in 1324 when King Edward II decreed that three average size barleycorns, placed end to end, equalled one inch. At the same time, it was found that the largest normal foot was the equivalent of 39 barleycorns, or 13 in. This became known as "size thirteen." Due to the use of barleycorns as units of measurement for inches and feet, variations of one-third of an inch between full shoe sizes came into vogue and the system is still used. Half sizes differ from full sizes by one-sixth of an inch.

Then, some time during the seventeenth century a monk in Northampton, England, invented the sliding size stick; another English monk conceived of the pantograph. These two innovations made possible the development of standard shoe measurements and ultimately the modern last lathe.

In the United States, today, all lasts are made from kiln-dried, rock maple (or sugar maple) most of which comes from forests in western New York, northern Pennsylvania, Wisconsin, and Vermont. After being cut into blocks and roughly turned, the wood is air-dried in sheds for about nine months. At this point, the moisture content is 25% to 30%. The blocks must then be kiln-dried to reduce the moisture content further until it is only about 5%.

Rough blocks are placed on last-turning lathes. These remarkable machines can duplicate the shape of a hand-carved model as a "model wheel" about an inch and a quarter wide and three inches in diameter rotates slowly over the master last from toe to heel. At the opposite end of the lathe, a circular cutter the same shape and size as the model wheel shaves the block of wood, which is being

120

As shoes move along a conveyor in the packing room of United States Rubber Company's footwear plant at Naugatuck, Conn., workers insert laces.

In the stock-fitting room of a modern shoe factory, operators attach upstanding tape ribs to Goodyear Welt insoles with specially designed machines.

rotated on a spindle at the same speed as the model. Gradually, an exact duplicate of the model is cut from the maple block. Lasts for right and left feet are produced simply by reversing the rotation direction of the block and model.

Another feature of the last lathe is its ability to reproduce enlarged or reduced sizes from the master last, by the adjustment of gears. Also, by controlling the relative rates of travel of the model wheel and the cutter, lasts may be lengthened or shortened. As these size variations are limited, however, several master lasts must be made to reproduce all the required shoe sizes. Master lasts are made by skilled craftsmen in the model rooms of last factories. Working with spokeshaves and files they sculpture maple models with an artistry that comes only from long years of training and practice.

In the United States and Canada there are about thirty last manufacturers which employ between twelve hundred

and fifteen hundred persons and do an annual business of about ten million dollars.

SHOE CONSTRUCTION

In "building" a shoe there are three principal steps which include making the shoe upper, sole assembly, and final assembly consisting of "lasting," "bottoming" and finishing. First, materials are selected and sorted. Leather linings and trimmings are stitched. The various pieces are cut by hand or with die-cutting machinery. As in the case of dress manufacturing and the making of other wearing apparel, skillful fitting of parts in a jigsaw puzzle arrangement on the material is essential to minimize waste.

When various parts of the upper assembly have been stitched, they are ready to go on the last. Meanwhile, the apparently simple sole assembly requires an amazing number of steps. Outersole, welting (the Goodyear welt method of construction), insoles, counters, toe boxes, and

(Left) Loading a roughing lathe at the United Last Division's styling center in Lawrence, Mass. The rough shapes for both right and left shoes are turned from solid maple blocks in less than a minute. (Right) One of several high-speed finishing lathes used to turn production lasts to finished dimensions after rough turning. Lasts are then hand fitted with heel plates, reinforcing edges and hinges and given a high-luster wax coating.

heels are joined together. Counters and toe boxes, made of stiff leather to provide heel and toe rigidity, are inserted between the lining and outer leather. First the parts are roughly cut, then finished in a rounding machine. The outsole is calendered to compress fibers, while a splitting machine reduces it to a uniform thickness.

In the "lasting" operation, the upper assembly is fitted snugly over the last and temporarily tacked in place. Since the fit is tight, considerable pull is required, and a "pulling-over" machine has been developed to replace hand lasting. A trimming machine and a series of wipers serve to smooth rough edges and to iron out all wrinkles. Next a beating machine hammers the leather into the exact shape of the last.

By the Goodyear welt method of shoe construction, the insole and upper are joined by means of a welt, a narrow strip of flexible leather along the edge of the shoe, with the result that the stitches do not penetrate the shoe's interior. To accomplish this, a special machine with a curved needle is employed.

Somewhat simpler and less costly, the McKay method produces a sturdy but less comfortable shoe. In this case the outersole is attached to the upper by stitching all the way through the insole. For heavy work shoes, pegged or standard screw construction is used. This consists of attaching the upper to the sole with metal pegs, wooden pegs, or wire. Many children's shoes are produced by the stitchdown method. With the upper turned out instead of under the insole, a single stitching joins the sections together.

In recent years the Compo shoe has become increasingly popular. This simple process, which produces a light,

A master last model is being hand finished by a master craftsman. Slightest deviation in dimensions might impair the comfort of thousands of shoes.

flexible, easily styled shoe, is a method of cementing sole to upper. Originally used primarily for manufacturing women's shoes it is now coming into vogue for men's shoes as well.

U.S. SHOE INDUSTRY TODAY

Due to the complex problems brought about by constant style changes and the need to supply many different sizes of each design, specialization has subdivided the shoe industry into hundreds of comparatively small plants. Companies specialize in making such items as women's, men's, or children's shoes. They may carry specialization a step further by limiting their production to certain classifications, such as sport, dress or work shoes, "sneakers," moccasins, and other novelty styles. Some plants make nothing but parts of shoes: heels, soles, or uppers.

As an illustration of the reason for plant specialization, a manufacturer of men's shoes needs about 1,000 lasts of different sizes just to make a complete line in a single category.

There are well over 1,000 American producers in the various categories. These firms employ a quarter of a million workers and gross about three billion dollars annually, producing some six hundred fifty million pairs of shoes. Twenty of the largest companies make about 37% of the nation's shoes, and among the leaders in this group are International Shoe Company, General Shoe Company, Brown Shoe Company, and Shoe Corporation of America. The larger shoe manufacturers have their own tanneries to produce a major proportion of the leather they use. In addition, about 50% of retail shoe stores are operated by manufacturers. Annual retail sales in the United States amount to nearly five billion dollars.

Until 1900, most American shoe manufacturing was done in New England, but the trend has been toward decentralization due to a shifting labor market and to the rapid growth of midwest leather tanneries near the meat-packing centers.

There is little indication of great future growth of this industry. It is highly mechanized and technically mature. Other than increased overall production due to normal population growth, it is doubtful that any significant changes will occur in the foreseeable future. However, some interesting experiments with injection molding of shoes could alter this picture. The process involves the injection of liquid plastic into a metal last containing the material of which the shoe upper is to be made. When the plastic solidifies, the upper becomes molded to the sole. Great savings in labor and other production costs can result from the perfection of the injection molding process, and some producers claim that, although shoes made in this manner cannot be repaired, their soles will outlast the uppers.

Whatever future technological developments may occur in the shoe industry, it is certain that style changes, multiplicity of sizes, and fierce competition will continue to be the manufacturers' chief problems. It is equally certain that the six hundred twenty to six hundred fifty million pairs of shoes sold to Americans each year will continue to represent one of the largest and most essential of the nation's industries.

122

As a model in muslin poses, an artist paints the dress in color for use on a pattern envelope and counter catalog. The dress designer will check the illustration before it is reproduced.

20 Fashions

As the wearing apparel industries are greatly affected by style changes, the question arises, "who sets the styles?" Somebody has to design the clothing that will appear in the shops next season.

Logically, it would seem that each garment manufacturer would have his own staff of designers. Many of the larger firms do, but the designers employed by manufacturers do not set the styles and fashions; they merely adapt the current fashions to their particular products. Brilliant fashion designers are rare, and when they are successful their patterns are so much in demand that they command fabulous prices for them. Because of this, a separate and distinct industry has grown up around a small group of topflight designers in such fashion centers as New York, Paris, London, and Rome.

For many years, Paris has been considered the fashion capital of the world. At certain seasons, especially in the spring, great fashion houses in Paris unveil their latest creations at special showings, and representatives of fashion magazines, as well as manufacturers from all parts of the world, observe these showings with intense interest. Since World War II, when Paris fell to Nazi Germany, New York fashions have gained in prestige, not only to American consumers but in the eyes of other nations as well.

The New York Dress Institute, now known as The New York Couture Group, Inc., was organized in 1941 by union and management leaders in the U.S. garment industry. It has become a recognized international clearing house for fashion information. The Institute sponsored a series of special showings of new dress designs, calling these semiannual showings "National Press Weeks." They feature creations of American designers and are attended by fashion writers and style editors from all parts of the United States. Eleanor Lambert, a New York publicist of the U.S. fashion industry for many years, was responsible for this idea, which has contributed greatly to making New York a world fashion center.

The New York Couture Group maintains a continuous flow of fashion news to newspapers, magazines, and broadcasting stations throughout the world. The Group's showings include accessories as well as newest dress designs, fabrics, children's clothes, jewelry, and cosmetics. Among the members of the group have been such well-known names and firms as Oleg Cassini, Christian Dior (N.Y.), Anne Klein, Rudolf Gowns, Ceil Chapman, Hannah Troy, Adele Simpson, and Arthur Jablow.

WHAT IS THE FASHION INDUSTRY

Fashion begins in the studios of a few great design houses. It is the result of creations by individual designers who have gained preeminence, such as Christian Dior, Oleg Cassini, Ann Fogarty, Hattie Carnegie and Pauline Trigere. The latest designs of dresses, sport clothes, lingerie, beachwear, and various accessories are displayed at elaborate fashion shows, where buyers and their designers make sketches and notes.

Pattern companies are in the forefront of the businesses determining styles. At a major pattern firm, such as Simplicity Pattern Company, the development of a design begins with a study of all possible sources: American and Paris style services, motion pictures, museums, fashion shows, trade publications, and fashion magazines. Artists make hundreds of sketches every month, from which 40 or 50 may be selected for production.

When a sketch has been approved, drapers make a muslin model, draping the material on dummies the same size as the pattern. When the model garment has been approved, it is taken apart, piece by piece, and a master pattern is traced from the pieces onto heavy paper. Next, the master pattern goes to a testing room, where an actual garment is sewn in muslin and tried on a living model. Any flaws in design or construction are corrected and changed on the master pattern. At this point, the approved pattern goes to the grading department to be drawn in the various standard sizes, and to the primer department where sewing instructions are written and illustrated.

Finally the patterns are printed on tissue, along with the sewing instructions, and are packaged in paper envelopes.

Patterns of this type are sold by the millions to American women who use them to make their own clothes. Over a hundred million printed patterns are sold each year. Similar patterns are purchased, copied, or designed by garment manufacturers around the country.

Although dress patterns as we know them are a comparatively modern innovation which began only about 100 years ago, tailors to the Egyptian Pharaohs used guides cut from pieces of slate to trace the outlines of royal garments. Similar slate guides have been found in the catacombs of Rome and are believed to have been used by early Christian monks in making their vestments. When a French tailor conceived the idea of making patterns on thin wood in the thirteenth century, the Tailors' Guild put a stop to the idea, not wishing its secrets to become public property.

American paper pattern-making began in New England in 1863. There a tailor named Butterick, seeing his wife painstakingly cutting out pieces of material for shirts, decided it would be easier if she first cut the shapes from paper, which then could be used again and again for making any number of identical shirts. Soon neighboring women were asking for copies of Butterick's paper patterns. Thus started the first pattern business.

Not long afterward magazines, such as *Pictorial Review* and *Vogue,* began the practice of illustrating latest styles and printing the basic patterns from which the garments could be made.

FASHION SHOWS

Outside of the sports and entertainment industries, no business activity is quite as colorful or as entertaining as the fashion show. For six or eight weeks prior to the important showings, designers work at white heat to produce the season's "collection" for their firm. When the collection is ready, it is paraded before the professional critics, the editors, the buyers from department stores, by chic models. Many of the New York shows are filmed for the newsreels and television, and the more sensational designs are photographed to appear in newspapers and magazines from coast to coast.

Despite all the fanfare, many of these new offerings fail to meet public approval. American women do not, as has sometimes been claimed, wear anything or everything simply because it is the latest style. Dresses that are bought enthusiastically at the showings by buyers for large stores may die in the stores. Others, considered "flops" by the experts, have become national sensations. As one observer remarked, "The good is not always new, and the new is not always good."

Nevertheless, with all the hazards of style and fashion in women's hats, shoes, dresses and sportswear, more American women are wearing more fashionable clothes than in any other country of the world; and the American fashion and pattern industries are setting a pace which the Paris salons are having difficulty matching.

In the proving room, executives of a pattern firm inspect the second muslin, which has been made from the master pattern.

At the Simplicity Pattern Company plant in Niles, Mich., workers trace master pattern markings on transparent glassine sheets.

21 Furs

In a fur merchant's storerooms are pelts from American farms, fields, and forests, as well as special furs from every other continent. Fox, mink, squirrel, muskrat, and Persian lamb pelts are being inspected by a fur buyer.

The skins of animals have provided mankind with clothing since prehistoric times, and furs have never been surpassed for their comfortable warmth in cold climates. Because many fur-bearing animals possess coats of rare beauty, furs have always been prized for decorative purposes even where the climate was mild. Over 3,500 years ago fur on clothing designated personages of high degree. The ancient Greeks and Romans used furs which they brought back from wars with their northern neighbors. From very early times, ermine was a symbol of purity, royalty, or power. Laws were actually passed in medieval times forbidding commoners to wear these prized pelts. The use of furs was by no means limited to female attire. On the contrary they were probably more in evidence as trimmings on men's clothing.

FUR INDUSTRY IN AMERICA

Early colonial exploration was spurred by the quest for two principal products: gold and furs. In fact, most of the French and English push westward was brought about by the fur-trapping industry, and one of the great American family fortunes, that of John Jacob Astor, was built on furs. Fur trading resulted in the founding of Detroit, St. Louis, and St. Paul. Some chapters of early American fur-trading history were written in blood, for representatives of Astor's American Fur Company and many of the pioneer trappers were unscrupulous in their dealings with the

Indians. They set up trading posts where cheating Indians was part of their stock in trade. By paying low prices for furs and charging exorbitant rates for items sold to the native trappers, the white traders accumulated quick fortunes. Naturally, the Indians occasionally showed their resentment with violence. This lucrative fur trade helped open up the continent and led to exploration of the vast, rich territory of the Northwest. By 1850 the old-time fur trading had come to an end as a major industry, and while some trapping of wild fur-bearing animals continues to this day, most skins for the modern fur industry are provided by fur farms or ranches.

NORTH AMERICAN FURS

The most popular furs from North American animals are fox, mink, beaver, muskrat, seal, squirrel, marten, ermine, and lynx.

Fox furs are available in a great many natural and "mutation" colors. The natural colors are silver, white, blue, and red. Mutations include beiges, grays, and browns. There are also a number of dyed fox furs of various colors, including black. Fox is noted for depth and softness of underfur and long, glossy guard hairs.

The most fashionable fur in recent years has been mink, which comes from a small, rat-like animal. Its soft, dense, brown fur has a natural luster and an evenness of texture, silky to the touch. Both wild and ranch mink are used;

mutations from careful ranch breeding provide grays, beiges, white, and a variety of brown shades. Pieced mink coats are made by combining small, well-matched skins in chevron patterns or with spotted white on a dark brown or gray background.

Beaver, which used to be one of the most highly prized pelts in early fur-trapping days, is less popular today, but it is one of the warmest of furs. Beaver, identified by dense, silky underfur of a deep brown color, is sometimes bleached or dyed white, beige, or gray. In its natural state it has long, hard guard hairs, which are usually plucked before coats are made.

Comparatively inexpensive, but an excellent and serviceable fur, muskrat is used for a variety of dyed and sheared furs to simulate mink and seal. Natural seal has a unique velvety texture. It is a short fur, frequently dyed black or various shades of brown.

Squirrel is a dense fur with soft, silky texture, and lightweight. Only the clear gray is used in its natural color. Most squirrel fur is dyed shades of brown.

Another luxury fur is stone marten with its deep, dense texture and dark brown color hiding a whitish underfur.

Chinchilla, the tiny animal which originated in South America, is now widely raised on ranches in the United States. Its slate-blue, dense, soft fur has made it one of the most desirable of fine pelts.

Ermine and lynx furs come mainly from Canada; both are light in color. Ermine is usually from that animal's winter coat of pure white. It is exceedingly dense, soft, and silky to the touch.

The greatest variety of fur-bearing animals is furnished

The cutter, one of the highest paid of all fur craftsmen, is shown in the first step of "letting-out" mink skins. Cutter's skill takes many years to acquire. Mistakes are very costly.

Sections of a Persian lamb coat are being sewn together in the important "closing" operation. Each section is made of skins that have been expertly worked into perfectly matched areas. Closing transforms the individual parts into a whole garment.

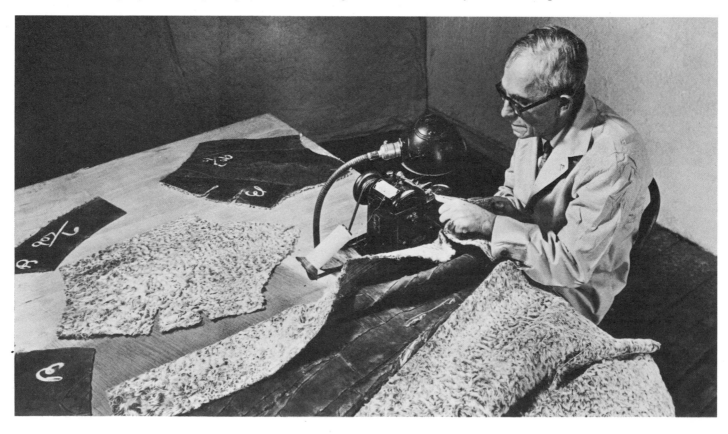

This machine operator is patiently sewing strips of fur into a long "let-out" skin. Letting-out results in supple skins of great beauty.

After being wetted, skins are tacked to a board, fur side down, in shapes required for finished coat. Skins will maintain shapes after drying.

by North America. In the United States alone, there are 40 different native furs available for commercial use. While the industry draws heavily on fur farms, many fine pelts are still furnished by trappers, both amateur and professional, who sell their catch to itinerant buyers. The best skins come to the large auction houses in New York, St. Louis, Minneapolis, Seattle, Winnipeg, and Montreal where they are graded and auctioned to fur buyers. These experts have their own unique, mysterious language for indicating their preferences with a system of signs and signals understood only by the initiated.

FUR FARMING

Privately operated fur farms are widely spread throughout the United States and Canada. Contrary to the belief of old-time trappers, ranch-grown furs are often superior to the wild product. The notion that fur-bearing animals would not thrive in captivity has been proven wrong. Scientific breeding, controlled diets, and environment are producing finer furs than ever before in the history of the industry.

On Prince Edward Island in Canada fur farming was first tried in 1887. Today Canadian fur ranches, particularly those for silver fox, represent the major industry in several provinces.

DRESSING FURS

The skins for furs must be dressed and treated with great care by the manufacturers before they can be made into finished garments. The first step is proper skinning, which must be done by the trapper or rancher. The skins are cleaned and stretched before delivery to market.

Modern machinery is employed for scraping, soaking, rinsing, drying, tanning, shaving, and clipping. All furs must be washed and soaked in chemical solutions; then treated with oils to make the skins soft and to prevent drying and ultimate cracking. These operations are followed by many cleanings in sawdust-filled drums. The furs are next beaten and carefully combed.

Final finishing involves plucking of guard hairs for certain furs; shearing; dyeing; bleaching by various processes, depending upon the style or type of fur. In many fur-dressing plants, these processes are closely guarded secrets.

The fashioning of furs into a garment is a highly complex handicraft, largely carried out by individual fur workers or small shops which make a specialty of the craft. In New York City alone there are some 2,000 such fur-fabricating shops. The cutter is the highest paid worker in this profession because he must be highly trained. To prepare fur for a mink coat, for example, he must carve every skin into diagonal strips only one-fourth to one-sixteenth of an inch wide. These strips are sewn together into a long, narrow strip, with thousands of seams in a supple line from collar to hem. Every step is done by hand. There is no assembly line for making a fur garment.

After skins are cut and sewn in conformity with the designer's pattern, a "nailer" wets and tacks them with the fur side down into the prescribed shape of the finished coat. When dry, the skins will hold to the curves or straight lines as positioned by the nailer. At length the dried sections are "closed" or sewn together by a skilled sewing machine operator; buttons, hooks, loops, and other trimmings are put on.

Because the fur industry is dependent upon changes of fashion, its volume fluctuates as favorite styles come and go. However, the need and desire for fine fur coats, and for decorative fur pieces has persisted through the ages. Fur seems destined to remain an important status symbol to say nothing of providing warmth in biting, cold weather.

22 Automobiles

When the body and chassis lines meet at the "body drop" or "mating line," the two components are joined, and the car begins to take final shape.

If one should ask what makes the United States different from any other nation on earth, there could be a number of valid answers. Yet a keen observer, even one who had previously been unfamiliar with American life, could scarcely fail in a very few days to pick the automobile as one of the most significant factors in making the United States unique. America is literally a nation on wheels. From Henry Ford's earliest vision of the inexpensive family car to the latest high-speed streamlined model, the automobile has transformed America from a slow-paced country of scattered rural communities to a fast-moving, closely integrated nation. Accordingly, the entire concept of life has changed in America. Swift, long distance travel has become an individual prerogative, requiring little or no planning or effort. By means of the automobile, Americans have given the world a new declaration of independence—they have declared themselves free to travel anywhere on their vast continent virtually at will.

The results of this new automotive freedom have not all been good. But good or bad, the average American spends a considerable portion of his life moving swiftly on his privately owned and operated set of wheels. The industry which makes this possible is one of the world's greatest.

HOW DID IT ALL BEGIN?

Unlike many other inventions, the "horseless carriage" cannot be attributed to a single inventor; nor is it possible to establish a definite date for its earliest successful model. For at least 50 years before 1900, both in Europe and in the United States, mechanics and inventors had been tinkering with motors and power-driven vehicles. A "gas carriage" was driven through the streets of Paris in 1863 by its inventor, Etienne Lenoir. With benzine as the fuel and large, clanking pistons, the engine propelled this clumsy carriage at a slow pace for several hours. But the achievement, though significant, was not good enough to be a commercial success.

The first internal combustion engine was made probably in 1878 by the German, Carl Benz. By 1883, Benz had succeeded in building a gasoline-propelled carriage. With

128

the rapid growth of the petroleum industry came more and more efforts to use gasoline as a motor fuel. (See *Petroleum*) In 1885, Gottlieb Daimler made the first motorcycle. Two years later the Daimler automobile appeared.

American inventors were some years behind in automotive developments. Not until Charles E. Duryea fastened a gasoline engine under the seat of a one-horse buggy did Americans see a successful "homegrown" automobile. This was in Springfield, Massachusetts, in 1892 or '93 (the exact year is in doubt). Soon afterward, similar horseless carriages appeared in other parts of the country. One was made by Elwood Haynes in Kokomo, Indiana, in 1894. Meanwhile, the Dodge brothers had turned their efforts from bicycle manufacturing to the building of automobiles. A carriage firm operated by the Studebaker brothers also began to work on gas cars.

At about the time that Charles Duryea finished making his first automobile, a young man in Detroit was working on gasoline engines in a brick shed behind the rented, two-family house where he lived. His name was Henry Ford. Ford completed his first car in the spring of 1896. Fitted with a two-cylinder steam engine, bicycle wheels, and two belts to provide two forward speeds, this first Ford had no reverse, no steering wheel, and no brakes. But it was the beginning of one of the world's great industrial empires.

While David Buick, the Dodge and the Studebaker brothers, and many others developed elaborate custom-built luxury cars, Ford concentrated on the idea of producing an automobile that every American family could afford. After some early successes in winning races with his cars, Ford organized the Ford Motor Company with $28,000 invested by 12 shareholders. Two of these original investors, who had contributed $5,000 each, sold their holdings a few years later for twelve and one-half million dollars. The famous Model T first appeared in 1908; fifteen million were produced during the next nineteen years.

HENRY FORD

Probably Ford's greatest achievement and his most important contribution to all industry was his creation of the moving assembly line. Both Henry Ford and R. E. Olds, creator of the Oldsmobile, were striving to produce a car within the means of the average working man. Ford devised two innovations which made his dream a reality. First, he recognized the value of vanadium steel, a strong lightweight steel of English invention, as a material with which he could reduce the weight of his cars by two-thirds and thus use a cheaper engine. This steel had been introduced to America in 1905 by the U. S. Steel Corporation. Second, he used Eli Whitney's old principle of interchangeable parts, (*See Machinery*) together with the precision of up-to-date machine tools. This enabled Ford's engineers to do away with individual grinding, tooling, and fitting of the many pieces of an automobile. They set up power-driven conveyor lines, using belts, chains, and rails. The parts moved now in endless lines to the workmen, each of whom was assigned a specific assembly operation. The first actual trial of the moving assembly lines took

129

The Model T Ford became an institution in American life of the early 1900's. Fifteen million of them were sold from 1908 to 1927.

place in August, 1913. The day of modern mass production had dawned.

MACHINES OF THE DEVIL

Despite the quick acceptance of Ford's cheap car, some segments of the public bitterly resisted the encroachments of the noisy, diabolical machines. A "Farmers' Anti-automobile Society of Pennsylvania" demanded that, when driving at night, a motorist should stop every mile, send up a warning rocket, and wait ten minutes to be sure the road ahead was clear before proceeding. They also suggested, somewhat facetiously, "If a horse is unwilling to pass an automobile, the driver should take the machine apart as rapidly as possible and conceal the parts in the bushes."

The devilish machines continued to roll off the assembly lines in ever increasing numbers. Other manufacturers soon followed Ford's lead in setting up mass-production methods, and in spite of bad roads, tire troubles, hand-cranked starters, the dust, grease and discomfort of early motoring, America rapidly became the land of automobiles. As the automobile industry grew, giant companies were formed. By 1909, the four firms of David D. Buick,

A Ford of the future is the X-2000, one of many advanced and experimental models built to test new concepts of automotive design.

Henry M. Leland's Cadillac Automobile Company, the Oakland Motor Car Company, and the R. E. Olds Company were merged into what is now known the world over as General Motors Corporation. Louis Chevrolet's Company joined the giant corporation in 1918. Walter P. Chrysler, another of the early entrants in the automotive field, established the third of the three major giants of the industry.

AUTOMOBILE PRODUCTION TODAY

The major automobile producers are all billion-dollar corporations and are among the real giants of industry. The all-time U.S. production peak was reached in 1955, with a record of nearly eight million units. Translated into money, this represented factory sales of about fourteen billion dollars. Since that time, annual sales have averaged between six and six and one-half million units, or between ten and eleven billion dollars. Aggregate retail sales of cars, trucks, tires, gasoline, and accessories amounted to fifty-seven billion dollars in 1960. Such

tions required to process and assemble all of its parts. Then try to picture the plant that can do this job from start to finish. "The Rouge," as automotive men refer to it, covers over 1,200 acres. It has docking facilities for ore boats, gigantic ore bins, blast furnaces, coke ovens, open hearths, and steel mills for rolling, stamping, and casting steel parts. (See *Primary Metals*) River Rouge contains a complete glass factory, a paper mill, and its own power plant, along with the numerous assembly operations. More than 100 miles of railroad track, 81 miles of conveyors, and 4 bus lines link the various plants and buildings. Within the gates of The Rouge, some sixty thousand employees are paid approximately a million dollars every working day.

THE ASSEMBLY LINE

Today's automobile costs at least four or five times what Ford charged for his miraculous Model T. Without taking inflation into consideration, the modern car is well worth its price, even by 1910 standards, for it is easily

Final assembly line operations add window glass and interior trim. The completed automobile passes through a water test and receives a wheel alignment test and final inspection. Then it is driven off the line to start its journey to a dealer.

gargantuan volume has a profound influence on the entire American economy, and its effects are felt in many other industries. Manufacturing the modern automobile involves such materials as steel, malleable iron, copper, aluminum, lead, zinc, nickel, glass, rubber, plastics, cotton, wool, and leather. In the United States, automobile manufacturing is, without doubt, the largest and most important of durable goods industries. Six huge corporations are currently making more than three hundred models of about fifty brand names. There are automobile assembly operations in 36 cities scattered throughout 20 states. Probably the world's largest industrial operation is the Ford Motor Company's River Rouge plant in Dearborn, Mich. This astounding factory complex handles every step in the production of cars from iron ore to steel, silicates to glass, and component parts to finished automobiles that are driven off under their own power.

Examine your car and visualize the thousands of opera-

20 times as complex as its ancestor. In a typical automatic transmission unit there are 400 principal parts joined on 15 subassemblies. Yet so well organized are the assembly lines that only a little over an hour and one-half is required for complete motor assembly from the starting point to the motor drop where it is attached to the chassis. The body assembly line requires about eight and one-half hours from first welding jig to body drop. A complete automobile, depending on the model, is assembled in 9 to 20 hours.

At the Plymouth factory in Detroit, a typical assembly plant, the automobile begins to take form at the "gate line," where sides, floor, and roof are welded into a single unit. Floor pans are carried to the line on moving "trucks," while sides are swung into position by means of huge clamps called "fixtures." Roofs are put on by hand. As soon as the sections are welded together, the body is put through a grinding and finishing operation, then through an electronically controlled system which cleans, dries, primes, paints, bakes, and cools the finish. The bodies are also dipped in a giant "bathtub" of anticorrosive paint.

On an S-shaped assembly line, skilled workmen add the body hardware, which includes wiring harness, brake assemblies, interior lights, steering wheel, instrument panel, windshield, and exterior and interior moldings.

Meanwhile, the chassis has been advancing along a separate line where frame, transmission, engine, wheels, drive shaft, etc. are assembled. When the body and chassis lines meet at the "body drop" or "mating line," the two components are joined, and the car begins to take final shape. It moves to an inspection site where the engine, transmission, and the electrical system are checked and tested.

Final assembly line operations add window glass and various elements of interior trim. The completed automobile passes through a water test—280 gallons per minute applied with hurricane force—receives a wheel alignment check and final inspection. Then it is driven off the line to start its journey to a dealer. Such assembly operations cover as much as a million and one-half square feet, with lines about three and one-half miles long. Cars are turned out at the rate of approximately one every minute.

FROM FACTORY TO CONSUMER

In the United States there are about 40,000 franchised, new car dealers who handle sales of American and foreign makes as well as used cars from trade-ins. In addition there are many independent used car and truck dealers who have no connection with any of the manufacturers.

Most automobile dealers furnish their own capital to start their businesses, although manufacturers sometimes offer financial assistance. Depending on the size and location of the dealership, the investment may range from a hundred thousand dollars to well over a million. Large city dealers may sell several thousand new cars and an equal number of used cars each year. Many dealers have their own service and repair shops, and all must carry large inventories of parts and accessories.

Assembly operations cover a million and one-half square feet, with lines about three and one-half miles long. Cars are turned out at a rate of about one every minute.

AUTOMOBILE SERVICE IS BIG BUSINESS

In addition to the repair services offered by dealers, there are about 80,000 independent repair shops and over 185,000 gasoline service stations in the United States. The wholesale value of automobile parts and accessories sold each year amounts to between two and three billion dollars. To supplement the supplies made by the major automobile manufacturers, hundreds of smaller companies do a large volume of business manufacturing seat covers, batteries, tires, brake fluids, antifreeze chemicals, glass, and dozens of special automotive extras such as car radios, mirrors, flashlights, and other luxury items.

Some 12,000 independent wholesalers maintain automobile-parts warehouses. They do business not only with new car dealers but with specialized retail automotive stores, department stores, and mail-order houses.

TRUCKS

It is estimated that U. S. production of trucks accounts for at least 50% of the world's total. About one out of five American-made trucks is sold to the foreign market. Truck transport has been increasing rapidly in America in recent years, partly due to the great strides in superhighway construction.

New cars move from factory to dealer on specially constructed truck trailers which are sometimes loaded on railroad flat cars for long hauls.

An aerial view of the Ford Motor Company's River Rouge plant in Dearborn, Mich., where automobiles are produced from raw iron ore to finished cars.

Justly proud of his rig was this driver of a Mack Junior two-ton truck in 1911. Under the hood was a 30-horsepower four-cylinder engine.

In the all aluminum cab of a modern trailer truck, the driver has everything he could wish for comfort and efficiency. Instruments and controls are easily accessible, and the cab is fully insulated.

Major truck manufacturers are Ford, Chevrolet (General Motors), Dodge (Chrysler), Studebaker, and the specialized companies which do not make passenger cars (International Harvester, Divco-Wayne, Willys Motors, Mack Trucks, and The White Motor).

Although the manufacturing of trucks does not represent as large a volume of business as passenger units, it is nevertheless a giant industry. In the early 1960's, production exceeded a million units with a wholesale value of more than two and one-half billion dollars. Of this quantity, some 60,000 units were truck trailers.

While farmers make up the largest market for light and medium trucks, some 18,000 interstate, trucking firms are purchasing great numbers of heavy motor trucks and truck trailers. About a million and one-half of these larger trucks, with a capacity of five tons or over, are operating in the United States. According to the Automobile Manufacturers Association, approximately seven and one-half million people are employed in the truck transportation industry, which is growing steadily. The scope of trucking in the early 1960's may be judged by the fact that truck owners were averaging fourteen and one-half billion gallons of motor fuel each year and spending almost four billion dollars annually on new equipment. Every year they contributed close to three billion dollars in taxes for the maintenance of highways. In order to increase load capacities without materially increasing the weights of trucks, large trailer trucks are utilizing more and more aluminum. (*See Primary Metals*)

New developments in the trucking industry include the production of compact trucks designed to compete with foreign all-wheel drive units; improved trailer designs for refrigerated products and for the hauling of such "fluid solids" as cement and flour; and the increasing use of "pickaback" rail transport of trailer units for some long hauls. (*See Railroads*) New air-conditioned buses are appearing on the highways, both for long distance runs and for local transportation. Prospects for the trucking industry indicate considerable expansion within the next 5 to 10 years in the production of new units and in the amount of freight transported by trucks and trailers.

WHERE DO WE GO TOMORROW?

The automotive industry faces the dilemma of keeping pace with its own high-speed creations. With the building of more and better highways, the steady increase of "two-car" families, the recent popularity of compact cars, and the technological advances coming with bewildering rapidity from drafting rooms and laboratories, it would appear that America is on the threshold of another explosion of new ideas in motor travel. Such luxuries as air-conditioning and anti-smog devices were once considered laughable. Now they are approaching the status of standard equipment. New materials are gradually revolutionizing automobile construction. More plastics, aluminum, and synthetic fibers are appearing in the new cars.

In the design departments of automobile manufacturers are plans years ahead of the current models. How is the idea for an automobile developed? First, the opinions, ideas, and suggestions of thousands of car owners are sifted. Hundreds of sketches are drawn showing body styles, upholstery designs, instrument panels, and interior trim. When a committee of top management personnel approves a set of plans, a full-scale model is constructed of clay. This clay model, or "mockup," is used to take accurate measurements, to make templates, working drawings, and blueprints which go to the machine shops. Because paper is subject to shrinkage and expansion, master body drafts, accurate to one-hundredth of an inch, are drawn on sheets of aluminum.

In every set of new plans, engineering improvements are sought for several areas: driving safety, durability, comfort, smooth performance, and smart styling. Products of this type of research are such improvements as safety glass, all-steel bodies, tubeless tires, and automatic transmissions. Prior to its actual installation in new cars, each mechanical device is put through every conceivable test. Engines, brakes, fuel, and cooling systems are endlessly subjected to severe trials on vast company proving grounds where test drivers do their best to make hardy machines cry "uncle." Chemists study every raw material and every component that make up the modern car. Tensile strength of metals, resilience of natural and synthetic rubbers, and the toughness of various plastics are measured in the laboratories. There, scientists are at work on stronger, lighter materials and on ways to increase both the power and the efficiency of motors. After test cars have been driven about 20,000 miles, they are taken apart and analyzed, piece by piece, to determine the degree of wear.

Patterns for new styles or redesigned engine parts are painstakingly made by hand. Skilled craftsmen are employed to carve some of the components in wood. Sheet metal is hammered into shape over wooden forms. The resulting custom-made master models may cost anywhere from fifty thousand to a quarter of a million dollars.

Despite all the wonders of the automotive age, it has brought with it many sobering problems which will require the best minds of future scientists, engineers, and mechanics. Highway injuries and deaths reach staggering numbers every year. Road congestion, especially on the approaches to large towns and cities, is becoming acute. Highway engineers admit they are several years behind in the solution of problems caused by increased automobile traffic.

Still, the car of tomorrow is taking shape on the drawing boards. Cars that float on cushions of air; radio-powered and radio-controlled cars that travel on highway beams at incredible speeds; strange, streamlined, plexiglass all-weather bubbles, fully air-conditioned and heated—these and many other "Buck Rogers" vehicles of the future are already in the planning stage.

Whatever the future of the automobile and the automotive industry may be, one thing is certain—it will be big, dynamic, and exciting. By its very nature, this is an industry of movement, whose rapid progress forecasts an auspicious future.

Making clay cars and mock-ups in an advanced styling studio, skilled craftsmen prepare the full-size master models for next season's cars. Such custom-made models may cost a manufacturer from fifty thousand to a quarter of a million dollars.

A powerful four-unit diesel pulls an eastbound freight train through the Cascade Mountains of Washington.

23 Railroading

The thunder of a growing nation found expression in the rumble of iron wheels on iron rails, and in the deep-throated puffing of steam-powered locomotives. As American industry exploded into the Machine Age, and as restless pioneers pushed into the western wilderness during the early years of the nineteenth century, steel bands were laid to join the east coast to the far west. The United States needed speed. Railroads provided it. As soon as rail transportation of freight and passengers linked up the farms to the cities, the forests to the lumber mills, the wheat fields to the grain elevators, and the mines to steel mills, America began to stir as a giant awakening from sleep. New towns and cities sprang up within months or even weeks. Agricultural and industrial production increased and distance no longer prevented trade. In 1830, when railroads first began to operate on a commercial basis, there were fewer people west of the Mississippi than there are today in the city of Richmond, Virginia. In the entire United States, only five cities had populations larger than 25,000—they were Philadelphia, New York, Baltimore, Boston, and New Orleans. All were located at or near the seacoasts. Now some 500 U.S. cities have more than 25,000 inhabitants and they are scattered through-

out the country. Railroads have played a leading role in bringing about these vast changes.

EARLY LOCOMOTIVES

Steam engines had begun to alarm the world with their unfamiliar snorting and puffing as early as 1769, when Captain Nicholas Cugnot ran a machine through Paris streets at a little over two miles an hour. Designed to haul guns for the army, it was condemned as too dangerous a contraption for practical use. Not many years later, however, English inventors were experimenting with steam locomotives. William Murdock built a foot-high working model in 1784. On a dark night, he lighted the spirit lamp under the small locomotive's boiler and started it chugging along a lane near his house. When a local clergyman, out for an evening stroll, saw this fire breathing, coughing engine approaching him, he rushed to the church, believing he had seen the devil himself.

Another Englishman, Richard Trevithick, built a more practical steam locomotive for mine service in 1802. By 1804 he had put his engine on a wagon which pulled other ore wagons along rails. By this means he hauled ten tons of iron at a speed of five miles an hour. But the locomotive's weight was too great for the roadbed, and for the time being railroading ground to a halt. Then George Stephenson, another mine worker, tried his hand with steam power. Because his locomotive roared so loudly that it frightened miners and horses, he contrived to funnel the escaping steam into the engine's stack. This served to increase the draft and, consequently, the steam pressure. Soon afterward, Stephenson helped to build England's first operational railroad, the Stockton-Darlington Line which opened in 1825.

Meanwhile Americans were also experimenting with rails. In 1815, John Stevens was granted a charter by the New Jersey State Legislature to construct a railroad between Trenton and New Brunswick. By 1823 he was working on an 80-mile line from Columbia, Pennsylvania to Philadelphia; this was the beginning of the mighty Pennsylvania Railroad. Yet his progress was slowed by lack of funds. It was not until 1834 that horse-drawn trains were making the Columbia-Philadelphia run in nine hours.

America's first steam locomotive was brought from England in 1829 by a civil engineer named Horatio Allen. The engine, called the *Stourbridge Lion* after the town where it had been built, performed well enough by itself but lacked power to pull the heavy coal carts for which it had been purchased. Later that same year, Peter Cooper of New York tested his *Tom Thumb* locomotive in Baltimore. This was the first American-built steam locomotive to operate on a U.S. common carrier railroad.

From that time, one railroad experiment after another was recorded. Despite a few serious accidents, such as the blowing up of *The Best Friend of Charleston* when a slave employed as a fireman tied a rope around a valve to stop the noise of escaping steam, the railroad age had begun. By 1835 more than a thousand miles of track had been put into operation and some 200 railway charters had been granted.

TRANSCONTINENTAL LINES

While railroads spread their steel bands in networks throughout the East and in the South, the dream of a transcontinental line kept nagging at rail enthusiasts. Although many of the problems involved seemed insurmountable, plans were laid before Congress as early as 1844. Not until 1864, however, was a U.S. government charter granted after the Central Pacific and the Union Pacific Railroads had been organized. President Lincoln established the Missouri River at Omaha, Nebraska Territory as the eastern terminus. The western terminus was to be Sacramento, California. While the Union Pacific built westward, the Central Pacific pushed toward the east. Each company was hampered by great difficulties. Most of the Central Pacific's tools and materials had to be transported by ships all the way around Cape Horn or carried across the Isthmus of Panama. Their roadbed was built through the rugged Sierras. On the other hand, the Union Pacific, working on comparatively level ground, was harassed by Indians, and the farther west it advanced, the less timber and other supplies were available.

But at last the two railroads met, and the famous gold

Streamlined locomotives of this type, in use on the Southern Pacific's "Daylight Specials" running between San Francisco and Los Angeles, are among the last of a proud but dying breed of iron horses.

The first train of passenger cars to run in New York State was pulled by the De Witt Clinton locomotive, August 9, 1831, from Albany to Schenectady.

The Stourbridge Lion, purchased in England for the Delaware and Hudson Company, introduced steam locomotives to America. Horatio Allen drove it three miles on August 8, 1829, at Honesdale, Pa.

Still in operating condition today, the Atlantic locomotive pictured above was built by Phineas Davis of York, Pa., and went into service on the Baltimore and Ohio Railroad in 1832.

Blazing new trails in the West and South, railroad construction crews, like that in this motion-picture scene, faced danger and hardship.

spike was driven to connect the last section of rail on May 10, 1867 at Promontory, Utah. Since telegraph wires had been strung along the right of way, the nation was now joined from the east coast to California by rail transportation and by swift telegraphic communication. (See *Telegraph*)

THE GIANTS OF IRON HORSE DAYS

Railroading as an industry in America was big business almost from its inception. It required big thinking, big money, big effort, and big risks. To assist vast enterprises such as the transcontinental railroads, the U.S. government offered federal land grants. These were not outright gifts, however, but were made on condition that the railroads would carry U.S. troops, property, and mail at substantial discounts. It has been estimated that until the repeal of the special government provisions covering rail rates in 1941 and 1946, the railroads repaid about one hundred twenty-five million dollars' worth of land approximately ten times.

Still, for almost a century railroads prospered, and some of the country's greatest fortunes were built on rails. One of the famed multimillionaires of the late nineteenth century, Cornelius Vanderbilt, acquired a veritable railroad empire. Starting with the New York and Harlem Railroad, the Hudson River and the New York Central Railroads, he expanded westward to control the Michigan Central and the Canada Southern Railroads. While some of the financiers involved used unscrupulous methods in the cornering of railroad wealth, the resulting consolidations had one highly important beneficial result: passengers were enabled to travel from New York to Chicago or make other extended journeys in one continuous trip. In the earlier days of railroading, a multiplicity of short lines made the changing of trains and arranging of schedules a frustrating problem for the traveler. The greatest single period of railroad expansion was in the ten years from 1880 to 1890, when more than 7,000 miles of track were added to the nation's railways each year—a total of 70,300 miles in the decade.

RAILROADING SINCE THE TURN OF THE CENTURY

By 1916, the U.S. railroads had reached their peak with two hundred fifty-four thousand miles of road in operation. Since that time, the total mileage has dropped slightly, but this does not mean that the aggregate amount of track has decreased. Actually, by laying multiple tracks, rail capacity has been increased by the railroads so that with two hundred twenty thousand miles of distance, the roads are using some three hundred eighty thousand miles of track.

In 1960, the Association of American Railroads reported that American railways were carrying 30% of all commercial passenger traffic and 45% of the nation's freight. They were also transporting 75% of U.S. mail. Despite their great size and vital service to the nation, the railroads in the 1960's found themselves in serious trouble. Nearly all the major roads were operating at a loss. Passenger travel declined and many passenger lines have been discontinued in recent years.

The reasons for the decline in railroading are many, but the foremost ones are, of course, the newer, competing forms of transportation. Automobile travel, with its improved cars and superhighways, has been cutting deeply into rail travel, especially on commuter lines. (See *Automobiles*) For long distances, more and more people are using the airlines. Even heavy freight is being shipped by air and by truck.

Part of the railroad industry's difficulty has been its slowness to recognize the vast changes taking place in transportation. With the arrogance of their former exalted position the major railroads did not keep pace with their brash young competitors, the airlines, in offering service and comfort to customers. But it is clear that now the railroads have been aroused. The public, too, has begun to realize that railroading must be rescued from its current difficulties, since its role is still of vital importance to the nation.

GOVERNMENT RESTRICTIONS

One important area where help can come to the railroads is through changes in federal legislation. In an era when other forms of transportation were seriously cutting into railroad volume, rates of all railroad freight movements were still tightly regulated by government while two-thirds of truck traffic and nine-tenths of inland waterway traffic were unregulated. At the same time, huge federal spending for improved highways has aided trucking during a period when truck traffic expanded three and one-half times. Similar situations existed in regard to airlines and waterways. Meanwhile, up to the early 1960's, the railroads built their own rights-of-way at their own expense and also paid heavy taxes on them. In 1959, four hundred twenty-two million dollars of more than a billion dollars in railroad taxes were paid to state and local governments. For the same year, truck lines paid twenty-two million dollars in comparable taxes and airlines paid about six million dollars. Proportionately, the railroads paid state and local governments close to three times as much as bus lines, ten times as much as truck lines, and fourteen times as much as airlines. There have been other inequities in restrictive laws applicable to railroads, many of which have outlived their original purposes or usefulness.

CHANGES IN RAILROADING

In the past 25 years, railroads have undergone some drastic changes. Some have been forced changes; others have been brought about by forward-looking railroad men. Consolidations have continued to take place so that from

1911, when there were 1,312 operating railroads in the United States, the number of companies has dropped to less than one-half. Further consolidations with a view to increased operating efficiency are likely to take place in the future.

Meanwhile a physical change has brought sorrow to thousands of railroad enthusiasts. The "iron horse" has virtually disappeared from the rails. As recently as the 1950's, magnificent, puffing steam monsters could be seen hauling freight, even on eastern electrified roads. But steam, which gave birth to the railroad, was inevitably doomed to obsolescence. Powerful diesel locomotives, far more economical to operate, have taken over the chores of freight hauling, just as they did for passenger service a few years earlier. Though they are far less dramatic to watch, the smooth efficiency of the diesel engine is what the railroads need to compete with other modern forms of transportation.

Fortunately, for those who enjoy the nostalgia of former eras, many of the old steam locomotives are being preserved and operated on special scenic excursion runs. One such operation is on the 129-year-old Strasburg Rail Road in Pennsylvania. Pulled by a genuine "iron horse," sightseeing passengers ride in coaches 60 to 75 years old. This four and one-half mile line is one of the few U.S. railroads operating its passenger service at a profit. The Reading Lines also sponsor a series of "Iron Horse Rambles" through Pennsylvania.

Significantly, in 1962, the American Car Foundry in Berwick, Pa. closed its doors after many years of profitable operations. Since this manufacturer of railroad cars employed 1,900 people, representing 40% of the town's work force, the closing brought about a serious economic dislocation which will have far-reaching effects for some time to come. No one blamed anyone. It was simply a case of not enough orders. Eastern railroads were buying fewer cars, and their needs were largely being filled by their own car foundries.

MODERNIZATION

Railroads are now making a concerted effort to overcome their recent losses by improving service and the efficiency of their operations. There are many advantages to rail transportation which the individual companies and the Association of American Railroads are endeavoring to exploit and promote. One feature of modern freight operations is that a shipper anywhere in the United States, Canada, or Mexico can load a freight car for delivery at any station in these countries. With fast diesel trains, rail freight is being moved at greater speeds than ever before in railroad history.

To expedite the movement of fast trains, great improvements have been made in the rails on which they travel. Through research by metallurgists and engineers, rails are now made heavier, stronger, and safer than they were even a decade ago. Standard length of rails has increased from 33 ft. in 1920 to 39 ft. today, and some modern lines use rails 60 to 80 ft. long for special sections of track. Continuous rail has also come into use with joints welded together for spans of a mile or more.

Meanwhile, streamlined passenger trains have provided greater comfort for riders. Modern lightweight aluminum cars feature soft, indirect fluorescent lighting, adjustable upholstered seats, air conditioning, tavern cars, glass-dome observation cars, cafe cars, coach sleepers, roomette cars, and lounge-parlor cars.

New types of locomotives are fast, streamlined and even more powerful than the old steam giants. A gas-turbine, electric locomotive burning fuel oil can develop 4,500 to 8,500 horsepower. There is also an ignitron-rectifier, electric freight locomotive with 4,000 horsepower per unit.

So rapid has been the changeover in locomotive power that since 1941, total locomotive hours performed by diesels has grown from 12% to nearly 98%. In freight service, the change has been even more startling, for at the beginning of World War II diesel-electric locomotives pulled only one-fifth of 1% of the gross ton-miles of cars, whereas now the proportion is about 95%.

Freight equipment, too, has been undergoing drastic changes. Modern freight cars are designed to carry 40 to 80 tons each, with some specially constructed cars having 250-ton capacity. Stainless steel and aluminum are being used for freight car construction. (See *Primary Metals*) Many new types of tank, refrigerator, and hopper cars have been built to handle every sort of chemical, liquid, or powdered product.

Working on the principle, "if you can't fight 'em, join 'em," the railroads devised the scheme of "piggyback" or

A modern steam locomotive pulling a train of loaded coal cars in the Appalachian Valley. Diesel-electric locomotives now haul about 95% of gross ton-miles of freight cars.

The Jet Rocket is one of the newer streamliners. Its articulated, guided car wheels and low center of gravity enable it to take curves at higher speeds than conventional trains.

"pickaback" service. Special flat cars are used to transport loaded truck trailers over long distances, speeding truck deliveries on certain hauls. A specially designed fork lift is used to load the trailers onto the railroad cars and to remove them at their destination. There the trailers are once more coupled to trucks and driven to their local delivery points.

Another recent railroad innovation is the use of the

Growing popularity of "pickaback" service stems from the fact that it provides fast, door-to-door delivery of undisturbed trailer loads.

Up to 3,000 freight cars a day can be handled in the Englewood Radar Yard at Houston, Texas. An electronic brain and five miles of pneumatic tubes are included in its automatic equipment.

Assistant general yardmaster at the Houston, Texas, Englewood Radar Yard can contact all other parts of the yard and radio-equipped trains through this communications panel in the bowl tower.

"Ticketfax" machine which handles pullman reservations electronically. The old handwritten, yard-long tickets are rapidly being eliminated. Developed by Western Union, the Ticketfax works on the principle of the wirephoto. When a customer asks for a reservation, no matter what his point of departure or destination, the order is flashed by facsimile to a central office. The ticket is transmitted electronically back to the waiting customer. The time consumed is about one minute between sending and receiving operators. One of the first users of this system was the Pennsylvania Railroad, which also uses a microfilm system for getting information on routes and fares for each of several thousand rail points. With this, ticket attendants can answer queries in a matter of seconds whereas several minutes were formerly consumed while lines of impatient customers waited their turns.

At the New York Pennsylvania Station, closed circuit television is built into the ticket and reservation system. Ticket sellers can glance at a TV screen to see what space on a given train is available.

Television controls are also being used extensively for railroad traffic direction and dispatching. By means of closed circuit TV screens, operators in control towers can see the movement of trains and locomotives in sections of track out of sight of the towers. Complicated operations in the freight yard can now be remotely controlled comfortably and accurately.

WHAT OF THE FUTURE?

Some experts can see nothing but gloom in the future of railroading, and certainly events in the past 10 years have not been encouraging. What the railroads really need, today, is some of the good, old-fashioned American pioneering of the type that built the early railroads against seemingly impossible odds. Men and women with imagination are needed to envision and carry out plans for new concepts in railroading. Because the highways have become so congested, a great opportunity exists for railroads to recapture a large number of commuters and travelers who have become disenchanted with fighting traffic. Motorists are in a frame of mind to change. But the railroads must offer really attractive service and extra comforts. Many modern trains have the ultimate in smooth riding and comfortable seating. But too many other trains do not. By a vicious circle of events, lack of customers has caused railroads to discontinue passenger lines or to cut down on service. This in turn has driven more customers away.

As far as freight is concerned, railroads unquestionably still have the advantage over all other forms of land transportation. Yet, to maintain that position, railroad engineers must think in terms, not merely of gradual progress, but of real breakthroughs in speed, minimum problems for the shipper, and better accommodations for all types of materials and merchandise.

Railroads are entirely too vital a factor in American economy to be permitted to strangle themselves by default. Here is an industry that offers one of the greatest challenges to young people—a great industry requiring great thought and ingenuity. Its future can be as promising as its personnel can make it.

From the control tower at the Washington National Airport, controllers keep all aircraft moving freely and safely into the terminal area and onto the ground as they make the transition from center to tower control.

24 Aviation

The inventive process follows curious paths. Sometimes a great invention comes in a flash of inspiration to a single individual. In other cases, centuries of slow development and of trial and error by hundreds of people contribute to the final technological breakthrough. Such was the case with the flying machine, which was conceived many centuries before men had the technical knowledge to build a successful airplane. In his early legends, man expressed his dream of flying. The Greek story of Daedalus and Icarus, the *Arabian Nights* tale of the magic carpet, both reveal a yearning for flight that must have been felt by the most primitive peoples as they watched birds soaring through the air.

As might be expected, the earliest attempts at flight were patterned after the birds themselves. Men attached wings to their shoulders and tried to stay aloft by flapping their arms. In the fifteenth century, Leonardo da Vinci made drawings in his notebooks, indicating that he recognized the principles of the helicopter. His machine had rotating wings, and his invention of the propeller, designed for flight experiments, proved valuable for ships long before it was applied to practical aircraft.

During the eighteenth and nineteenth centuries balloon flights reached considerable heights in the atmosphere, but in all cases a source of motive power was the missing ingredient. Lighter-than-air craft merely drifted with the wind, completely at the mercy of fickle air currents.

In 1891, a German named Otto Lilienthal built the first glider. Only a year later Samuel P. Langley was building experimental airplanes in the United States. By 1903, Langley was ready to try a power-driven monoplane, but it failed to leave the ground. Meanwhile a Frenchman, Louis Bleriot, was making progress in his aircraft experiments.

Then, on December 17, 1903, came the first successful flight of a heavier-than-air machine when Wilbur and Orville Wright flew their biplane at Kill Devil Hill in North Carolina. A reporter, who flashed the news to his newspaper in New York, was discharged for spending so much money telegraphing nonsense.

Without question, the gasoline motor was largely responsible for making airplane flight possible, for this gave inventors a comparatively lightweight power plant that could rotate propellers at high speed. Steam engines were entirely too heavy, and no other type of engine up to that time was capable of generating sufficient power. Curiously, the jet propulsion principle, known long ago in ancient Greece when early experiments were conducted with steam, was later to give aircraft the jet engine which is rapidly replacing the gasoline piston-type motor.

The Wrights were followed in quick succession by other successful flyers, including Louis Bleriot who flew across the English Channel in 1909 and Glenn H. Curtiss, a motorcycle manufacturer who, with Alexander Graham Bell, had formed the Aerial Experiment Association at Hammondsport, N.Y., in 1907.

This picture of a biplane in the U.S. Aerial Mail Service was taken about 1918, in the earliest days of flying the mail. Many of the pilots were World War I flyers who had difficulty convincing the public that the airplane was here to stay.

As the design of aircraft improved, so did the engines to power them. By the outbreak of World War I, airplanes were equipped with 200-horsepower engines. They could cruise up to 600 miles nonstop and reach an altitude of about 13,000 ft.

EARLY DAYS

No industry has developed more rapidly or made more spectacular strides than the aircraft industry. In a period of 60 years the airplane has advanced from the Wright Brothers' frail craft to supersonic jet planes which streak through the stratosphere, and luxurious passenger airliners which carry many passengers across oceans and continents in a matter of hours. Nor is the end of progress in sight. Planes now on the drawing boards will make present aircraft obsolete.

Although the manufacture of aircraft has expanded rapidly in all parts of the world, it was inevitable that the United States with its vast industrial capacity would be a leader in the field. Due to the airplane's importance in modern warfare, a large segment of the industry is devoted to making military and naval aircraft. As a result, the U. S. Government has a huge stake in the industry.

In World War I, American production never got into high gear until the last weeks of the war. Consequently, the U. S. Air Force lagged behind those of European nations. The American public seemed unaware that an air age was dawning. However, a small group of adventurous and dedicated young fliers, the "barnstormers" of the 1920's, bought surplus warplanes, established individual passenger and mail service, and earned a few dollars by exhibition flying at county fairs. It was this group rather than government officials or farseeing industrialists who kept the United States from falling completely out of the air, as it were.

One of these intrepid flyers was Charles Lindbergh, whose New York to Paris flight on May 20, 1927, in his tiny single-engine monoplane, "The Spirit of St. Louis," electrified the entire world. This first transoceanic flight, which took 33 hours, served at last to convince the American public that air travel was a practical reality. In the meantime, another man was battling public apathy in another direction. This was General Billy Mitchell whose appreciation of air power drove him time and again to seek support of Congress for increased air defenses. For years, his was a lone voice crying in the wilderness, and although he was court-martialed for bringing discredit on the services, he continued his campaign to arouse Americans to the need for air power.

A DIVERSIFIED INDUSTRY

The aircraft manufacturing industry is not easily coordinated or concentrated into single-operation plants where, as in the case of automobiles, new models can be put into mass production in a matter of months. New airplane designs sometimes require several years of planning and testing before they can be put into full production. Also, modern aircraft are so complex that as many as 2,000 subcontractors may be working on a single program at one time. The aircraft company itself performs the task of final assembly for thousands of components which come from other plants in all parts of the nation.

The problem of building a huge air force or a great fleet of passenger planes for commercial traffic is a formidable one. When World War II began, President Roosevelt's call for production of 50,000 planes a year seemed to many persons an impossible task. In 1938, the American aviation industry had produced only 3,675 planes of all types, of which 1,800 were military craft. Yet so great was the urgency that American industry accomplished another of its many wartime miracles. By 1944, U.S. production had nearly doubled Roosevelt's request with an output of 96,000 planes.

A modern airplane assembly plant is one of the most fascinating of factory operations. Because of its scale, the construction of a large jet airliner is an impressive process. Sections of the plant are devoted to constructing main wing sections, body sections, wing leading edges, horizontal stabilizers, nose sections, and other large assemblies. Before these components, along with thousands of smaller parts, are brought at last to the final assembly area, a whole series of subassembly operations must be completed. Some of the machining is done on complex machine tools, such as giant extrusion and forging presses, and highly specialized jigs. Stretch presses are employed to wrap sheet metal around the most precisely engineered contour dies. Every part must be tooled with utmost accuracy. Since the heat generated in jet engines would melt ordinary steel or aluminum, the use of such metals as titanium requires new types of machine tools.

At a plant in Renton, near Seattle, Wash., there are three major assembly lines. Two lines, one long and one short, are engaged in assembling jet tankers for the U. S. Air Force. Another huge horseshoe-shaped line is producing commercial jet airliners. From eight to eleven planes are in various stages of assembly on a line at a given time. Main body and wing sections have already been joined in an adjacent building. In this vast enclosure, the planes slowly take form appearing as monstrous birds waiting to try their wings. Intricate electrical systems are installed; the huge jet engines are joined to the nacelles; interior trim, furnishings, and instruments are put in place, checked, and tested. A dark protective coating is applied to the aircraft for the final assembly operation. This is removed before the plane is moved to the paint hangar for its finishing and airline markings.

In place of mass-production standardization common to automobile assembly, aircraft manufacturers use a system known as "flexible mass production." Designs change rapidly as aerodynamics technology advances. As a result, seldom more than several hundred identical aircraft of a given model are produced.

Behind the machining and the physical job of putting the parts together is the design department. Here, experts in many fields pool their knowledge, because the design of an airplane involves various aspects: acoustics, aerodynamics, structural design, stress, vibration, weights, tensile strength of various materials, and hours of physical research. Before the B-52 could make its maiden flight a total of four million eighty-five thousand engineering manhours was consumed. To accomplish such a herculean task obviously requires the service of hundreds of skilled technicians. One man doing the job would need to work 450 years, assuming he had mastered the many necessary skills.

Approximately 30 companies make up the aircraft-manufacturing industry insofar as final construction and assembly are concerned. These companies must, in turn, purchase engines, supplies, instruments, and parts from some 35,000 other firms. Foremost makers of military aircraft are Boeing, Douglas, Lockheed, Martin, Grumman, General Dynamics, Fairchild, and Republic. Boeing, Douglas, and Lockheed dominate the commercial plane market, while for small, private aircraft the leaders are Beech (Beechcraft), Piper (Piper Cub), and Cessna. Aircraft engine manufacturers include Curtiss-Wright, Pratt and Whitney, Fairchild and Avco Manufacturing Corporation.

THE JET AGE

Athough jet planes were in active military service before the end of World War II, it was several years before civil

use of jet engines was an important factor of the industry. Now, giant jetliners capable of 600-mile-per-hour speeds are rolling off the assembly lines of the major plane manufacturers and are flying regular schedules across the United States, as well as over the ocean to Europe.

What is jet propulsion? As a law of physics, it was first stated by Sir Isaac Newton, the British physicist: For every action, there is a reaction, equal in force and opposite in direction. This law is demonstrated when air is permitted to escape rapidly from a toy balloon, causing the balloon to shoot across a room. In a modern jet engine, air drawn into a chamber of the engine by a compressor is squeezed, and pressure is raised. The highly compressed air rushes into a combustion chamber where it is mixed with a liquid fuel, such as a high-grade kerosene. As the mixture is

Two views of the final assembly area for Boeing 707, 720, and 727 jet airliners at the Boeing Transport Division plant in Renton, Washington. Alongside the commercial jetliners, Boeing KC-135 jet tankers and C-135 jet transports are being built for the United States Air Force. Dark protective coating is removed before planes are moved to the paint hangar.

141

ignited, pressure increases still more until the air, having nowhere else to go, rushes with great force out of the "back door" of the engine, or the jet's nozzle.

The same principle is used in the turboprop engine, but instead of acting upon pure thrust, the force of escaping air is used to turn a propeller. Although they produce far more power than conventional piston engines, jet engines weigh no more. As a result, four jet engines are equivalent to 40 piston-type motors. Since jet planes use fuel about five times as fast as do piston planes, wing tanks must be designed with a larger capacity. This is accomplished by the swept-back design permitting thicker wings.

Some of the newer jetliners are 150 ft. long, accommodate 150 passengers, plus as much cargo as can be put into the entire fuselage of the DC-4 cargo plane. Their span from wing tip to wing tip is greater than the distance

Two jet combat planes for the U.S. Navy: the Grumman F9F-8 Cougar (top) and the Grumman F11F-1 Tiger (lower). Jets are rapidly replacing propeller-driven planes in all categories of commercial and military aircraft.

flown by the Wright Brothers on their first flight. One plane costs between five and six million dollars.

Among commercial jet planes are the Boeing 707; the DC-8, manufactured by the Douglas Aircraft Corporation; and the Convair 880. There are also a number of turboprop planes, such as the Vickers Viscount, Lockheed Electra, and the Fairchild F-27.

Jets fly higher than conventional planes, generally cruising at about eight miles above the earth. Cabins are therefore pressurized to maintain equal air pressure at all altitudes. Noise is subdued inside the planes, and there is little vibration. Because of the tremendously increased speeds, flights between widely separated cities can be accomplished in less time than it takes to drive a few miles in congested traffic. For example, a jet plane makes the 400-mile journey from Toronto, Canada to Idlewild Airport in New York in the time required for a bus to travel the 18 miles from midtown Manhattan to the airport. New York to Los Angeles flights are expected to be made by supersonic jets in 76 minutes.

TRANSPORTATION PROBLEMS IN THE JET AGE

This new burst of air-travel speed has created problems. While the major airlines are committed to increased use of jet planes, they are harassed by irate citizens who object to the noise, by new traffic problems, and by the need to streamline their methods of handling passengers and luggage. Even though jet travel is quieter for the riders, it has created a particularly irritating level of noise in and around the airports. In order to minimize this, engine thrust has been increased from 14,500 to 17,000 lb. in order to achieve faster takeoff and climb, thus carrying the great planes out of range of residential districts as quickly as possible. Airport authorities strictly enforce rules to minimize noise, which they measure with scientific instruments.

As the number of air travelers increases constantly, ground traffic problems multiply. Having gained a reputation for efficient service early in their existence, the airlines are now battling to overcome customer resistance to long waits for luggage, seemingly endless walks from ticket areas to boarding ramps, and the necessity of locating jet ports miles from congested metropolitan centers. They are solving at least some of these problems in interesting ways. For passenger convenience in boarding or leaving the planes, telescoping walkways have been constructed. These devices automatically extend an enclosed ramp from a central tower to the doors of the planes. Passengers are thus enabled to board or leave the aircraft without exposure to weather and without climbing long flights of steps. Still more amazing are the mobile lounges, comfortably appointed waiting rooms mounted on giant truck chassis, which roll from plane to airport terminal and back while passengers relax in upholstered lounge chairs. To speed up the trip from town to airport, helicopter service is being offered in most large cities.

AIR TRAFFIC CONTROL

As farsighted engineers predicted some years ago, air traffic congestion has reached problem proportions. A

This structure is one of over 1,200 VORTAC installations being constructed by the FAA. The station broadcasts direction and distance information to pilots. VORTAC's are part of a vast web of airway aids forming an invisible electronic network across the nation.

traffic control system has been worked out for the safety of commercial airlines and military aircraft. This system, which is owned and operated by the Federal Government, integrates all types of planes receiving this separation service into a single network of air highways. It allots moving blocks of airspace to every plane in flight. Planes are "fed" into the system from control points in such a way that they are timed to have ample space ahead and behind, while they are separated vertically at 1,000-ft. intervals below the 29,000-ft. altitude level and 2,000 ft. above 29,000 ft. Nevertheless, even this system is becoming inadequate to control the great number of planes in flight at all times. The U.S. private and commercial fleet comprises more than 80,000 planes; the military operate well over 35,000. Although airlines fly only a small portion of the commercial fleet (some 2,000 aircraft), they are in the air a far greater proportion of the time than any other class of planes. New and more efficient radar, electronic systems, and divisions of airspace are being devised to take care of the rapidly increasing traffic.

AIR SAFETY

While automobile fatalities have consistently stayed at an alarmingly high level in relation to the number of miles driven, airline fatalities have decreased to the point where there has been less than one death for every one hundred million passenger miles. This is about six times safer than automobile travel.

Increased air safety has resulted from better designed aircraft, more efficient engines, improved instruments and controls. Confidence in the safety of air travel is expressed in the steady increase of passengers, year after year. In 1960, airlines carried sixty-six million passengers and it is authoritatively estimated that in the 1970's they will carry more than one hundred twenty million passengers a year.

FINANCIAL PROBLEMS

Despite great advances in aircraft technology, expanding traffic, and American "air-mindedness," U.S. airlines face financial difficulties. Unlike the railroads, many of whose problems stem from antiquated equipment and old-fashioned thinking (See *Railroading*), the airlines can scarcely be said to suffer from lack of modern ideas. Air travel is the ultimate in modern transportation and, in most departments, its service is unexcelled. Nevertheless, due to the gigantic costs of operating and maintaining up-to-date equipment, rising wages, and the necessity of maintaining fares competitive with other forms of transporta-

This Air Route Surveillance radar installation at Suitland, Md., is one of 46 located around the U.S. They monitor air traffic within a 360° radius, 200 miles from location.

tion, many lines lost money. As in a number of other industries, there was a trend toward giant mergers in the early 1960's in a move to consolidate operations, pool capital resources, and eliminate competition.

The rapid emergence of the jet age has been one of the greatest financial burdens which the airlines have had to bear. The change-over to new, multimillion-dollar jetliners and facilities to service them, while essential to the future of any progressive airline company, required an aggregate investment of more than three billion dollars during the late 1950's and early '60's. This in an industry which entered the jet age with a total investment of only one and seven-tenths billion dollars in 1958!

THE AIRCRAFT INDUSTRY

Several major segments of the aircraft industry comprise a gigantic overall activity. Aircraft construction is divided into two parts, commercial and military. As mentioned earlier, so complex is the building operation that literally dozens of industries and hundreds of plants throughout the United States are involved. However, a major portion of the construction industry is concentrated in the West Coast area. Many of the large aircraft companies are also working on the construction of rockets and missiles (which see). In recent years, the manufacture of helicopters has grown tremendously. During the Korean war, the use of military helicopters, many of them Sikorsky S-55's, proved the versatility of this type of aircraft by hauling equipment and supplies to inaccessible mountain tops, evacuating wounded, and doing valuable observation work. Sikorsky, Piasecki, Hughes, Bell, Hiller, and Doman are well-known names in the field of helicopter construction. Russian-born Igor Sikorsky conducted many of America's pioneering experiments with single-rotor machines from 1939 to 1942. Now helicopters are used for commercial taxi service (midtown heliports to airports),

land surveys in map making, crop dusting, ferry service between land areas and ships at sea, shuttle transport of airmail, police patrols, and rescue work, as well as a great variety of military missions.

U. S. air transport is now a massive industry, consisting of about 60 airlines connecting nearly 750 cities. It employs some one hundred seventy thousand people with an annual payroll in excess of a billion dollars. This industry carries about a quarter of a billion ton-miles of mail each year, sixty to seventy million passengers, and three-quarters of a billion ton-miles of commercial freight.

This multibillion-dollar industry, which has shown consistent gains and now leads all other travel facilities in passenger miles, is in need of some drastic remedies to prevent financial disaster. Like the railroads, it blames many of its present difficulties on government regulation and interference. Industry spokesmen complain of restrictive taxation, needless competition by the government-owned airline, MATS, and traffic-procurement practices that prescribe impractically low rates on airlines. Competition from foreign airlines, is becoming increasingly serious.

Because civil and military aviation are of the utmost importance to any nation's relative position in the world, the aircraft industry must advance at a rapid pace. To do this, skilled personnel in many departments are urgently needed. These include pilots, mechanics, flight engineers, aircraft designers, airline hostesses, as well as scientists, engineers, and technicians in a host of contributing industries such as electronics, chemicals, petroleum, primary metals, plastics, and radio communication. Vital to the industry's continued growth to maintain world leadership will be the attitude and actions of Federal regulatory agencies and a recognition by the American public that the United States simply cannot afford to take second place in aviation.

To control air traffic flying under Instrument Flight Rules on the 349,000 miles of Federal Airways, FAA has divided the country geographically into 36 areas. Each is under the jurisdiction of an Air Route Traffic Control Center like the one shown here, where controllers monitor aircraft on the television-like screen of a long-range radarscope.

A 30,000-ton tanker is launched at New York Shipbuilding Corporation for Atlantic Refining Company.

25 Shipping and Shipbuilding

As we now stand on the mysterious threshold of space, it is easy to forget that the sea was once a realm of equally awesome mystery, challenging adventurous men to explore its vast reaches and offering unknown hazards and horizons. The frail ships, in which sailors first ventured forth, were to the modern ocean liner what space capsules doubtlessly will be to future space-ships.

Earliest ship builders of record were the Egyptians, but of all the ancient peoples, the Phoenicians were the greatest ship builders and navigators. The Phoenicians developed the long fighting ships with triple banks of oars. These served as early models for the great Roman triremes which were often 160 ft. long and carried two masts with square sails bent to yards. Far to the north, the Norse sea rovers were also well versed in the building of seaworthy ships, though their vessels were generally smaller and less luxuriously fitted out than those of the Mediterranean empires.

SHIPBUILDING IN AMERICA

During the Colonial period of North America, shipbuilding was one of the major New World industries for obvious reasons. First, the vast forests provided ample lumber; particularly valuable was the tall, virgin timber for masts. Second, land transportation was limited. Actually, it was easier to sail from one coastal settlement to another than to push through the wilderness, and the early colonies subsisted largely upon sea trade, not only with Europe but with each other. The greatest shipbuilding activity was in New England, where numerous towns from Gloucester, Mass. to New Haven, Conn. grew up around this and the related fishing industry. (See *Fishing*)

From about 1800 to the time of the Civil War, American shipbuilding surpassed England's; the peak being reached in 1855 when more than 2,000 vessels were launched in U.S. shipyards. This was the time of the great clipper ships, the world's fastest and most efficient sailing vessels. Before the era of steam and steel, American ship-building supremacy remained unchallenged.

STEEL SHIPS

Then came the great revolution in ships and shipbuilding. Despite the experiments of Robert Fulton and the strides in American steam-driven railroad trains, American ship builders were slow to make the transition from sail to steam. This was due partly to a reluctance of New England yards to abandon their prized clipper ships and of American shipmasters to believe that the newfangled steam could replace the glorious white-winged sailing ship; partly to the difficulty of changing a long and proud tradition of design and building concepts.

In any case, England again gained ascendancy in the realm of the sea and ships. In England from 1860 to 1870, the great transition from wood to steel and sail to steam took place, for at that time the iron and steel industries themselves were 50 years farther advanced than they were in the United States. As a result of these factors the American shipbuilding industry steadily declined. Only during World Wars I and II did U.S. shipbuilding revive sufficiently to challenge Britain's preeminent position. In 1917, when Germany's submarines were threatening to destroy the world's merchant shipping, the United States entered the war and immediately stirred its shipyards to feverish activity. Although they turned out more than 2,000 ships in a period of about two years, American ship builders slumped into the doldrums as soon as the war ended.

To stimulate the industry Congress passed the Merchant Marine Act of 1936, establishing a program to build 500 vessels in a 10-year period. The intent was for the Federal government to pay approximately half the cost of the construction of ships that could be quickly converted to military use. However, shortly after this program got under way, World War II brought about a situation almost identical to that of 1917. As in the first World War, mass-production techniques were applied; welding was used in place of riveting, and huge subassemblies were prefabricated in separate plants and brought together for final assembly in the shipyards. From 1941 through '46, the American shipbuilding industry surpassed all previous historical records and reached a miraculous peak production of twelve and a half million gross tons in 1943.

The feast or famine instability of this industry is illustrated by the fact that from the 1943 peak, American ship production dropped to one hundred thousand gross tons in 1955.

AMERICAN COMPANIES

Largest of U.S. shipbuilding companies, equipped to make almost any type of vessel from small freighters or tankers to the largest luxury liners or aircraft carriers, are such firms as Bethlehem Shipbuilding Corporation, Newport News Shipbuilding and Dry Dock Company, and New York Shipbuilding Corporation. Smaller firms include Bath Iron Works, Sun Shipbuilding and Dry Dock Company (which specializes in oil tankers), and Federal Shipbuilding and Dry Dock Company, a subsidiary of U. S. Steel.

American companies in peacetime are faced with serious and almost insuperable problems, foremost of which is the high cost of U.S. labor. Because shipbuilding has not been extensively mechanized, the cost of constructing a major vessel is prohibitive in comparison with foreign competition. To operate a ship under the United States flag costs more than it does for any other nation of the world. For example, monthly wages on a Norwegian ship are less than one-fourth those paid to an American crew on the same type of vessel.

To help combat this problem the Federal government has heavily subsidized shipbuilding activity. American taxpayers sustain about 40% of the cost of most merchant vessels to enable U.S. shipping concerns to compete with foreign companies. At the same time, a trade-in program of obsolete tankers allows companies to sell the government ships 10 or more years old, provided they build replacements in American shipyards.

Fortunately for the shipbuilding concerns, they are not dependent upon merchant shipping alone but are kept active with construction of destroyers, cruisers, aircraft carriers, submarines, and other vessels for the U.S. Navy.

HOW STEEL SHIPS ARE BUILT

Except under the duress of wartime emergencies, ships cannot be mass-produced in the manner of automobiles or even aircraft. Every ship is custom-built to a customer's specifications, and the larger vessels are among the most elaborate and expensive of human creations. A modern ocean liner may be nearly a quarter of a mile long and cost many millions of dollars to build.

Due to its size and complexity, a large ship requires hundreds of drawings, plans, and blueprints before any construction can begin. After engineers have made up the basic designs, a large staff of draftsmen may work for several months on the detailed blueprints for every part of the ship, such as electrical circuits, pipes, power plant, cargo space, staterooms, crew's quarters, and so forth. Engineering of a ship requires specialized knowledge of the stresses and strains to which it is subjected. A ship must be watertight, stable, and so balanced that in rough seas its center of gravity will always return to a normal upright position. These factors are greatly affected by the type of service a ship will be expected to perform: the size and weight of its cargoes, the desired speed, length of voyages, and consequently the amount and kind of fuel

The world's first nuclear-powered merchant ship, "N. S. Savannah," slides down the way at Camden, N.J. The "Savannah" carries a fuel supply sufficient to propel her for more than three years.

it will carry. Designing involves roughly 8% to 10% of the cost of building a ship.

After the blueprints have been completed, they are taken to a vast room called the "mold loft," where large wooden or composition patterns (templates) are made. These full-size patterns are laid out on the floor of the loft. Curving lines of the ship's hull are cut from basswood or pine scantling. Each pattern section serves as a model for a steel plate which must later be precisely and accurately machined. Symbols marked on the templates indicate the type of steel to be used, thickness of the plate, and where it is to be joined in the ship's assembly.

Next, the templates go to a fabricating plant, known as the "plate-and-angle" shop where steel parts are shaped and machined to conform with the patterns. Plates, which must be bent to sharp angles or curves, are heated in furnaces until they are sufficiently soft to be worked. Some pieces are joined into large sections by riveting or welding before being sent to the ways for final assembly. In the forge shop and foundry, meanwhile, propellers, engine parts, and other working parts are being made and machined.

ASSEMBLING A SHIP

As every school child knows, the first step in ship assembly is called "laying the keel," but few people know exactly what this means or how it is done. After the timbering, or scaffolding, has been erected on the "way," keel plates are laid along a series of wooden supports called keelblocks. Next, the vertical keel, a long girder which extends the entire length of the hull, is put in place. Generally the keel is laid on a slope, with the stern end toward the water at a lower level than the forward end, to facilitate launching. The keel is constructed in the form of an I-beam: the bottom horizontal plate being known as the "keel proper," the vertical keel providing the upright portion of the beam, and the top horizontal plate forming the "keelson."

After the keel is placed, often with prefabricated portions of the side plates attached, vertical girders are welded at each end. These are the "stempost" and "stern-post." Next, curved girders, or "ribs," are attached to each side of the keel and along its entire length, while various steel plates for the shell of the hull are brought from the plate-and-angle shop. Transverse beams are joined between each pair of ribs to give them support, as well as to provide a base for the deck. Working from amidships, the construction crew builds outward toward each end. Gradually the ship's skin of steel plates is laid over the ribs and skeleton framework and the hull begins to take shape. Engines are installed, along with propeller shafts and their supporting "thrust blocks." As the riveting of overlapping, inch-thick steel plates on a large vessel proceeds, the noise is deafening. However, the trend nowadays is toward welding of sections, many of which are brought to the ways as subassemblies already prefabricated.

On the inside surface of the ribs, a second inner skin is fastened, forming a "double bottom." This increases the strength and seaworthiness of the ship. It also provides a storage space between the inner and outer skins for ballast, fuel oil, and water.

Designing a ship involves 8% to 10% of total cost. This view shows only part of the drafting rooms at New York Shipbuilding Corporation.

Under construction in the building dock is the "U.S.S. Kitty Hawk." Workmen of 30 to 40 trades are involved in constructing a large ship.

Crosswise partitions, known as bulkheads, are built inside the hull. The watertight compartments thus formed help to prevent a ship from sinking should a part of the hull be pierced. In some cases, watertight doors in bulkheads are electrically controlled from upper decks.

While the main framework is being assembled, wiring, steam pipes, and other installations are put in place by workmen who swarm over the scaffolds. In the course of the construction, between 30 and 40 different trades will be represented.

When the hull is ready to be floated, the launching takes place. This is done by removing the keelblocks, thus allowing the ship to slide majestically down the way and into the water. At this point, the vessel is by no means completed. The fitting out often requires more time than does the initial hull construction. In a special berth called the fitting-out basin, interior painting, furnishings, and fixtures are added. Finally the vessel is ready for her trial run.

FUTURE OF AMERICAN SHIPBUILDING

As mentioned earlier, U.S. shipbuilding seems destined to suffer long periods of quiescence, although government contracts and various forms of subsidy will undoubtedly serve to keep the industry alive. Despite some rather gloomy predictions there are encouraging signs. The maiden trip of the "Savannah," the world's first nuclear-powered merchant ship, from the New York Shipbuilding Corporation's yards in Camden, N.J., on January 31, 1962, was a portent of a new era in American shipbuilding and shipping. This cargo-passenger vessel costing fifty million dollars had been launched in July 1959, fourteen months after the laying of her keel. Designed to carry 60 passengers, a crew of 110, and 10,000 tons of dry cargo, the "Savannah" is 595 ft. long and has a 22,000-ton displacement. Her power plant is a pressurized water atomic reactor encased with six inches of lead and twelve inches of a plastic material. The reactor's lower half is surrounded by four feet of concrete. The nuclear power plant will furnish 74,000 thermal kilowatts to produce steam needed to drive a turbine propulsion system developing 20,000 horsepower. (See *Power*) She carries a fuel supply sufficient to propel her for more than three years.

Forerunners of such atomic merchant ships were the miraculous nuclear-powered submarines built by General Dynamics Corporation's Electric Boat Division at Groton, Conn. The first of these was the "Nautilus," completed in 1955. This was followed by more advanced types including "Seawolf," "Skate," "Skipjack," "Triton," "George Washington," and "Patrick Henry." Others have been built to carry and launch Polaris missiles and to find and destroy enemy submarines beneath the surface.

The trend in passenger, dry cargo, and oil-tank vessels has been toward greater size and speed, and with the perfection of nuclear power plants speeds of more than 20 knots will be considered commonplace, where only a few years ago, 14 or 15 knots were fast for cargo vessels. As the efficiency and safety of ships are increased, it is possible that American-operated vessels may once again be in a position to compete with foreign shipping lines, but the problem of costs remains a serious one.

A section of the main machine shop of a large shipbuilding company, equipped with standard and specialized machine tools. Work ranges from turbine blades weighing a few ounces to machinery parts weighing 100 tons.

THE U.S. MERCHANT FLEET

The U.S. merchant fleet consists of vessels engaged in coastal, Great Lakes, and river trade, as well as international commerce on the seas. There are more than 3,000 vessels larger than 1,000 gross tons, including an oil tanker fleet of about 400 ships. Three groups of ocean-going ships ply domestic ports: first, those in service between Atlantic ports, Pacific ports, and between Atlantic and Gulf ports; second, those traveling between Atlantic-Gulf ports and the Pacific Coast via the Panama Canal; third, those serving Puerto Rico, Hawaii, Alaska, and other offshore territories.

There is, likewise, an important amount of shipping on the Great Lakes, where between 350 and 400 American vessels are largely engaged in carrying ore, grain, coal, and other raw materials. Because the size of ships engaged in Great Lakes-ocean trade is limited to the capacity of canal locks through which vessels must pass to and from the St. Lawrence River, the United States and Canada have cooperated in enlarging the waterway between Lake Erie and Montreal. This system, known as the St. Lawrence Seaway, has greatly increased the scope of American shipping by giving seagoing cargo vessels access to the Great Lakes ports.

Meanwhile, river shipping has greatly increased on America's inland waterways in recent years. In the years between 1940 and 1955, ton-miles of boat traffic on the Mississippi River more than tripled, while industrial growth along this mighty river stream and its tributaries (a system of more than 7,500 miles of navigable channels) has been phenomenal.

Viewing the U.S. shipbuilding and shipping industries as a whole, the latter half of the twentieth century seems to hold more promise than did any peacetime period since before the Civil War. It is to be hoped that continued progress in ship design, construction and propulsion systems, improvements in American inland waterways, and harbor facilities will signal a new era for this vitally important activity.

26 Missiles and Rocketry

A Martin SM-68 Titan missile roars upward from Cape Canaveral Missile Test Annex. A data cassette was recovered from the nose cone after its reentry and recovery during this highly successful test.

In one sense it may appear strange to include a chapter on missiles under the heading of transportation. Rocketry has been so intimately associated with weapons and push-button warfare that it is sometimes difficult to think of the missile as a vehicle for transporting people and freight. Yet the time for interplanetary transportation is approaching, and it is by no means inconceivable that rocket flights halfway around the earth will one day carry passengers, mail, and cargo.

The underlying principle of rocketry is Sir Isaac Newton's third law of motion: For every action, there is an equal and opposite reaction. Long before Sir Isaac Newton's time, the jet propulsion principle had been observed and even put to use. (See *Power*) It is believed that the Chinese had fireworks 5,000 years ago, but in any case, an actual document tells of rockets being used in 1232 during the Mongol siege of the city of Kaifeng. The chronicler tells of an "arrow of flying fire," propelled by rocket power instead of by a bow. About three centuries later, in 1500, a Chinese scholar attempted to fly by means of rockets. Wanhu carried two paper kites, one in each hand, and sat in a chair to which 47 rockets had been attached. At a signal, assistants ignited the fuses and Wanhu took off. Unfortunately he was never seen again.

The father of modern rocketry was an American, Robert H. Goddard, who stated to the amazement and incredulity

149

of the public in 1920 that a rocket capable of soaring from the earth to the moon is feasible. Goddard had tried to send a gas-filled aluminum balloon into the upper atmosphere as early as 1898. In 1926, using liquid propellants, he developed a rocket motor and was the first to work out a practical system of multistage rockets. Despite the fact that he was ridiculed and ignored by most people, his research resulted in more than 150 patents, and since his death in 1945, he has become recognized as the world's greatest rocket pioneer.

Had American military men paid more attention to Dr. Goddard's work, they would doubtless have been farther advanced in rocketry than they are today. It was the Germans with their V-2 rockets during World War II, who set the stage for later intercontinental missiles and space exploration.

On October 4, 1957, the first man-made satellite was fired successfully into orbit around the earth. This Sputnik, or "baby moon," was a Russian not an American device, and it signaled the beginning of a great race for the moon between the two powers. John H. Glenn's historic triple orbit of the earth and successful reentry on February 20, 1962, contributed greatly to narrowing the gap in this race, though the odds still favored Russia to be first on the moon.

HOW ARE ROCKETS PROPELLED?

Unlike airplanes, rockets do not need air in order to move forward but can travel in a vacuum or in empty space beyond earth's atmosphere. Many people still wonder how a missile can be propelled when there is "no air to push against," but Newton's law explains this. In a rocket engine, the explosion of burning fuel exerts force in all directions, but because the outer shell of the rocket prevents side thrust, the explosion must push in only two directions: backward to allow exhaust gas to escape, forward to propel the vehicle. A rocket flies solely by the pressure of its exhaust.

Modern rocket engines use various types of liquid fuel, such as kerosene-and-lox and hydyne. Various combinations of liquid and solid fuels have been tried in order to attain greater thrust. Hydrazine hydrate, used as a fuel, may be combined with nitric acid which supplies oxygen for efficient combustion. The problem is to find fuels which burn with tremendous exhaust velocity. Present research by rocket engineers working in aircraft company laboratories, the National Aeronautics and Space Administration (NASA), and at such firms as General Electric, RCA, Westinghouse, Du Pont, and the large chemical companies, is concentrated on three main types of rocket engines: chemical, nuclear, and electric.

Chemical systems are the ones now in use, and while they have been greatly improved, their potential thrust is limited to the energy content of the fuel and its oxidizer.

A nuclear rocket will differ from chemical rockets in having a nuclear reactor as a means of heating chemical fuels to velocities two or three times greater than is possible with hydrogen and oxygen combustion systems.

Ultimately, for deep-space missions, electric rockets using ion propulsion systems are expected to produce jet velocities up to two hundred thousand miles per hour. In an ion rocket engine, the propellant is given a positive charge, or is "ionized," after which it is passed through an electrostatic field. This serves to speed up the positively charged propellant. In order to generate sufficient electrical energy for such an engine, a nuclear reactor will provide heat for a turbine-driven electric generator.

BUILDING ROCKETS AND MISSILES

Like the aircraft industry, rocket construction is so complex and requires so many thousands of parts that many industries contribute to the final product. However, the aircraft companies do most of the final assembly, and as one industry spokesman has put it, aircraft manufacturers seem to be "researching themselves out of existence." For as spacecraft and missiles take the place of military aircraft, the entire aircraft industry must undergo drastic changes, possibly with two industries emerging: one devoted entirely to the building of commercial transports and private airplanes; the other, to military missiles and spacecraft.

At the moment, though, missile building comprises a segment of the aircraft industry. (See *Aviation*)

The link between aircraft and rockets is the X-15 rocket-propelled airplane. Developed for the purpose of testing manned space flight prior to actual orbital or inter-

Launcher tube sections for Polaris missiles are shown in the assembly area of a Westinghouse plant, where research and development of launching and handling systems for future Polaris submarines are being carried on.

Astronaut Alan Shepard, inside his space capsule, is surrounded by complex electronic devices.

of the most precise timing mechanisms, cameras, radio and television transmitters, and hundreds of complicated controls. Compared to its instrumentation and telemetry, the rocket's fuel tanks and engine are simplicity itself, yet the instrumented nose or capsule of a rocket may comprise less than 5% of its total bulk and weight. In order to carry a single pound free of earth's gravity, 10 to 15 lb. of fuel must be consumed by chemical rocket engines.

To achieve greater efficiency, rocket engineers are working on two problems simultaneously: improving the efficiency of propellants and propellant systems and reducing the weight of the ship. Not only may lighter materials be used to achieve this objective, but the electronics industry's progress in miniaturization of instruments has been accelerated by the demand for compact, lightweight rocket controls. (See *Machinery*) Tiny printed electrical circuits, transistors, and micromodules make it possible to pack the most amazing collection of instruments into a capsule the size of a basketball. In the field of instrumentation and scientific study of space American rocketry appears to be well ahead of Russian. Possibly, therefore, Russia's early lead in propulsion systems may prove to be a blessing in disguise, as it has forced U.S. technicians to find ways of reducing the sizes and weights of pay loads in order to make the most of the available American rocket engines.

IMPORTANT AMERICAN MISSILES

The U. S. arsenal of military missiles is made up of many specialized rockets, each designed for a specific type of mission. Best known of these are the Jupiter, Thor,

planetary flights, this rocket ship has reached altitudes of 32 miles and speeds over 3,300 miles per hour. It is designed to soar into space 100 to 150 miles above the earth at 4,500 miles an hour. The plane is launched from under the wing of a B-52 bomber after the mother ship attains an altitude of about 40,000 ft. A rocket engine, with some 55,000 lb. of thrust, rapidly propels the X-15 beyond the earth's 20-mile atmospheric layer. After the fuel is exhausted, the pilot guides the plane back to the Air Force base for a landing.

Because air friction creates tremendous heat as the X-15 reenters the atmosphere, it was necessary to find new materials for its superstructure. A special steel alloy, known as Iconel-X, has been used for this purpose. Skin temperature is raised to 1,200° F. by aerodynamic heating during the reentry.

While these experiments in manned space flight proceed, NASA continues to prepare orbital flights and to plan for unmanned and later manned flights to the moon and beyond.

Since the cost of such programs is immense and since there is no possibility of any commercial return on the investment in the foreseeable future, space projects are at present financed by the Federal government. But private industry is doing the actual work of designing, engineering, and construction, with the result that a vast and complex industry for rocket and missile manufacturing has come into being within the past few years. One of the most important aspects of this work is in the field of electronics and instrumentation, for a rocket's pay load is a package

Major components of the Tiros III weather satellite are spread out on a table beneath the satellite itself as an inspector checks the parts at the RCA Astro-Electronics Division in Princeton, N. J.

Titan, Atlas and Dyna-Soar long-range missiles, and the Polaris, used for launching from nuclear submarines. There are also a large number of smaller ground-to-air anti-aircraft missiles, such as the family of Nike rockets, air-to-air, air-to-ground and ground-to-ground missiles. Currently attempts are being made to develop an effective antimissile missile.

PEACEFUL EXPLORATION OF SPACE

The most intriguing possibilities of rocketry are in the peaceful exploration of space. So new is this realm of science and the industry supporting it that its future can be only a matter of pure speculation. There is little question, however, that it will provide one of the most dramatic chapters in human history.

Among the early results of sending unmanned satellites into orbit are these: the discovery of radiation belts; mapping of the geomagnetic field; discovery that the earth is slightly pear shaped; new knowledge of the earth's heat balance; solar effects on the upper atmosphere; electron distribution in the upper ionosphere. Such scientific information has been sent to earth by the Vanguard, Explorer, and Discoverer satellites. By measuring reflected and reradiated energy from earth, the atmosphere, and clouds, meteorologists have gained new insight into heating and cooling processes which affect the weather. Important new information about the moon is being gathered, and within a very few years men will be getting such information first hand as they travel to the moon and explore its surface and subsurface. Knowledge thus gained could conceivably unlock the secret of the formation of the entire solar system.

Meanwhile, the United States and Canada are developing orbiting astronomical and geophysical observatories. These giant satellites, some weighing several thousand pounds, will contain optical systems to study the universe, as well as many different types of instruments for reporting data from 40,000 to 50,000 miles in deep space.

The most immediate practical results of space probes are improved weather forecasting and the work being done by the communications industries. (See *Telegraph, Telephone*) On April 1, 1960, the Tiros I satellite began transmitting pictures of the earth's cloud cover. Some of these photographs encompassed areas of five hundred thousand square miles. Within six hours after the pictures were taken, they were being studied, and the resulting analysis forwarded by facsimile transmission to the National Meteorological Center of the U.S. Weather Bureau at Suitland, Md. A second Tiros satellite was launched in November, 1960, and the program of weather satellites continues to represent a major revolution in meteorological forecasting techniques.

Meanwhile, Echo satellites demonstrated the practicability of world-wide communications by means of reflecting or retransmitting very high-frequency radio signals, "bouncing" them from the satellites to distant points on the earth. So successful were the first Echo tests that the Bell Telephone System is preparing to finance a system of communications satellites as a commercial venture.

Echo I was a sphere 100 ft. in diameter, launched by

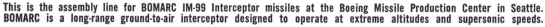

This is the assembly line for BOMARC IM-99 Interceptor missiles at the Boeing Missile Production Center in Seattle. BOMARC is a long-range ground-to-air interceptor designed to operate at extreme altitudes and supersonic speeds.

The first unmanned Mercury spacecraft to orbit the earth made this Super Anscochrome of the West African Coast, from the Strait of Gibraltar to Cape Juby, Morocco. Cloud cover hangs close to the coastal area and the Atlantic Ocean appears in the top left of the picture. Astronauts Glenn and Carpenter saw views like this as their capsules orbited the earth at about 17,500 miles per hour.

folding it inside a 26-in.-diameter container. Once in space, a sublimating powder inside the satellite evaporated and inflated the sphere. Among the industrial firms which contributed to this experiment were General Mills Corporation, which developed cutting processes for the Du Pont Mylar, of which the sphere was made; and the G. T. Schjeldahl Corporation, which worked out a method of joining the pieces together. Meanwhile, Bell Telephone Laboratory at Holmdel, N.J. had developed a new powerful transmitter and receiving system in cooperation with NASA.

Newer Echo spheres are made of two layers of aluminum foil ¼-thousandth of an inch thick on either side of a ⅓-thousandth inch thick sheet of Mylar plastic. It is planned to put a number of these 140-foot diameter spheres into orbit simultaneously to provide a complete communications network.

A more advanced, "active," satellite relay station is being built by the Radio Corporation of America. This will contain a transmitter powered by the sun through solar batteries.

While the United States puts these instrumented packages into orbit for scientific and technical purposes, the giant rockets and future spaceships are gradually taking form. The names Saturn C-1, Saturn C-2, Nova, Centaur and Apollo signify man's ultimate flights to the planets. An idea of the scope of future rocket construction may be gained by statistics on the Saturn rockets which are expected to carry men to the moon and possibly to Mars. One version of the Saturn stands 18 stories high. Its fuel and oxygen system includes eight tanks 70 in. in diameter, clustered around a central tank 105 in. in diameter. The booster has 8 Rocketdyne kerosene-oxygen engines, *each* of which develops 188,000 lb. of thrust. Compared to the Atlas, which furnishes 360,000 lb. of thrust, the Saturn has a thrust of one and one-half million pounds. Saturn C-3 will be twice as powerful as that!

To build vehicles of this kind will require the utmost resources of industry and science. It is too early to predict exactly how the rocket industry will develop, or what commercial uses will be made of space technology. But the probabilities are, judging from lessons of the past, that the wildest guesses will look mild by comparison to what actually takes place. It is safe to assume that even the most imaginative space scientists will be surprised by what comes of their efforts.

153

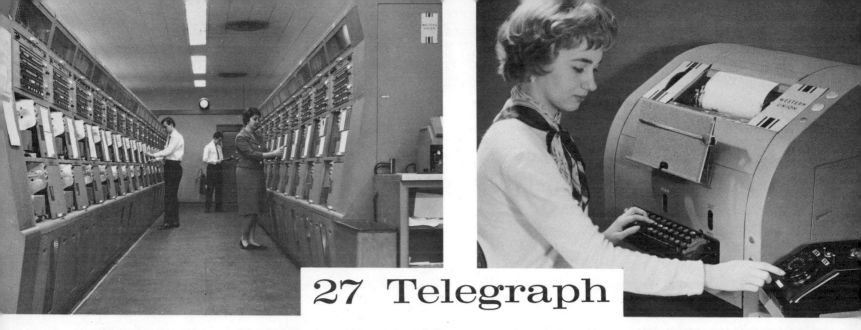

27 Telegraph

Aisle view of the New York Center of the "Bank Wire," through which over 25,000 messages are transmitted daily to and from other switching centers on the network.

By Western Union's new "dial-direct" Telex system, subscribers may send messages to any point on the network by dialing another subscriber's number.

The communities of the world have been tied together by so many highway networks that today the expression, "It's a small world," is literally true. There are concrete highways for automobiles and trucks, air lanes for thousands of plane flights, shipping lanes across the seas, and steel highways for the railroads. And there are the millions of miles of wire, the highways of electrical communication over which messages may be flashed around the earth in a fraction of a second. With the telegraph and the telephone, mankind overcame the limitations of time and space and found a way to communicate instantly with almost any part of the globe. Now we are learning to use pathways through outer space for the transmission of messages.

Although Samuel Finley Breese Morse is credited with the invention of a practical telegraph, Roger Bacon as long ago as 1267 pondered using electricity for distant communication. He was put in jail for dabbling in black magic. In 1726 an Englishman named Wood proved that electricity could be conveyed through metal, and only a few years afterward men were sending electrical impulses through several hundred feet of metal wire. André Ampere demonstrated a way to signal the 26 letters of the alphabet by placing magnetic needles at the ends of 26 wires, and a captain in the Russian army, Baron Schilling, actually made a working telegraph in 1820.

There were others who had built electric telegraphs before Morse. But in 1832, Samuel Morse conceived of the "dot and dash" principle of transmitting messages. With a small salary from New York University where he was a professor of the Literature of the Arts of Design, he rented rooms in Washington Square where he built his first telegraph instrument. He used an ordinary pencil on a pendulum to produce the dots and dashes of his new code.

Following a demonstration in 1837, Morse received financial backing from Alfred Vail, who became his assistant. When his improved instruments were shown to President Van Buren and his cabinet, congressmen called

it a "crazy scheme." At last, however, Morse succeeded in getting Congress to appropriate money for an experimental telegraph line. This was in 1843. The following year, on May 24, 1844, over the line which had been built between Baltimore and Washington, the famous first message was transmitted: What hath God wrought!

When government officials decided that the project could never serve any practical commercial purpose, Morse sought private capital and succeeded in raising enough funds through the sale of stock to extend the line to New York in 1846. Then he licensed others to build telegraph lines connecting a number of eastern cities. Lines were generally strung along the routes of railroad tracks, and today, most of the nation's two and a half million miles of telegraph wire follow the railroad lines. (See *Railroading*)

FORMATION OF WESTERN UNION

Until 1851, telegraphy was carried on by about 50 independent companies whose service was dubious and whose finances were shaky. In order to consolidate service on a national scale, Hiram Sibley used the resources of the New York and Mississippi Valley Printing Telegraph Company to buy out the smaller firms. In 1856, Ezra Cornell, whose line was one of those purchased, proposed the name Western Union Telegraph Company.

As thousands of people moved into the vast new western territories, the need for long-distance communication in America became so great that Western Union began to plan for a transcontinental line. Mail, carried by ship and across the Isthmus of Panama, was over a month in transit from coast to coast, and although stagecoach mail was a little faster, it was unreliable. For a brief period of 16 months, in 1860-61, the Pony Express carried mail and telegrams between St. Joseph, Mo. and Sacramento, Calif., a distance of 1,400 miles in eight days. But Western Union was stringing its telegraph wires in an effort to link the East and West Coasts. From the east, Edward Creighton supervised the construction, while James Gamble built eastward from California. When the two construction crews met and joined their lines at Salt Lake City on October 24, 1861, the romantic days of the Pony Express came to an end.

For many years, Western Union continued to extend its service and to acquire independent lines. Finally, in 1943, the company absorbed the last of its competitors, Postal Telegraph, Inc. Like the telephone, telegraph communication must be unified in order to provide efficient service on a national scale.

HOW THE MODERN TELEGRAPH WORKS

Until the early part of the twentieth century, the Morse key sender to produce dots and dashes was used for most telegraphic messages, but now telegrams are transmitted by automatic printing and facsimile methods, such as the teleprinter and Desk-Fax. Operators use letter keyboards similar to those on typewriters. Each time an operator taps the keyboard, holes are punched in a paper tape: these code holes represent letters of the alphabet. Written letters also appear along the top of the tape. As the perforated tape moves through an automatic transmitter, the letters are instantly flashed to an electronic brain in the nearest message center. This machine, guided by the coded tape, automatically selects a circuit over which the message will travel. Seconds later the words are being recorded at their destination. At the receiving end, machines print the messages on paper tapes which are then pasted to the familiar yellow blanks for delivery.

The teleprinter machines are designed to transmit electrical impulses over wires to the printers at the other end of the line. Thousands of teleprinters are in use in business offices, newspapers and magazine-publishing firms; many large companies lease private wire systems from Western Union. In offices which do not have teleprinters, call boxes are often employed. Turning a small handle signals the nearest Western Union office that a messenger is wanted.

New Telex machines can be used to dial direct to other subscribers in the network, making it possible to transmit written messages in the same manner as a dial is used with the telephone. After dialing the desired number, the sender uses a typewriter keyboard to compose the message. Telex subscribers also can get direct connections with subscribers in nearly every country in the world.

Telefax is a machine used to transmit handwritten or typed messages telegraphically. When a message is inserted into the machine, it is scanned by an electric eye as it moves around a revolving cylinder. The Telefax transmits the markings on the paper over a wire to a receiving instrument which makes an exact copy of the original. The same principle is used to transmit "wirephotos" for newspapers. A compact adaptation of the Telefax used in many thousands of modern business offices is Western Union's Desk-Fax. This electronic messenger sends and receives messages in facsimile form automatically. It is operated by pushing buttons for outgoing and incoming messages.

MICROWAVE BEAM

Telegraphic communication makes extensive use of radio beams which carry over 1,000 messages simultaneously in each direction. Western Union has constructed a network of radio beam towers, about 100 ft. in height (some as high as 300 ft.) and spaced 25 to 30 miles apart, so that microwaves, or short radio waves, flash instantly from tower to tower until they reach their destination. Since microwaves travel in a straight line, they will not follow the curvature of the earth. For this reason, relay points are needed. The waves are "bounced" from large, saucer-like reflectors with radio antennae in the centers.

With the launching of communications satellites in space, long-range microwave communication will be possible, the messages being beamed at the satellites and reflected back to points halfway around the globe.

Messages transmitted by microwave may ultimately be used in nearly all long-distance telegraphic communication. This system, in addition to multiplying the number of messages which can be transmitted simultaneously, also has the obvious advantage of eliminating interruptions in service due to storm breaks in the wire lines.

TELEGRAPHY NOW AND TOMORROW

Western Union operates many millions of miles of telegraph channels which handle nearly two hundred million telegrams and ten million telegraphic money orders annually. This does not include the hundreds of millions of messages and data transmitted over the private wire systems of large firms, the government and the armed forces. The company owns 26,600 nautical miles of ocean cable, 21,000 offices and agencies. Its service to leading stock exchanges involves the use of over 3,500 quotation tickers. (See *Finance*) Some 50,000 clocks are electronically synchronized with Naval Observatory Time every hour in 2,000 cities. Telegraphy is used to transmit complex figures to data-processing machines thousands of miles apart; to send letters, orders, requisitions; to duplicate documents with photographic accuracy; to transmit railroad Pullman and reserved coach tickets from one station to another via "Ticketfax" (See *Railroading*); to send candy with telegraphic messages by the transmission of "Candygrams"; to wire orders for flowers from one city to another. Among the special services offered by Western Union are "singing telegrams" for birthdays or other anniversaries, "wake-up telegrams" for heavy sleepers, and a hotel-motel telegraphic reservation service.

A brilliant future is assured to communications engineers and technicians, for telegraphy, today, involves more than the transmission of wire telegrams. Western Union now offers private wire, alternate voice and record service and will soon introduce a new record and voice service called "broadband switching," providing instantaneous, direct customer-to-customer connections which can be used for transmitting voice as well as data, facsimile, or other types of record communication. Western Union is today a complete telecommunications company. Complex modern instruments require service technicians and repairmen, operators, experts in radio and electronics. In the dawning space age, telegraphy, rocketry, and satellite instrumentation are all closely allied, for it is in the communications industries that space technology will probably have its first and most important commercial applications.

A central office switchman is shown installing a wire connection on a translator frame, part of the automatic message accounting equipment needed to identify automatically the calling station's telephone number.

28 Telephone

The name of Bell is so intimately associated with the telephone industry that it almost seems to signify the ringing of a 'phone. That tinkling sound which summons us to speak with a caller who may be hundreds or even thousands of miles away, is jokingly referred to as one of the tyrants of modern living; yet in the vast majority of instances it brings good tidings: a business order, a friendly call, or news from some loved one.

For centuries, men had only dreamed of being able to communicate over many miles, and with the invention of the telegraph in 1837, it appeared to many that the ultimate in long-range communication had been reached. But Alexander Graham Bell had a still greater concept. He believed he could make a mechanical eardrum to transmit spoken words electrically. Bell, a teacher of elocution and a student of electricity, began working with thin strips of spring steel and, in 1875, created a transmitter which sent sound vibrations to a receiver. His first idea was to improve on the telegraph so that by means of complex vibrations, several messages could be transmitted simultaneously over a single wire. During his experiments with the "harmonic telegraph," he developed a speaking instrument. On March 10, 1876, he succeeded in telling his assistant in another room, "Mr. Watson, come here, I want you." Nearly 40 years later, in 1915, when the first transcontinental telephone line was put into operation, Bell transmitted the same message from New York to Thomas Watson who was listening in San Francisco.

Marvelous as the instrument proved to be, Bell's telephone was nearly ignored by judges at Philadelphia's Centennial Exposition, in the summer of 1876. Not until the emperor of Brazil listened in the receiver while Bell talked at the other end of the line did anyone realize that here was perhaps the greatest invention in an age of great inventions.

HOW THE TELEPHONE WORKS

According to Thomas Watson, Alexander Bell came to him for technical advice at the electrical workshop where he was employed. "If I could make a current of electricity vary in intensity," Bell later told Watson, "precisely as the air varies in density during the production of a sound, I should be able to transmit speech telegraphically."

This basic principle had been formulated by Bell during his work as a professor of Vocal Physiology at Boston University. Yet for several months, he and Watson were unable to make instruments that would produce the desired result. The great breakthrough came on June 2, 1875. At that time, Bell discovered that, when a section of magnetized spring steel in contact with an electrical circuit was made to vibrate over the pole of its magnet, it produced a current of electricity that varied in the same way as the air density was varying within hearing distance of the humming spring.

Thus, as sound waves cause air molecules to dance and to make the ear drum vibrate, the same sound waves set up vibrations on the diaphragm of a telephone transmitter. Behind the diaphragm in a modern transmitter is a tiny chamber filled with granules of carbon. When these carbon granules are more or less compressed by the "bouncing" of the diaphragm, they transmit corresponding impulses of electricity through the connecting wires. At the receiver end of the line, the dancing electrons cause the receiver diaphragm to reproduce identical vibrations.

In the receiver is a thin iron diaphragm and a small electromagnet. If the electric impulse is strong, the magnet pulls the diaphragm toward itself. As the impulse weakens, the diaphragm springs away from the magnet. In this way, the vibrating diaphragm transmits its sound vibrations to the listener. Naturally the action is at the speed and frequency of the original sound vibrations.

GROWTH OF THE GREAT BELL SYSTEM

Alexander Graham Bell was not himself enough of an electrical technician to carry his marvelous invention beyond its primitive beginning, but like all great inventors he had the vision to see the potentialities of his creation. In 1878, only three years after he had made his first talking instrument, Bell said, "It is conceivable that cables of telephone wires could be laid underground or suspended overhead, communicating by branch wires with private dwellings, country houses, shops, manufactories, etc., uniting them through the main cable with a central office where the wire could be connected as desired, establishing direct communication between any two places in the city. . . . Not only so, but I believe . . . a man in one part of the country may communicate by word of mouth with another in a different place."

In 1875, Bell signed an agreement with two backers, Thomas Sanders of Haverhill, Mass. and Gardiner G. Hubbard of Cambridge, Mass., to form the Bell Patent Association. A patent application on improved telegraph instruments was filed in the Patent Office in Washington on March 6, 1875, and the patent was issued a month afterward, covering his improvements in transmitters and receivers for electric telegraphs. Then, in 1876 he patented his speech transmission instruments. As other patents quickly followed, the Bell Patent Association became the nucleus of a new industry.

On July 9, 1877, the telephone business was legally established when the Bell Telephone Company, with Gardiner G. Hubbard, Trustee, was formed. Thomas Watson was employed to handle the early technical work of making the invention commercially practical. Though he had no scientific education, Watson superintended the making of telephone instruments and solved many of the early operational problems. Under Hubbard's business management, the new company established a leasing and licensing system whereby telephones were leased, not sold, to users. Although the original ownership of the company was divided equally between Bell, Hubbard, and Sanders, it was soon broken up into 5,000 shares of stock, distributed in varying amounts among the three men, members of their families, and Thomas Watson.

The undertaking was a gigantic one, much too large for the company's limited resources. Sanders, the principal backer, invested a hundred ten thousand dollars before he got a dollar in return. In order to expand the service, Sanders finally interested a group of Massachusetts and Rhode Island businessmen who formed the New England Telephone Company in 1878. With its main office in Boston and a capitalization of two hundred thousand dollars, the new firm was committed to setting up telephone communication in the New England area. Under a licensing agreement, it was to buy its instruments exclusively from the Bell Telephone Company and was not permitted to sell any instruments or equipment to subscribers. The two companies also agreed to cooperate in extending telephone service beyond the confines of New England territory.

By 1879, the National Bell Telephone Company had been set up and the telephone began to emerge as a national utility. The problem, however, was to achieve unified service in a situation where more and more local companies were merely being licensed to use Bell instruments.

Switchboard operators still manually plug in telephone circuits as they did many years ago, though more and more automatic equipment is being installed. At the left, an old-time switchboard, about 1900. At right, a present-day long-distance traffic operator. Shown under her left hand is a multileaf bulletin containing information for her use in push-button dialing (key pulsing) the call to the distant telephone or long-distance office.

TELEPHONE

Bell's chief competitor was the Western Union Telegraph Company. This company owned important telephone developments by Thomas A. Edison and others and established the first telephone exchanges in several cities. Bell interests fought this and won the right to control all telephone business while Western Union continued to operate all public telegraph message service.

It quickly became clear that national telephone service required so vast an operation that complete reorganization of the company was needed to cope with the situation. Under an act of the Massachusetts State Legislature, the American Bell Telephone Company was formed on March 20, 1880. At the end of that year, there were 540 stockholders, 14 of whom held the majority of the shares.

Finally, in 1885 a new company was formed to build long lines connecting various city exchanges. This was the American Telephone and Telegraph Company, which started out as a subsidiary of American Bell, but which today is the mammoth parent firm federated with some 23 associated companies.

THE BELL SYSTEM TODAY

In the telephone federation, each associated company provides local service within a given state or states and is subject to the regulations of those states. Meanwhile, American Telephone and Telegraph, or A.T. and T., coordinates the interconnecting long-distance lines, subject to regulation by the Federal Communications Commission. A.T. and T. maintains the Bell Telephone Labora-

Bell plant department employees pay out telephone cable made by the system's manufacturing arm, Western Electric Co., for underground installation.

tories, Inc., which conducts research and development programs, and it also controls the Western Electric Company, a supply and manufacturing facility for the overall system.

MIRACLE OF THE DIAL

Whenever you make a call to a person whose line connects with a central office other than your own, a special connection must be made between the two central offices, via a trunk line. This connection may be made by an operator in your central office, or by an automatic mechanism. Originally, every call, even one to a next-door neighbor had to be connected by a human operator. When you lifted your receiver, a small light signaled the operator that your line was open. She answered, listened while you gave her the number, and then plugged a cord into the proper line to give you the connection you wanted. Now, except in a few isolated districts, virtually all calls are dialed; even when you wish to signal the operator, it is necessary first to dial "O."

The dial system must do mechanically what the operator does by hand. In order to handle the thousands of telephone calls being made at all hours of the day and night, the dial-switching equipment is necessarily extremely complex. When your receiver is lifted a switch closes and current starts flowing from a central office battery through your line. This surge of current causes an electromagnetic switch at the central office to connect you with the dial mechanism. As the dial turns it clicks once for each digit, sending an electrical pulse through an electromagnet at the central office. The combination of clicks is what directs the dial apparatus to select the proper line for your connection.

The speed of these complex operations is the speed of electricity, and a long-distance telephone line can carry the sound of your voice over thousands of miles in less time than it takes the same sound to travel through the air for half a city square.

With the development of transistors (See *Machinery*)

A cable splicer is shown working on polyethylene insulated conductor cable which contains wires that are color coded. The workman is wearing a safety strap around his waist and climbing spikes on his legs.

which were a product of Bell Laboratories research, more compact apparatus has aided the extension of dial service. Now, long distance dialing is spreading rapidly to include all parts of the country. An electronic "brain" receives the dialed numbers and almost instantly connects and completes the call. Simultaneously another electronic machine records the charges to the customer, punching a paper tape which later will be used for automatic billing.

But this is only the beginning of revolutionary changes which are about to take place in telephonic communications. People, who think sending rockets into space unnecessary, may be the first to complain if their global telephone service gives them bad connections. For it won't be many years before telephone calls and television transmission half way around the world will be handled swiftly and efficiently by active satellites which will relay messages from one land communications network to another. The Echo I balloon satellite, which was launched at Cape Canaveral in August 1960, was the first step toward accomplishing a global network of communication space satellites. Sponsored jointly by the Naval Research Laboratory, National Aeronautics and Space Administration, the Jet Propulsion Laboratory, and the Bell Telephone Laboratories, the Echo project proved conclusively that the idea is practical.

However, Echo I was a passive satellite. It merely reflected signals sent to it from the ground. The active satellites receive signals, amplify them and send them on to another point on earth. During 1962 a number of experimental active satellites are scheduled for testing. These include the following: Telstar, a Bell System experimental satellite being launched in cooperation with NASA; Relay and Syncom, which are NASA sponsored satellites; and Advent, a Department of the Army satellite.

Telstar and Relay will be launched into elliptical orbits ranging between 600 and 3,000 miles. They will relay telephone, telegraph, and television signals, and high-speed data between ground stations in Maine, New Jersey, South

A two-man telephone crew uses an earth auger mounted on a construction truck to dig a hole for a telephone pole.

America, and Europe. Syncom and Advent are the forerunners of a synchronous (22,300 mile high) satellite system. They will transmit telephone signals and data during their tests.

HOW BIG IS BIG?

With all his prophetic vision Alexander Graham Bell could never in his wildest dreams have conceived of the present scope of the telephone industry. Recent figures show that in the entire world there are about one hundred forty-one million telephones, of which nearly eighty million are in North America, and seventy-five million in the United States alone. As a matter of fact, Americans have about 17 times as many telephones in proportion to U.S. population, as the rest of the world. Another interesting fact is that 99% of American phones are privately operated, while in Europe, where there are forty-three million phones, only 17% are privately operated. In 1961, Russia lagged far behind the U.S. in telephones, with only four million instruments in operation. Canada had nearly six million in the same year.

Nearly all the telephones of the world connect with the U.S. Bell System: 100% of those in North America, almost 95% of those in Europe and 90% of the phones in Asia. Bell lines connect with approximately 3,200 independent telephone companies.

So vast a network produces astronomical income figures. The Bell System's operating revenues and other income

This fantastic maze of electrical panels is only a part of Bell Telephone Company's Central Office equipment.

amounted to more than eight billion dollars in 1961. It paid over five billion dollars in operating expenses and one and nine-tenths billion dollars in taxes. Its earnings provided $5.52 per share on more than two hundred thirty-two million shares of A.T. and T. stock outstanding in 1961. The stock was held by more than two million shareholders.

Bell's seven hundred twenty-six thousand employees are engaged in manufacturing, installing, and operating communication facilities. They are planning, inventing, researching, and designing for a future that will undoubtedly make statistics of the 1960's look small.

NEW DEVICES

What does that future hold in store for us? The new developments are coming at such a rapid pace that it is impossible to foresee all the possibilities or to list in a short space what is known to be in planning. But in addition to global communication by means of space satellites, here are a few of the latest developments.

TASI, or Time Assignment Speech Interpolation, is now in use on transatlantic telephone cables. This amazing system can automatically assign channels to voices when a simultaneous conversation on another channel pauses or lags. Within one-millionth of a second, the equipment can shift the voice channels so as to make maximum use of all lines available every second, thus increasing the capacity of existing equipment. The shifting from channel to channel does not interrupt conversation or invade its privacy.

TELPEK service provides for large users of communication between specific points, whether for telephone, teletypewriter, telephotograph, facsimile or high-speed

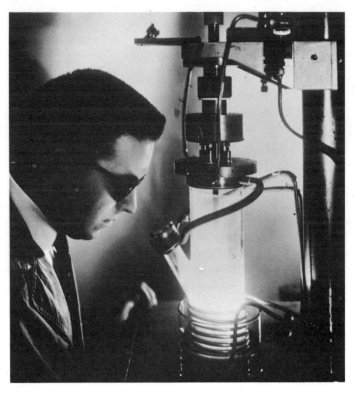

In a Bell laboratory a technician examines apparatus for growing single crystal germanium. A grayish white, metallic element, germanium, is important for making transistors as it is a semiconductor of electricity.

data. It is done by providing broadband channels of various sizes, each of which may be subdivided into a number of narrower channels to fit the customer's specific needs.

Wide area telephone service at a fixed monthly rate connects a customer's line with the nationwide dialing network so that he may make as many long-distance calls as he pleases within a specified area at no extra charge per call. The size of the calling area ranges from nearby states to the entire country, with basic rates varying accordingly.

DATA-PHONE service interconnects business machines by the simple process of dialing a telephone number. In this way, business branch offices in different cities can feed data to a centralized computer or receive data from the central computer. The system can transmit any data code from machines using magnetic tape, punched cards, or paper tape.

New electronic central offices are being built to handle calls at split second speeds. Similar to electronic computers the electronic switching system can store millions of items of information on minute photographic plates, or "memory plates." Among other things, it will automatically dial any one of several, frequently used numbers the moment it receives a simple signal from a caller.

Meanwhile, the former competitors, now the two giants of communications industries, seem to have come full cycle and are once again involved in overlapping services. While Bell offers a form of telegraphic service in its Data-Phone, and Telpek, which can handle various types of silent communication, Western Union is now providing private wire, voice service and alternate voice-record services whereby customers may switch from one type of transmission to another. Telephone equipment and instruments are furnished by Western Union. Contracts, be-

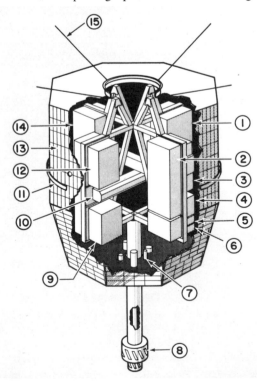

Project Relay active communications satellite, developed at the RCA Space Center, contains these: (1) traveling wave tube power supply, (2) radiation effects experiment, (3) receiver exciter, (4) encoder, (5) decoder, (6) receiver and subcarrier demodulator, (7) radiation sensors, (8) wide-band antenna, (9) receiver and traveling wave tube exciter, (10) traveling wave tube, (11) altitude control coil, (12) traveling wave tube power supply, (13) solar cells, (14) batteries, (15) telemetry antenna.

tween American Telephone and Telegraph Company and Western Union, now provide for the Telegraph Company to lease circuits from the Bell System and for private Western Union voice circuits to be connected with the telephone toll networks and Bell System's general exchange.

While systems and services are rapidly improving and changing, the telephone instrument itself has undergone a major face-lifting. Smooth, simple, compact design has replaced the old-time mouthpiece and receiver. The neat instruments are made in attractive colors to go with virtually any decor. Wall phones are available for use in kitchens or other convenient locations.

For communications between automobiles, trucks, boats, and planes, mobile telephone service is available. Calls from mobile phones can be connected with any other telephone in the network.

Office phones with built-in call selectors make it easy for busy executives to look up and dial frequently used numbers. The new "Rapidial" instrument actually dials the numbers on its selector automatically.

WORLD'S GREATEST INDUSTRIAL LAB

In the opinion of *Fortune* magazine, an opinion shared by many others, Bell Telephone Laboratories, Inc. is the world's most impressive scientific enterprise. It is in the giant research center at Murray Hill, N. J. and in the laboratories in New-York City, Whippany, N.J., and Holmdel, N.J., that tomorrow's wonders of communication are being formulated. With more than 12,000 employees, the Laboratories' costs for research and development, including military, have passed three hundred million dollars per year. Their scientists, engineers, and technicians are engaged in developing new devices and systems for military as well as public telephonic communication. About 500 mathematicians, physicists, chemists and other specialists are performing some of the most brilliant feats in the scientific world. Engineering of the vast, 600-million-dollar DEW (Distant Early Warning) Line, which stretches from Alaska to Baffin Island, was carried out by Bell Laboratories. Television network systems are likewise a part of Bell's responsibilities. (See *Television*) Such brilliant men as Hendrik W. Bode, leading authority on electrical network theory; Walter H. Brattain, one of the three Nobel Prize-winning transistor inventors; and Warren P. Mason, who has gained 159 patents, have made up a scientific "brain trust" second to none in the world.

A 45-year-old electronics expert at Bell Labs, Jack A. Morton, was the creator of an amplifier tube that made Bell's 31,000-mile microwave relay network possible. A crossbar-switching mechanism, which can provide pathways for 20 separate phone conversations, was conceived by A. J. Busch, a Bell engineer. The system is one of the most intricate mechanisms ever built by man.

So it goes. The achievements of Bell Laboratories and the projects now in process are so fantastic as to seem impossible. But the word impossible is unknown to the modern communications scientist.

MAINTENANCE

One of the most colorful aspects of the telephone industry is its remarkable maintenance service which keeps telephone lines in operation through every conceivable weather condition, fires, floods, and other disasters. Along with courageous operators, who have saved many lives at the risk of their own by staying at their posts, maintenance crews repairing broken lines are at work at the very height of storms and floods.

To expedite maintenance the telephone crews are equipped with an amazing variety of tools and machines. From powerful trenching machines that bury telephone cable to delicate instruments for locating broken circuits, the repairmen and linemen have everything science can devise to meet emergencies. Still it is the man himself who must do the work and who must brave blizzards, ice, hurricanes, and fires to keep your telephone line open to every part of the United States and to most of the world as well.

(Left) A mechanical trench digger is used for laying underground telephone cables in a new housing development. **(Right)** Stringing cable from a Telsta truck with electric lift. The telescopic boom is designed to help construction crews work efficiently while minimizing hazards.

One of the largest and most fabulous of modern mechanisms is the Fourdrinier papermaking machine which converts what appears to be a thin stream of milky water into a continuous web of paper. Shown here is the "wet end" of a machine at International Paper Company's Mobile, Alabama mill.

29 Paper

The book you are reading is a miracle of modern technology. Its type was set on typesetting machines, the color plates were made by a complex series of photographic processes, and the printing was done at high speed on giant presses which can control the registration of color with thousandth-of-an-inch accuracy. All of these processes are described in appropriate chapters, but before any printing can be done, there must be material to receive the ink. Most printing is done on paper. Paper in this twentieth century is in such abundant supply and used so widely by millions of people and by all industry, that it is easily taken for granted. Yet papermaking is a complicated process requiring great technological skill, monstrous machines that cover acres of factory floor space, and vast amounts of fuel and power. Modern chemistry has found ways of making paper in a great variety of forms, with surfaces and textures for many purposes. Paper was one of the first synthetic materials to be devised by man, for it is made by breaking down the structures of raw materials and reconstituting them in a new form.

WHO MADE THE FIRST PAPER?

Man with all his inventive genius cannot claim the honor of being the first of earth's creatures to make paper. Millions of years ahead of him, hymenopteron, the paper wasp, was making paper as he does to this day. By chewing up dry wood, he grinds it into tiny fibers, masticates it, and produces a true paper to cover his nest. How he learned to do this is a mystery of nature, and in aeons of time he has never improved upon his own secret process.

Man may have been a slow starter in the paper field, but he has made tremendous strides both in his production methods and in the quality of his product. Centuries before the time of Christ, the Chinese used flattened strips of bamboo and palm leaves for writing and drawing. Ancient Egyptians used the reedy plant called papyrus as a writing material. After cutting the pith of the reed into long strips, they laid the strips side by side, then crosswise, forming a sort of mesh. This was dampened, pressed, or pounded together with a stone and allowed to dry. Several papyrus sheets were then pasted together to form rolls. While the word "paper" is derived from the ancient papyrus, modern papermaking is in no way related to the pressed reeds of early times.

The so-called Oriental "rice paper" was not made of rice but, like papyrus writing sheets, from the soft pith of a Formosan plant. Although the rice kernel itself cannot be used to make paper, the stalks or leaves of the rice plant furnish a paper pulp.

About the beginning of the Christian era, parchment came into use. This was made by soaking the skins of lambs or calves in lime, stretching them on frames and scraping them. Use of parchment and vellum made from animal hides continued through Medieval times, and most of the early Bible manuscripts were written on parchment.

Probably the first true paper was made in the year 105 by Ts'ai Lun in the court of the Chinese emperor Ho Ti. Although silk had been used as a writing material for many years, it was costly, and Ho Ti wanted a more economical substitute. Ts'ai Lun's answer was a paper made from waste silk, hemp, and mulberry bark. He soaked his raw materials in water, beat them to a pulp with a wooden mallet, and spread the mixture onto coarsely woven cloth, which acted as a sieve and allowed the water to drain away. The dried pulp formed a tough sheet, which Ts'ai then rubbed smooth with alum. His process remained a secret of the Chinese court for about 600 years. When Arabs conquered western Asia in 704 they brought the papermaking process back to the Western world, and by the latter part of the twelfth century, papermaking was an active industry in Italy, Spain, and soon afterward in other European countries.

PAPERMAKING IN AMERICA

The American paper industry began with a mill near Philadelphia in 1690. Papermaking was still a laborious hand process, although water power was used to reduce cotton, hemp, and linen rags to pulp in a stamping mill. Ts'ai Lun's use of a coarse cloth mold had been refined somewhat with the introduction of a wire screen stretched within a wooden frame. Workmen dipped the screens into vats of liquid pulp, lifting out enough of the mixture to coat the screen mesh. As the water drained away, the screen was expertly shaken to "felt" the fibers. The "deckle," or wooden frame, was then removed. The screen was turned upside down placing the damp paper pulp against a piece of felt which pulled the fibers away from the screen. After another sheet of felt was used to cover the paper, the procedure was repeated until many layers of felts and paper sheets had reached a depth of 10 or 12 in. Excess moisture was removed by pressure, and finally the paper was hung on racks to dry.

In 1799, a Frenchman named Nicholas-Louis Robert thought of joining a series of screens together to form an endless conveyor, with open vats underneath to catch the water as it drained off. This was the first machine to produce paper in a continuous roll. After five years of experimenting, Robert had no funds to apply for a patent, but then he received a 3,000 franc national award which enabled him to take out a 15-year patent. His employer bought the patent, took it to England where he interested the Fourdrinier brothers, Henry and Sealy, in building a papermaking machine in 1803. Today's largest papermaking machines still have many of the original Fourdrinier features, and the wet end of the paper machine is known to this day as "the Fourdrinier."

From that time forward, basic principles of paper manufacture did not change, though speed and mass production have advanced steadily. Where the Fourdrinier machine could produce 35 ft. of paper per minute, modern giants run off as much as 3,000 ft. per minute in rolls up to 12 ft. wide.

The first Fourdrinier machine to be operated in the United States was built in England and assembled at a plant in Saugerties, N.Y., in 1827. In 1830, an economic depression caused a paper manufacturer in Massachusetts to seek a low cost raw material. He tried waste manila rope and thus started the manufacture of manila paper.

Probably the most important development in papermaking during the nineteenth century came in 1850 when Frederick Gottfried Kellar of Germany studied the work of our old friend, the paper wasp, and determined to find a way of making paper with wood fibers. Up to that time, hemp, linen, and cotton rags had furnished the pulp for paper mills in all countries. With the help of a mechanic named Voelter, Kellar succeeded in grinding up wood into minute fibers and making paper from a pulp which was composed of both ground wood and rag. By 1867, ground-wood paper was being made in America.

Meanwhile experiments were being conducted to reduce wood to pulp by means of chemicals. The earliest patents on this process were taken out by Hugh Burgess, an Englishman, who secured American patents in 1854. The following year the Warren Mill in Maylandville, Pa. was making paper by the soda pulp process. An American chemist, C. B. Tilghman, was experimenting with fats which he put in wooden vats. When he discovered that the wooden bungs in the vats were softened up by the action of the fat solution, causing leakage, he decided to set up a chemical wood pulp mill in 1865. Tilghman registered the first American patent for a chemical wood-pulping process by which he treated the wood with calcium bisulphite and cooked spruce, hemlock, poplar, and willow at 127° C. for about eight hours.

VISITING A MODERN PAPER MILL

Although a great many different kinds of paper are made today, the fundamental steps are much the same in all mills. First there must be a source of pulp. This may be linen or cotton "rag," hard or soft wood, or certain combinations of these raw materials. Nowadays, only certain higher grade papers have a percentage of rag content; wood pulp is the basic ingredient of the great majority

At the wet end of the Fourdrinier machine, a solution of wood pulp, about 99% water, flows from the head box (right) onto a wire screen. Agitation of the screen serves to knit pulp fibers together as water drains away.

In the woodyard of a paper mill, logs are stored in monstrous piles containing several million cubic feet of lumber.

of papers. A recent and important development has been the making of "permanent" paper from wood pulp. This is produced in an alkaline environment. Paper made in this fashion will last at least 300 years under proper conditions.

The story begins with the cutting of trees. (See *Lumbering*) Logs, mountains of them, are stockpiled outside the paper mill in wood yards which may accommodate several million cubic feet of lumber at a time. Log piles a hundred feet high and occupying the space of entire city squares are familiar sights near large paper mills. The supply does not last as long as you might think, for the daily consumption of the mill we are visiting would fill many railroad log cars. Large paper companies have their own carefully reforested tree plantations to supply at least a good portion of their needs.

First, the logs are brought by mechanical conveyors to the wood room. They are cut into uniform lengths and then put into "debarking drums," where they are tumbled against one another with a thunderous noise until the bark has been rubbed and pounded off. Water pressure washes away dirt and loose bark. From the drums they emerge as clean "sticks" ready to be ground or chipped.

Groundwood pulp, used for newsprint and other low-cost papers, is made by subjecting the debarked logs to grinding stones, four or five feet in diameter and revolving at four thousand five hundred feet per minute. Logs are forced by hydraulic or mechanical pressure against the grinders, which are cooled by water. The water also serves to carry off the ground pulp.

Better grades of paper containing longer fibers are made from a pulp derived from wood chips which have been chemically treated. Logs fed into the chippers are broken up into small pieces about three quarters of an inch square. Next the chips are poured into huge "digesters," tanks several stories high where a cooking liquor of calcium bisulphite reduces the wood chips to pure cellulose. The cooking takes about 12 hours. To process 125 tons of *sulphite pulp* requires the burning of 20,000 lb. of sulphur at temperatures of 1,800° F. This produces calcium bisulphite for use in the digesters. (See *Mining*)

Chemical cooking completed, the cellulose mass is discharged into a blow pit where it is broken up into fibers. After cooking liquor has been drained away, the pulp is put through several washings until all impurities have been removed. Samples are taken for careful laboratory scrutiny at every stage of the process.

Next the pulp is bleached white with chloride of lime. It is washed with water after every step of the bleaching, then it enters the "beaters." These large tubs, through which the creamy mass of wood pulp flows like a sluggish river, are equipped with rapidly revolving multi-bladed drums. The bronze blades rotate over a "bed plate" of opposing blades. The action serves to reduce the wood fibers and fray them so that they will lock together and form a strong bond in the paper. This process is known as "fibrillation." Another important result of the beating process is "hydration," or the combining of fibers and water into a gelatinous substance which later serves as an adhesive to hold the interlocked fibers together.

Another type of wood pulp for papermaking is known as *sulphate pulp*. In this case slightly larger chips than those used for sulphite pulp are made from spruce, jack pine, or poplar. About forty tons of wet chips are dumped into the digester and are cooked for three or four hours in a solution of sodium hydroxide and sodium sulphide. The resulting pulp, if unbleached, is a dark brown color and is used in the manufacture of kraft paper.

There are still grades of paper, particularly in the stationery categories, which are "rag content" papers. In some cases the raw material used includes old rags which must be washed, and their dyes removed. However, better quality papers contain a greater proportion of clean, new cuttings of cotton and linen cloth processed from

This view of a Natchez, Mississippi, paper mill woodyard shows the gigantic log piles needed to feed the mill's insatiable appetite for pulp.

Heavy logs are put through a debarking drum, where they are tumbled against one another with a thunderous noise until bark is rubbed and pounded off.

squeeze out still more water, at the same time compressing the fibers of the paper sheet.

A long battery of steam-heated drying cylinders removes the rest of the excess water from the paper web. At this stage, about two pounds of water are removed for every pound of paper produced. Because a vast volume of water is required in paper manufacturing, mills are generally located on deep, swiftly moving streams. Many large mills are found in New England, where timber and water supplies are abundant.

We have followed the course of the paper web through the gigantic machine—a distance greater than the length of a football field—and now we see the finished paper moving through calender rollers which impart a hard, smooth surface to the web. Finally the paper is wound onto a reel. The huge paper rolls, weighing many tons, are automatically lifted off the machine; the web is broken and fed onto a new reel without the machine ever stopping its high-speed production.

the textile trades. These cuttings are carefully sorted by hand according to classifications of fibers. They are cleaned, then cooked under steam pressure in an alkali solution. This softens the threads, separates dye, waxes, starch, and other unwanted materials. As with wood pulp, the rag pulp must be washed, bleached, and beaten until it is broken up into individual fibers. Finally it is pumped through a "wet lap" machine. Here most of the water is removed, leaving a thick "lap" ready to be mixed with wood pulp and made into paper.

THE PAPER MACHINE

We now move into a huge room where a miracle takes place before our eyes, the miracle of what appears to be a stream of water being transformed into a solid, tangible sheet of paper. The pulp, which we have seen made from heavy, four-foot logs, has been washed, bleached, and diluted until it is no more than a thin, milky water solution. Actually it is about 99% water as it flows from the "head box" onto the wire of the machine. This is the Fourdrinier, or "wet end" of the paper machine. At about eye level, we see the milky fluid flowing onto a screen, 15 to 20 ft. wide, which carries the watery pulp toward the press and drier section. As it moves forward, the screen of fine brass or bronze wire is agitated rapidly from side to side. This serves to knit the pulp fibers together as water drains away through the mesh of the screen. After traveling 40 or 50 ft., the "web" begins to form, as the pulp gradually solidifies. It passes under a roller called the "dandy roll." This may impart to the soft web of pulp a water mark, and it provides the surface texture known as "wove" or "laid," depending on whether the roll is covered with woven or parallel wires.

Under the dandy roll are suction boxes which draw off increasing amounts of water. Then the web leaves its supporting wire and for the first time appears as a cohesive sheet of paper. It is still about 80% water, however, and is extremely fragile. The edges are trimmed off by thin jets of water before the web is transferred to a woolen felt which carries it through a series of pressure rollers. These

PAPER FINISHES

Various finishes are put on papers by processes of calendering, embossing, and coating. Clay-coated paper, in a crude hand-applied form, was first made in the United States early in the nineteenth century, to facilitate finer printing of decorative wall paper. The paper-coating process developed slowly throughout the nineteenth and early twentieth centuries. One of the outstanding developments in papermaking during the last 25 years has been the dramatic increase in the use of pigments within and on the surfaces of printing papers, to provide a smoother and more uniform surface for printing. The coatings, made of clay, precipitated chalk, titanium dioxide, zinc oxide, and other pigments, are combined with adhesives such as glue, starch, casein, resins, and cellulose derivatives. Separate coating machines are used for the best grades, but "machine coated" papers are produced by adding the coating as part of the continuous operation of the papermaking machine. On modern equipment, coating

Wood pulp, shown here passing through a beater, flows like a sluggish river while rotary blades serve to reduce the wood fibers and fray them so that they will lock together, forming a strong bond in the paper.

165

In the finishing room of a large paper mill, sheets of paper are stacked and painstakingly inspected before they are wrapped, packed in cases or on wooden skids for shipment.

can be applied to both sides of the web at once. Hot air blasts dry the coating before the paper is wound at the end of the machine.

Printing papers, today, are being made with a much higher percentage of coating material than was the case only a few years ago. In 1929, English finish book paper was 17% pigment and 83% fiber. Today, it is about 23% pigment and 77% fiber.

A new family of papers, called "pigmented papers," has been developed. These are essentially uncoated papers but have a pigment content greater than any previously known uncoated papers. Fully coated papers, some of which are now actually double coated, have pigment contents exceeding 50%. This whole trend of increased pigment content yields papers with greater opacity, smoothness, and a higher degree of printability than ever before.

Various uncoated grades of paper include *antique,* rough surfaced paper run on a long-nap felt; *eggshell,* somewhat smoother, produced by special felts with more pressure; *vellum,* more finely grained than eggshell; *English finish,* smooth but not glossy, made by passing the paper through a calendering press in the drier section of the machine. Supercalendering is done on a separate machine to give a very high gloss to coated papers.

PREPARING PAPER FOR MARKET

The giant rolls of paper as they come from the machines are generally slit into narrower widths for use on various types of printing presses. Some presses take continuous webs, but a great deal of printing is on "sheet fed" presses. (See *Printing*) The sheeting and packing of printing papers is an exacting operation, requiring close-tolerance cutting

and trimming machines, as well as careful hand inspection of sheets before they are wrapped and packed in cases or on wooden "skids" for shipment.

Paper orders from publishers and printers are often filled directly from the mills. However, the marketing and distribution of printing paper is generally handled through independent wholesale distributors known as paper merchants.

PAPERS FOR HUNDREDS OF PRODUCTS

Although printing papers are the glamor products of the industry, they constitute only about one-fourth of the overall paper production. Boxboard, corrugated board, facial tissues, wax papers and other special wraps, carbon papers, and even paper printing plates for offset lithography are produced in tremendous volume. According to figures in a 1961 issue of *Pulp and Paper,* total U. S. paper production in 1960 was in excess of fifteen million tons, of which about two million tons were newsprint, five million were book papers, and another eight million tons were divided between wrappings, tissues, building papers, and a variety of specialized types. Another nineteen million tons of card and paperboards combined to make a fabulous overall production of thirty-four million tons. This volume was expected to increase steadily about 3.5% per year.

This greatly abbreviated list of paper products serves to reveal the vast complexity and versatility of the industry: acid-proof papers, asbestos papers, acoustical tile, gummed papers, electrical insulations, crepe paper, friction board, flint finished paper, napkins, special map papers, krafts, blotting, manila tag, tracing paper, photographic papers, bags specially made for hundreds of purposes (including meat, laundry, lunch, flour, sugar, thermoplastic coated, diaper, vacuum cleaner, clothing, garbage, shoe, and even casket bags), glassine, laminated paper, ice-cream and frozen-food container board, place mats, waxed papers, filter papers, leatherette, ledger paper, paper towels, and windshield wipes.

To produce these and hundreds of other papers, boards, and paper products, the industry employs about one-half million workers. Sales in the 1960's are averaging well over twelve billion dollars annually.

RESEARCH AND THINGS TO COME

In paper mills throughout America, research laboratories are busy making current methods obsolete. Since chemistry plays a leading role in papermaking, it is not surprising that the paper industry is one of the three largest consumers of chemical raw materials in the United States. Many of the large chemical firms have specialized departments devoted to paper research. They work in close cooperation with the laboratory technicians of the paper companies. To provide improved coated printing papers, new latex binders have been developed. Manmade latexes are made up of polymer (plastic) particles, often only .2 micron, or two tenths of 1/1000 inch in size, dispersed in water. Various formulations are being tested with excellent results, and as stated earlier, this use of new coatings has made possible a major revolution in the concept of paper manufacturing, with pigment constituting a major portion of the makeup of printing paper.

Research departments in paper plants include studies of color in paper and in inks, complete printing divisions for testing papers, water testing, photographic departments, and pilot plants. Ways of using hardwoods for newsprint pulp are currently being developed. This is opening up large new sources of raw material. Forestry research and field work are also vital industry operations.

Among the future paper products we may expect are clothes, fabrics, tents, sleeping bags, swimming pool liners, houses, paper that will conduct electricity and that will be useful in electronics, and elastic papers for stretchable bags.

One of the chief elements in papermaking is water. Every ton of wood pulp must be mixed with thirty-seven thousand gallons of water in the paper machine. A single mill may use thirty to forty million gallons of water per day. This means that the source of water for any large paper mill must be virtually inexhaustible. Studies of water conservation methods and of ways to make the most efficient use of water available are important aspects of the paper industry's technical program.

The recent rapid advances in paper manufacturing indicate that within the next decade more changes will take place than occurred during the past 500 years. Chemical research and the development of plastics will be closely tied to paper's future, and it is not unreasonable to suppose that a day may come when even hymenopteron, the paper wasp, will find his wood pulp paper obsolete.

Before being rewound on smaller reels. huge paper rolls from the Fourdrinier machine are slitted on this machine with rotary knives.

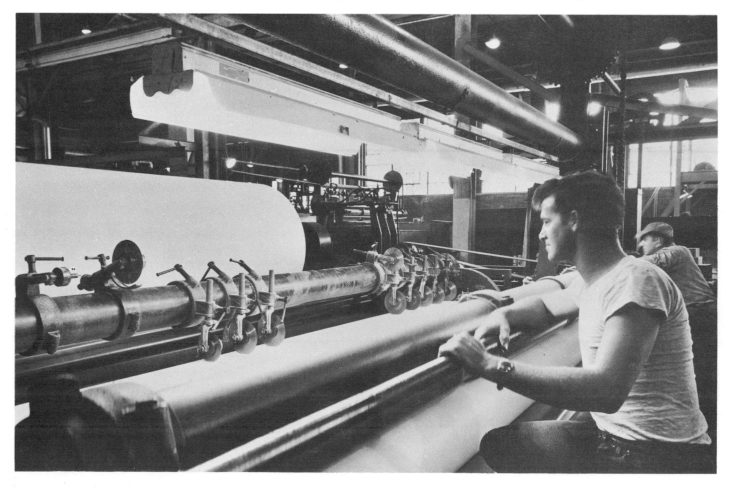

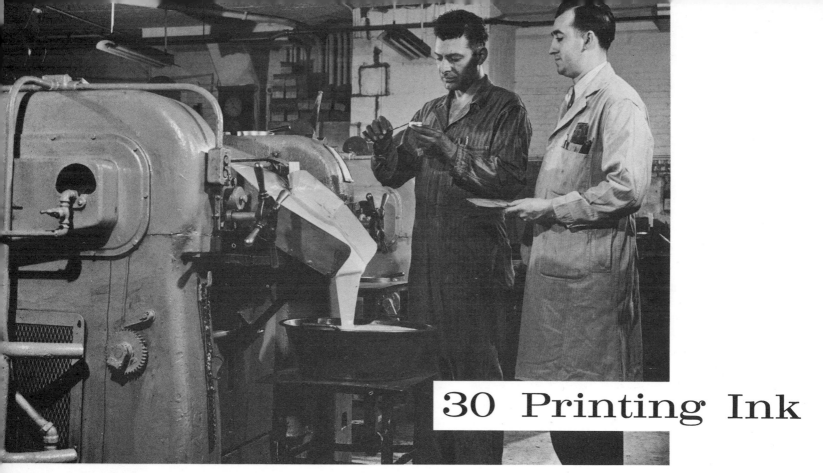

30 Printing Ink

A workman takes a sample of ink from a grinding mill with a spatula and puts it in a can which will be studied by the laboratory technician at right. Each production process is constantly checked through plant quality control.

When men had learned to make papyrus and various forms of paper, they needed a means of inscribing characters or making drawings on these prepared surfaces. Writing ink, the forerunner of printing inks, was used by the ancient Egyptians and Chinese as long ago as 2600 B.C. Generally this writing fluid was made of soot or lampblack mixed with animal glue or vegetable oils. Probably it was not long after the development of the first black writing ink before a variety of colored inks came into use. Pigments used in the making of paints and dyes were also available for inks. (See *Paints and Varnishes*)

Some 400 years before Gutenberg's invention of movable type, the Chinese were experimenting with hand-cut wood blocks to make ink impressions on paper. This was some time in the eleventh century. Then, after the printing of books began in fifteenth century Europe, ink manufacturing became an important industry in its own right.

The first printing inks, like the first writing inks, were black and were formulated in a similar manner. However, printers soon found that their inks had to be of a thicker consistency to perform properly. Originally, each printer made his own ink, combining lampblack with boiled linseed oil and grinding the mixture by hand with a mortar and pestle. But by the sixteenth and seventeenth centuries, ink factories were in operation in many parts of Europe.

Ink making in America began about 1742. Even at that time, color was rarely used, for the various mineral, vegetable, and earth pigments available were of poor quality. Only with the development of coal-tar colors and other synthetic pigments, did the great range of modern printing colors become possible. (See *Chemistry, Paints and Varnishes*)

Actually, the most spectacular advances in printing ink technology have been made in the last 20 or 30 years. While new developments in printing presses, photoengraving, and color photography have brought about many improvements in printing processes, no single element of the graphic arts industry has made a more important contribution than printing inks.

WHAT IS PRINTING INK?

Today it is impossible to define printing ink as such, for there are literally hundreds of different types of inks used for as many special purposes. First came new printing processes. The principles of lithography, discovered by Senefelder in 1796, required the formulation of an ink with entirely different properties from those in the traditional letterpress inks. In like manner, the introduction of the gravure process in the nineteenth century required special inks. (See *Printing*) But the different printing processes are by no means the only requisites for specialized ink formulations. Printing today is done on every conceivable surface: paper, plastics, metal, glass, cloth, foil, and ceramics, to name only a few. For every surface a special ink formulation is required. Even different papers take different inks, and there are hundreds of styles and surfaces of paper alone. (See *Paper*)

HOW INK IS MADE

The modern ink factory is a scientifically controlled

chemical plant and is similar in many respects to a paint factory. There are three main groups of ingredients necessary in the manufacture of ink: the fluids or vehicle, the solids or pigments, and the miscellaneous ingredients—principally driers and compounds. Formulations are worked out in laboratories, where pigments and vehicles are tested for color and chemical reactions to various printing surfaces.

The vehicle carries the pigment which furnishes color, and the nature of the vehicle largely determines the flow characteristics of the ink. Vehicles include several basic types.

Nondrying oils are absorbed into soft papers such as newsprint and are made from petroleum oils and resin oils mixed with various resins.

Drying oils, which dry by oxidation, include boiled linseed oil, China wood oil, cottonseed oil, castor oil, soybean oil, fish oil and a number of synthetic oils. These materials absorb oxygen, then harden as the liquid oils change to solid films. Gloss inks are made by combining certain synthetic resins with the oils.

Solvents: For gravure and flexographic printing, inks which dry by the evaporation of solvents are used. Solvent, or evaporation inks are used for printing on cellophane and metal foils. When gravure is employed to print on paper, low boiling, hydrocarbon solvents are combined with gums and resins. Such formulations evaporate rapidly with or without the application of heat.

Inks which dry too rapidly are difficult to handle on offset and letterpress equipment, for the obvious reason that they may harden in the press or on the printing plates before they can be imparted to the paper or other printing surface. Yet it is sometimes necessary to provide a method of instantaneous drying. The problem is solved with *heatset inks* which flow well on the press but which dry instantly as the printed material passes over a heating unit. These inks are made with high-boiling, slow-evaporating petroleum oils and solvents.

Precipitation-drying, moisture-set, and *wax-set* inks have vehicles consisting of resins that are insoluble in water and are dissolved in glycol type solvents. Glycol itself is soluble in water. When dampened paper or a fine water spray come in contact with inks of this type, the moisture is absorbed by the glycol, and the resin and pigment are precipitated from the solution. Wax-set inks perform in a similar manner, but the vehicle contains a resin which is insoluble in a solvent-wax system.

Quick-setting ink: A new type of ink has been formulated to dry almost instantly on contact with paper. Known as quick-setting ink, it contains a solvent that has an affinity for paper. As the solvent is absorbed by the paper, a relatively dry ink film of resin and oil remains on the surface.

Cold-set inks: Special presses are built to handle cold-set inks, which remain soft only when heated and which dry instantly on contact with paper. These inks contain a high percentage of waxes and resins.

After the correct formulation of an ink has been determined, pigment is mixed into the vehicle, as in the manufacture of paint. In large drum-shaped mixers, pig-

These change can mixers are used to churn pigment and vehicle before grinding. Center mixer shows the paddles with which the mixture is stirred.

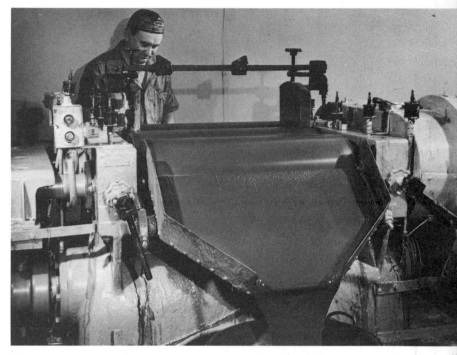

Ink is shown emerging from a milling machine. In this roll mill, pigment is dispersed in the vehicle by steel rollers revolving at varied speeds. Rollers are water-cooled to reduce heat generated by the grinding process.

Proof presses are standard equipment in printing ink plants. Many plants also have commercial presses to test inks under production conditions.

ment is gradually added to the varnish while revolving paddles churn the batch. The resulting mixture may then be put through a three-roll ink mill. This machine is constructed with a series of highly polished steel rollers which serve to "grind" the ink, dispersing the pigment thoroughly in the vehicle. Each roller revolves at a different speed, and all can be adjusted for greater or less clearance in respect to each other. In order to keep down the excessive heat generated by the grinding process, the hollow rollers are cooled with water.

Roll mills are used for grinding thick letterpress and offset inks. Other fluid inks are ground in ball mills or colloid mills. In the former type, steel balls or pebbles in a revolving drum serve to grind the charge as they tumble against each other. The colloid mill consists of a pair of grinding plates: a stationary, or "stator" plate, and a "rotor" plate which revolves rapidly. The ink is ground between the two plates after the operator has adjusted the clearance.

Newer methods of grinding inks by means of kinetic energy and ultrasonic waves are being explored to provide still better dispersion of pigment in the vehicle. There are many types of pigments, most of which correspond to those used in paint making. (See *Paints and Varnishes*) Selection of pigment depends on many factors in the ultimate use of the ink. Where lightfastness is required, only certain colors may be used. Today daylight fluorescent pigments are available in a limited number of colors, and metallic inks can be made with finely pulverized aluminum, brass, copper, and other metals. Mixed with colors, metallic powders provide a wide variety of brilliant inks.

WHAT KIND OF INK?

The most complex task of the ink maker is formulating ink to fit the press and paper or other material to be printed. Among the factors to be considered are the absorbency of the material, the exposure to sunlight, the printing process to be used (offset, letterpress, gravure, etc.), the possible contact with food, soaps, detergents, or chemicals. Lithographic inks must be resistant to the dampening solution which is applied to nonprinting areas of the printing plates. For packages or wraps which must withstand a great deal of abuse, inks must be formulated to be scratchproof. For printing on smooth and coated papers, a less viscous ink is used than for absorbent "antique" or "vellum" book papers. Ink for coated papers must be thin and well ground.

When printing is to be done on plastics, flexography and gravure are the printing processes most used. Flexography is a letterpress, or relief printing process employing specially formed rubber plates. The inks are highly fluid and contain fast-drying solvents.

Transparency or opacity of ink is another factor to be considered in its formulation. For the reproduction of most color pictures, transparent inks are used so that when they overprint, they produce secondary colors. For example, a transparent blue, printed over yellow, results in green. However, there are times when the ink must cover up the under color of ink, paper, or other material. Inks with high opacity are then employed. For the most complete coverage by opaque ink, such as a white ink on a black background, silk-screen printing gives the best results. Silk-screen inks are much like paints in pigmentation and consistency.

Toxicity of printing ink becomes a problem when it is used on food packages or on toys and books for small children. Special nontoxic inks can be formulated, but printers and users of printed products must specify what is required, since many ordinary inks do contain poisonous chemicals. Over 800 raw materials are used in ink manufacture, yet only about ten of these have been approved by the Federal Drug Administration as food additives.

THE MODERN INK INDUSTRY

Few people outside of the graphic arts industries themselves have any idea of the scope or the vital importance of the printing ink industry. Because its future is tied to a vast and growing demand for all types of printing inks and to the new frontier of chemical technology, the ink industry is a challenging field, with many opportunities for well-paid employment. Every industry, business, and profession uses printing ink constantly. Entire new ink markets are opening up, as in the case of the new magnetic inks for printing code numbers on bank checks (See *Finance*), postage stamps, and business machine cards. Chemists, mechanical engineers, machine operators, management and sales personnel are in demand. Many women are employed by the industry, particularly in the field of color control. Because it is not a seasonal business, a high level of year-round employment is maintained to serve more than 40,000 printers in all parts of the United States.

There are scores of local ink firms; even the largest national ink companies such as International Printing Ink (a division of Interchemical Corp.), maintain branches in many cities.

In addition to the research laboratories of individual ink companies, the National Association of Printing Ink Makers operates an ink Research Institute at Lehigh University, attacking ink problems common to all ink makers.

Over 300 printing ink plants in the United States employ about 8,000 people. Their products exceed 200 million dollars annually. There is also an active printing ink industry in Canada.

With constant development of new chemicals and with increasingly exacting demands being made by the mammoth printing industry, this uncrowded field is certain to offer some of the most promising of tomorrow's careers for young people.

High-speed web presses such as this require special inks and drying apparatus. The drying unit of this press was engineered by the ink maker.

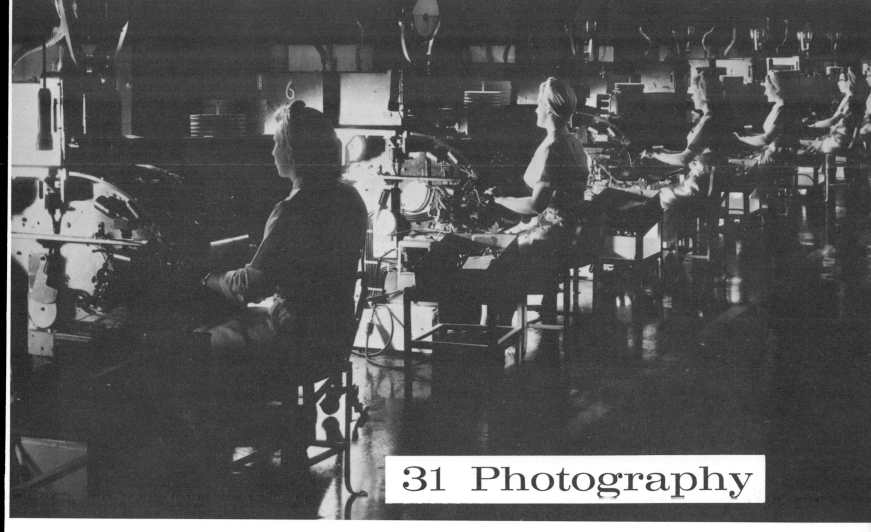

Kodak film is spooled in this darkened area of the Roll Film Division at Kodak Park Works, Rochester, N.Y. Picture was taken with infrared light.

Ever since primitive men tried to draw pictures of animals, people, and familiar objects in the world around them, the human race has sought better and faster ways of making pictorial records. The urge to make pictures springs from two important needs: satisfaction of man's hunger for beauty, and the practical need for authentic records. Although at its best, photography approaches the realm of art and can provide pictures of extraordinary beauty, its primary functions are recording, reproducing, and duplicating.

The basis of modern photography was J. H. Schulze's discovery in 1732 that chloride of silver darkens when exposed to light. A few years later, in 1737, a Frenchman, M. Hellot, developed a method of "invisible" writing with a solution of silver nitrate. Only when exposed to light did the characters blacken.

An early type of camera called the "camera obscura" recorded silhouette images on paper coated with chloride of silver. The camera itself was a simple box arrangement with a small hole and, later, a lens at one end. However, the pictures thus made quickly faded. Experiments by Fox Talbot, Rev. J. B. Reade, and Sir John Herschel, although conducted independently, resulted in making photographic prints permanent by using "hypo" as a fix. Meanwhile, J. N. Niepce had been working in France on a photographic process. Although he died before he achieved success, his work was carried on by L. J. M.

Daguerre, an artist, who finally perfected the daguerreotype in 1839. This process, used for portrait photography for many years, involved the development by mercury vapor of a thin, silver iodide-coated sheet of copper. Exposure required several minutes, a considerable strain on the models, who were forced to remain perfectly still for this length of time.

In 1841, Fox Talbot made an important stride in photography when he treated a sheet of paper with silver iodide. After exposing it in a box-type camera, he obtained a faint image. This he soaked in a solution of silver nitrate and gallic acid to develop a clear, strong picture. Later he hit upon the idea of making negatives for use in producing a number of duplicate positive prints.

Despite the efforts of many experimenters, photography remained for the most part a laboratory curiosity and might have continued to be so for many more years, except for a man named Eastman and the introduction of celluloid film by John Hyatt in 1868. (See *Plastics*) In 1888, George Eastman, a bank bookkeeper, invented the "Kodak" hand camera, a comparatively small and compact instrument for exposing film in continuous rolls. This popularized the use of photography and made possible the modern photographic industry. In order to fill almost immediate demand for his products, Eastman had established the Eastman Dry Plate Company in 1881. There he had perfected a paper-based film in 1884 and transparent roll

A baryta mixture of barium sulphate and gelatin is applied to photographic paper before it is coated with emulsion. Baryta fills in pores, gives gloss and provides a base for the emulsion.

film in 1889. With the building of Kodak Park in Rochester, N.Y., mass production of transparent film was begun by a process of drying a liquid cellulosic plastic on 200-ft. glass tables.

HOW MODERN FILM IS MADE

Today there are many different types of film for a great variety of specific uses, both for color and black-and-white pictures. Photographic film is a complex arrangement of chemical layers supported by a transparent base material. The light-sensitive layer is the "emulsion," made principally of gelatin and silver salts. The silver grains react almost instantly to light, forming what is known as a "latent image." A developing chemical then converts the exposed silver bromide to metallic silver, darkening all areas which received light. At this stage, a "negative" has been produced. The darkest areas are those which absorbed the most light; the light or clear areas are those where no light or very little light penetrated. The negative may be used as a mask to expose other film or light-sensitive paper to make positive film images or positive prints.

Kodacolor prints come off the driers in the Color Print Building at Kodak Park. From here they will be inspected, chopped, sorted, and returned to the photographic dealer from whom they came.

Silver is the essential ingredient of a photographic emulsion. Eastman Kodak Company alone uses about 16 tons of silver each week. Pure silver ingots, each weighing 80 lb., are first dissolved in nitric acid. The liquid is then pumped into 1,000-gallon drums called "crystallizers." Stirring and cooling produces silver nitrate crystals which are taken from the crystallizer and whirled dry in perforated drums. The process is repeated to purify the crystals further.

Meanwhile, photographic gelatin is being prepared as a medium to hold the silver salts. The emulsion is made by mixing the gelatin, silver nitrate, and potassium bromide *in darkness* because the silver salts are light sensitive. The potassium combines with the nitrate and carries it off, leaving only silver bromide crystals in the gelatin.

The photographic emulsion must now be applied to some kind of base. Transparent films look alike, yet there are many different types used for various purposes. In graphic arts and color reproduction, for example, high dimensional stability is essential for exact registration of the various colors. Special films have been created for this purpose. The raw material for most film bases is cellulose acetate, which is derived from cotton or wood fibers treated with acetic acid. The flaky, white cellulose acetate is transformed into a liquid, called "dope," by solvents similar to those used in lacquers. As the dope flows onto revolving chromium-plated wheels, it is heat dried and forms a thin, flexible, transparent film.

In a darkened room, the film is coated with the emulsion of silver bromide and gelatin, and backed, usually, with an antihalation coating which prevents unwanted halos in pictures. Finally the sensitized film is slit, wound on spools, and packaged for distribution to dealers.

COLOR FILM

In this age of color television, color movies, and color printing in newspapers, magazines, and books there is constant effort to increase and improve the reproduction of natural color through photography. Although some of the processes in making color film are similar to those for black-and-white film, the production is much more complex.

Light, as seen by the human eye, is composed of three primary vibrations: those which produce the sensations of red, green, and blue. These primary light vibrations are mixed in various proportions to produce all visible colors of the spectrum. In order to record these colors on photographic film, three layers of emulsion are employed. Each layer is sensitive to one of the three primary colors. This multilayer, "sandwich" type of color film was first successfully produced commercially by Eastman Kodak Company in 1935. Each of the layers is separated by one of gelatin, yet the total thickness of the emulsion is only slightly greater than black-and-white, single-layer emulsion.

Although a number of different color-sensitive films, such as Kodachrome, Kodak Ektachrome, Kodacolor, and Anscochrome, are processed differently, they all record primary light vibrations in the same manner. The blue-sensitive layer is on top, the green-sensitive layer in the middle, and the red-sensitive layer is next to the supporting film. As the top layer is sensitive only to blue light, green and red vibrations pass through it without affecting it. Excess blue light is stopped by a yellow filter layer before it reaches the lower emulsions. This yellow filter is later destroyed during processing. The middle emulsion layer is sensitive to both green and blue light, but as the blue vibrations cannot penetrate the yellow filter, only the green part of the image is exposed. Finally red light reaches the bottom, red-sensitive layer and completes the full-color exposure of the film.

After the color film has been exposed in a camera the latent images in the red-, green-, and blue-sensitive layers of emulsion are developed. With Kodachrome and Kodak Ektachrome processes, black-and-white developer is used to produce negative silver images in each of the three layers. By re-exposure, the remaining silver halide is fogged to prepare it for "coupler development." As the exposed silver halide becomes metallic silver, the developing chemical undergoes a change. It then combines with another chemical substance called the coupler. This reaction produces an insoluble dye which stains the photographic image with one of the three primary colors in proportion to the amount of silver developed.

In the Kodachrome process, coupler components of the dyes act upon the film from the processing chemicals. A separate color developer is used for each of the three layers of emulsion. Each layer must, therefore, be separately re-exposed before development, and the complex processing requires elaborate equipment and precise chemical control.

On the other hand, Ektachrome film is made with coupler components already in the emulsion layers, so that a single developing solution produces the three primary-color images.

After development, the color film must be bleached with a chemical that renders the silver soluble in hypo without affecting the dyes. It is then fixed in the hypo, washed, and dried.

Color negative films are made with coupler components of the dyes in the emulsion layers. These layers are exposed and developed on the same principles as positive color transparencies, but the final result is the reverse of the positive, all colors being complementary to those of the subject.

Because of the complexities of processing color films and photographic color prints, Eastman Kodak Company for years did all of the processing of its amateur color films, and the price of processing was included in the price of the film at the time of its purchase. Kodak now sells its color films and processing services separately, and many independent laboratories throughout the United States have been successfully engaged in the business of processing Kodak's color films.

PHOTOGRAPHIC PAPERS

In order to make photographic prints from transparent film negatives, special light-sensitive papers are manufactured. The process begins with papermaking. Most photographic papers today are made from specially prepared

This molten liquid will become the finest of optical glass in the Hawk-Eye Works of Kodak's Apparatus and Optical Division, where lenses for many different Kodak cameras are produced.

wood pulp with a cellulose purity equal to that of cotton. (See *Paper*) This paper is coated with a layer of barium sulphate and gelatin, which serves to fill in the pores and provide a base for the light-sensitive emulsion. The emulsion is chemically similar to that on transparent film and is applied in much the same way.

ANOTHER CHEMICAL INDUSTRY

Here is another in the long list of industries which rely on chemicals for their existence and their future progress. All photographic processes are based upon chemical action of light and of chemical solution upon chemically composed film emulsions. Kodak Park's chemical division produces 2,400 tons of film-base dope alone in a single week. With the most modern of push-button control equip-

On this machine, roll films are prepared for shipment. Starting at this point, the films proceed through the machine to be wrapped in foil, put into boxes with instructions enclosed, and date stamped.

ment, the Eastman Kodak plant mixes various photographic solutions in 5,000 gallon batches.

One of the chemical substances produced by Eastman is a basic material for developing powders. It goes by the nearly unpronounceable technical name of para-methyl-aminophenolsulfate or, for the purpose of everyday discourse, Kodak Elon Developing Agent.

Some organic chemicals are compounded by Eastman laboratories in minute quantities weighing only a fraction of an ounce, but whether the chemical production is in thousands of gallons or in milligrams, every batch is laboratory tested and carefully checked through all stages of manufacture.

CAMERAS AND LENSES

The manufacture of cameras is an exacting business requiring the same kind of close-tolerance operation as is found in miniature instruments and electronics devices. (See *Machinery*) Since there is a tremendous range of large and small cameras for a host of specialized and general uses, camera construction cannot be broadly standardized except in the case of popular commercial models. Many cameras for graphic arts and industrial purposes are engineered and custom-built to fit specific requirements.

There are a number of well-known companies active in the field of snapshot cameras, home movie cameras, and projectors. These include Bell and Howell, Eastman Kodak, Polaroid, Argus, and Keystone. Their products comprise an assortment of hand cameras. For example, there are telephoto rifle cameras, stroboscopic cameras, miniatures or "minicams," stereocameras, 35 mm. cameras for making color slides, and many styles of portrait and snapshot cameras. Home motion-picture cameras are made for both 8 mm. and 16 mm. film.

For years, German-made cameras were considered the world's best because of their excellent lenses, but recently American lenses have been improved to the point of offering important competition. Some of the finest optical glass in the world is now being produced by such American plants as Corning Glass Works in Corning, N.Y., Eastman Kodak Co., and Bausch and Lomb Optical Co. in Rochester, N.Y. (See *Glass*)

Basically, all cameras are designed on the principle of the original box camera, the box containing a place for the

A machine, designed and developed by Kodak engineers, electronically focuses the lens of the Kodak Automatic 8 Movie Camera. It ensures that the lens is locked exactly in its relation to the film plane.

film at one end and a lens and shutter arrangement at the other. The most complex part of a camera is the shutter. Some modern cameras have shutters that can operate at speeds up to 0.001 of a second. These delicate instruments, together with their diaphragm openings, are assembled by craftsmen who handle the tiny parts with the skill of watchmakers. On better cameras, timing mechanisms control the shutter speeds and can be adjusted for long "time" exposures or split-second operation.

Among the more recent developments are the automatic-exposure control devices which instantly adjust lens openings for the correct exposures under varied lighting conditions. The so-called zoom lenses in home movie cameras adjust automatically at the press of a button from wide-angle to normal or to telephoto focus. An electric eye controls exposures.

SPECIALIZED CAMERAS

In professional photography, expensive cameras are made for a variety of purposes. These include portrait cameras and those used by professional photographic studios for advertising setups; enlarging cameras for projecting images; astronomical telescope cameras; X-ray cameras; and aerial cameras for taking minutely detailed pictures from 20,000 ft. or higher and for use in below freezing temperatures encountered at 40,000 ft. Some aerial cameras are stereoscopic, that is, they produce pictures which can show, when seen through a stereoscope, three-dimensional topography of hills, valleys, roads, streams, buildings, and trees. Aerial photography is used extensively by cartographers, the military, and by the United States Forest Service. Aerial photographs are invaluable in flood control and studies of watershed protection.

Cameras to take pictures in total darkness have been developed, using infrared rays. The resulting pictures are as clear as those taken in daylight.

In order to capture motion in a series of still positions, stroboscopic cameras are used. An early version of this type of camera was invented by A. B. Brown in the nineteenth century. It employed a revolving shutter. In 1887, Ottomar Anschutz built an improved instrument called the "electrotachyscope." These were forerunners of the motion-picture camera, which is a form of stroboscope. (See *Motion Pictures*) But today's stroboscopic cameras for studying the flights of projectiles, or of other fast-moving objects, make rapid-fire exposures by means of an electric spark, which flashes on and off at a speed far greater than is possible with a mechanical shutter or with moving film. Lamps are fed current through condensers which allow a steady current to build up voltage until the condensers discharge. Such lamps can produce 1,500 flashes per second. By this means, a series of pictures are exposed on a single plate. While the shutter is left open, the camera photographs the moving subject in the dark, the only light being provided by the flashing lamp.

GRAPHIC ARTS PHOTOGRAPHY

One of the largest segments of the photographic industry is the manufacture of film, cameras, and other equipment for photoengravers and printers. (See *Printing*)

The consumption of film and chemicals in this field is gigantic. All printed reproductions of pictures begin with photographic film. After special negatives (or sometimes positives) have been developed, they are used to expose light-sensitized printing plates. This is true of all major printing processes, including letterpress, offset, gravure, and silk screen.

Because printing plates are made to impart solid areas of ink to paper or other material, pictures which have intermediate tones must be broken up into tiny lines or dots in order to reproduce properly. For this purpose, special film is made to record only black or white. No intermediate or gray tones appear on such film. However, the effect of gray tones is achieved by placing a fine screen in front of the film. The light reflected from the image is thus broken up into thousands of minute dots which vary in size in relation to the amount or intensity of light penetrating the screen. This is known as "half-tone" reproduction, and it is used for photographs, paintings, and nearly all full-color pictures printed by letterpress or offset lithography.

In the offset printing process, even type is first recorded on film negatives or positives and the film is used to expose the plates. So extensive is the use of this type of photography today that a number of phototypesetting machines have been created to set type automatically on film strips instead of on metal slugs. Actually, these typesetters are elaborate, keyboard-operated cameras which record film images of the letters as rapidly as the operator presses the keys.

For the making of printing plates, many special chemical solutions and emulsions are manufactured. These include various acid-resist coatings for making letterpress photoengravings, light-sensitive coatings for offset lithography, and gravure plates. While some of these materials are made by the manufacturers of home and studio photographic equipment, most of them are prepared by printing equipment firms, such as Harris-Seybold Company, makers of offset presses.

A MANY-SPLENDORED INDUSTRY

The photographic industry has so many facets today that it is one of the most complex of commercial activities. More than a billion and a half black-and-white snapshots and some four hundred million color prints are made in the United States annually. Wholesale value of American-made film and photographic equipment is over one and a quarter billion dollars annually. The primary center of production, New York State, accounts for about two-thirds of the total volume and employs 62% of the industry's production workers. The second ranking state is Illinois with a manufacturing volume of some one hundred fifty million dollars a year. Some of the yearly figures of specific photographic items reach staggering totals. Photographic lamps alone total six hundred seventy million units valued at fifty-eight million dollars. Some 3,500 U.S. camera stores report annual sales of three hundred eighty-five million dollars, while amateur-photographic product sales by drugstores and all other outlets, even excluding film processing and prints, amount to

An operator activates the automatic roll-on contact screen mechanism on a large graphic arts gallery camera. Regardless of size, all cameras are basically designed on the principle of the original box camera.

seven hundred eighty million dollars. U.S. exports of photographic products exceed a hundred twenty million dollars a year, and imports run as high as seventy million dollars. The largest imports are from West Germany, Belgium, and Japan.

As new uses of photography are constantly found for industrial, commercial, and defense purposes, the market for photographic products appears destined for steady expansion. With approximately 60,000 people employed, the industry offers a variety of fascinating occupations. Besides photographers and darkroom technicians, many skilled craftsmen and scientists are in constant demand. These include physicists, chemists, optical experts, laboratory technicians, and research personnel with many specialties. Portrait and commercial studios, finishing services, color-processing plants, printers, and photoengravers need skilled workers and aggressive sales and merchandising personnel.

Sensational discoveries in the realm of faster film emulsions, simpler and more accurate color processes, and improved cameras are being made and are waiting to be made by technicians of tomorrow. In the field of color, particularly, lies the greatest opportunity for the future, since no one has yet found a way to reproduce perfect natural color without complex processing and various methods of correcting errors inherent in present films and color-filtering systems.

One of the most remarkable recent developments in the industry has been that of the Polaroid Land Camera which makes possible the development of snapshots within the camera itself in a matter of seconds. In 1937, at the age of 28, Edwin H. Land organized the Polaroid Corporation, the company which was later, in 1948, to produce and market his sixty-second camera, considered the most revolutionary advance in photography since George Eastman's invention of roll film. In a few short years Polaroid, located in Cambridge, Massachusetts, has made enormous industrial strides. Although Eastman Kodak's overall position in the industry is out in front, General Aniline & Film (Ansco) and Polaroid are now strong contenders in the field.

The Land camera is a compact, self-contained photographic darkroom which exposes roll film negatives in the conventional manner, but which also contains a roll of positive paper. Attached to the positive paper are regularly spaced pods of a developing reagent. This jellylike substance is squeezed between two steel rollers as the exposed picture is wound into position for development. As the negative paper comes in contact with the positive paper, the developing jelly is pressed between the two rolls and acts upon the silver halide grains of the negative. A special solvent in the reagent transmits the unexposed silver to the positive paper. There, catalytic nuclei in concert with the developer convert the silver grains into a positive image. Within less than one minute after exposure, a positive print may be removed from the camera. The company is currently perfecting film and cameras to take and develop color snapshots in a similiar manner.

The chemical secrets of manufacturing the Land cam-

era's positive film are tightly guarded. All drums and bottles of materials in the Polaroid plant carry coded labels. However, the negative sheet, which is virtually the same as ordinary film negatives except that its base is paper, is made for Polaroid by Eastman Kodak and Du Pont.

Polaroid's history is one of the great success stories of this century, proving that American free enterprise can still confer great benefits upon people with ingenuity, drive, and a willingness to sacrifice. The Land family today owns stock in Polaroid valued at many millions of dollars.

In an article on Polaroid published by *Fortune* magazine in April, 1959, Land is quoted as telling his supervisors: "A country without a mission cannot survive as a country. . . . I want to talk about the proper role of industry. Its proper role, I believe, is to make a new kind of product—something people have not thought of as a product at all. When you've reached a standard of living high enough for most people, where do you turn next? It seems to me there is only one place to turn. Industry should address itself now to the production of a worthwhile, highly rewarding, highly creative, inspiring daily job for every one of a hundred million Americans."

In almost all its segments, the photographic industry is contributing to Land's objective. Certainly no other industry can claim more rewarding or inspiring work, or greater opportunity for inventiveness and for exciting progress.

This superb scene reproduced from an eight-by-ten inch Anscochrome transparency is shown broken down into its primary color images, as well as the black image used in the printing process.

32 Printing

This five-color Harris offset press with double delivery is used for high-quality color printing at the Western Printing and Lithographing Company. Such presses are used for printing modern children's books, textbooks, book covers, and jackets on large sheets.

Many people believe that Johann Gutenberg, the fifteenth-century German who produced the first printed Bible, invented printing. The fact is, Chinese and Korean craftsmen were printing words and characters from movable type as early as the ninth century and had experimented with other forms of ink transfer much earlier than that. In A.D. 175, the Chinese had a lithographic process consisting of engraving characters on a flat stone, pressing dampened paper into the depressions, then, after the paper had been allowed to dry on the stone, rubbing an ink-saturated pad of silk over the paper. The result was a "reverse" image of white characters on a black background, since the pad did not deposit ink in the character depressions. Actually, the ancient Babylonian method of impressing character stamps into wet clay to produce tablets was a form of "inkless" printing, practiced as early as 4000 B.C.

There is little question, however, that our modern printing industry and its near cousin, publishing (which see) really began with Gutenberg's Bible in 1452. Gutenberg's press, doubtlessly patterned after the wine and cheese presses of that period, forced a platen against the type form by means of a vertical screw. "Ink balls" made of wool-padded sheepskin attached to wooden handles were used to ink the type form. Since a good impression could be obtained from only one page at a time, the process was slow and laborious. But it was printing and was many times faster than the painstaking manuscript copying that had been Europe's only method of producing books and records for centuries.

In the course of his early experiments, Gutenberg learned that a heavy, less fluid ink than that used by the copyists performed better in printing. He turned to the techniques of German and Dutch painters to make a printing ink with boiled linseed oil. (See *Printing Inks*)

In order to finance his projects Gutenberg enlisted the help of a wealthy goldsmith, Johann Fust, who established the printing firm of Fust and Schoeffer. In a book which they printed in 1457 appears the first printer's mark, a double escutcheon, which is used today as the emblem of the Printing House Craftsmen.

Printing spread throughout Europe and the British Isles with amazing speed. A Frenchman by the name of Nicholas Jenson made an important contribution to the industry by designing the first "roman" style types with such perfection that they are still unsurpassed. Aldus Manutius, an Italian, cut the first italic (slanted) type and introduced the first "octavo" volumes which measured only four by six inches. This made possible the production of smaller, cheaper volumes and the printing of multiple-page forms.

By 1476 printing was being done in England, where

An old-time George Washington press, similar to the type used by Benjamin Franklin, is on display in front of the national headquarters of Printing Industry of America at Washington, D.C.

the great William Caxton set up his shop and began printing books and Bibles in the English language.

PRINTING IN AMERICA

Surprisingly, it was not in the northern British colonies that the first New World printing was done, but in Mexico City, where Juan Pablos published the first American-printed book in 1539; and in Lima, Peru, where, in 1584, the second New World printing shop was established. But it was only a few years after the Pilgrims landed that the first printing press arrived in the Massachusetts Colony. This was in 1638. The press was a new type developed by a Dutch printer, and its story is a notable one. It had been purchased by the Reverend Jose Glover, a clergyman, who, suspended from his pastorate in England for nonconformity with church principles, had decided to take part in the establishment of Harvard College. The press was to be used by the new college. Although Glover died during the voyage, his widow set up the printing plant as planned, assisted by Stephen Day and his son, Matthew. In January, 1639, they issued their first printed piece, *The Freeman's Oath,* which was no more than a single, small sheet. This was New England's beginning of what is today a multibillion-dollar U.S. industry.

The following year, Matthew Day published a book of 147 leaves entitled *The Whole Booke of Psalms Faithfully Translated into English Metre.* From that day, printing, publishing, and freedom of expression have advanced hand in hand as an integral part of American history.

BENJAMIN FRANKLIN AS PRINTER

As the eighteenth century began, Benjamin Franklin, one of the greatest names in American letters, learned the printing trade as an apprentice to his older brother, James. This was 1718 and Ben Franklin was only 12 years old. After hard years in which James forced his younger brother into some very unfair contracts and then persuaded other Boston printers to refuse him employment, Benjamin left home, went to New York, and finally to Philadelphia. It was there that Franklin eventually set up his own printing establishment, the firm becoming known as B. Franklin, Printer. Significantly, this great statesman, scientist, philosopher, and author chose to write his will with the opening phrase, "I, Benjamin Franklin, Printer . . ."

The story of Franklin's printing and publishing ventures would themselves fill a book. As an industry, printing was then very much of a hand craft, and although metal type had long been in use, it was set by hand, letter for letter, and printed in small sheets, a page or two at a time.

TYPE AND TYPESETTING

Printing from carved blocks of wood led to the development of type; yet curiously enough, woodcut pictures and even pictures with lettered inscriptions had been known for decades before anyone conceived of putting individual letters on separate blocks. Whether or not Johann Gutenberg is the true inventor of movable type, he was certainly one of the first to put the idea to practical use and to cast his letters on metal. Metal type, being far more durable than wood, made possible a greater number of impressions and produced a sharper, cleaner printed result. From Gutenberg's day to the present, typecasting has been a major segment of the printing industry.

If you pick up a piece of modern type, you will find that it has certain standard characteristics in common with any other type now in use, for standardization has been one of the important developments of the industry. All metal type in the United States, regardless of the size or style of the letter, is exactly the same height from the base to the printing surface, or "face." On one side of the block, or "body" of the type, is a small groove which tells the typesetter how to place the letter so that it will read correctly. Actually, type is cast in reverse, reading from right to left in English, so that when it is inverted to make an impression it will read correctly.

Type sizes are designated by small units of measurement known as "points," a point being approximately 1/72 of an inch. Generally speaking the smallest type in common use is six point, which means that the body measures six points high across its end, or "shoulder." The letter itself will usually be smaller than this point measure. Standard type sizes range from 6 points up to 72 points, the most familiar being 6, 8, 10, 12, 14, 18, 24, 30, and 36. This book is set in 10-point Times Roman type on a 12-point body, thus allowing a two-point space between each line.

The metal used in typecasting is an alloy of lead, antimony, and tin. For most letterpress printing there are three main classes of type: *Foundry type,* which consists of individually cast letters used for hand-setting of headings and for small amounts of copy; *Linotype,* set on a linecasting machine and used for setting the texts of most books, newspapers, and magazines; and *Monotype,* consisting of individual type letters set by machine.

Typography is both an art and an industry, involving skilled designers and craftsmen as well as the most modern machinery. Hundreds of different type faces have been designed since Gutenberg's day, and new styles are still being created. Yet some of the earliest designs, with slight variations, are even today considered among the best for long texts. These include Estienne designed by Robert Estienne (1503-1559); Garamond, by Claude Garamond (1501-1561); Bodoni, by Giambattista Bodoni (1740-1813). The creation of a new typeface is an exacting task for a skilled designer. Each letter is worked out in large scale sketches which are gradually modified until a final, master drawing has been made. The designer must consider how each character will combine with every other letter of the alphabet, both in capitals and in the "lower case," or small letter font. As the style will probably be cast in many different sizes, from the smallest, six-point, up to large "display" types, the designer may have to make separate drawings of some letters for the smaller sizes, making any thin lines and serifs somewhat heavier in proportion to the rest of the design for better printability. Most typefaces are designed with italics and bold face as well as the normal roman face. Special fonts are designed for ornate initials, unusual titles and other display headings.

When master drawings for the alphabet, numerals, and punctuation marks have been made, a complete font is ready to be cut and cast. The letters are engraved into a matrix by striking a steel punch into a copper bar, by the electrotype method, or by an automatic matrix-cutting machine which traces the original design and reduces it in size by means of a pantograph. After the matrix is inserted into a mold, molten type metal is pumped into it, thus forming a finished piece of type with its raised letter of the desired size.

The earliest typecasting machine was invented in 1838 by David Bruce, Jr., son of the David Bruce who established the firm now known as the American Type Founders Company. This mechanism forced liquid metal from a melting pot into the mold and matrix by means of a piston arrangement. At the same time, the mold was automatically closed, then opened to eject the finished type. However the type thus produced still had to be trimmed by hand. In 1888, an improved machine which cast and finished the type was invented by Henry Barth. Modern machines can cast letters at a rate of 1,000 or more per minute.

But the greatest advance in the typographic industry, and the one which made the modern daily newspaper possible was the Linotype. This marvelous machine, which sets type and casts a complete line in a single operation, was devised by Ottmar Mergenthaler during 10 years of experimentation and put into practical operation in 1886. At a keyboard, much like that of a typewriter, an operator releases brass matrices, called "mats," from a channeled container, known as a magazine, by depressing the

This cutaway view of a linotype machine shows the channels through which the matrices, or mats, travel from the magazine (top right) to the linecasting mechanism (at left) and then are lifted to the sorting slots at the top of the magazine.

The Intertype Monarch linecasting machine, designed for automatic tape operation, produces up to 14 lines of newspaper text per minute. Notice that there is no keyboard, as there is on a conventional linecaster.

keys. As the mats fall into place to form words, spaces, and complete sentences, they are conveyed to a carrier at the left of the keyboard where the operator can lift them out to make corrections if necessary, or he can insert extra spaces. An adjustment can be made to form lines of any desired length up to seven inches. Wedge-shaped space-bands serve to "justify" the lines, filling them out to the exact, prescribed measure. As soon as a line is complete, the operator activates a lever which carries the mats through a series of stages. First the line is struck from below by a bar which forces the wedges to expand the line to its full width. When the line of mats and the casting chamber come into alignment, molten metal is forced against the brass matrices, forming a solid line of raised type. This finished line, called a slug, is trimmed by knives that remove excess metal. While the slug drops into its place with previously cast lines, the mats are conveyed to the top of the magazine where, because each letter mat is differently notched, they are automatically sorted and distributed to their proper channels for reuse.

The entire operation of setting lines of type on a line-casting machine is carried on rapidly and continuously, so that a skillful operator can set about 250 to 350 newspaper column lines per hour.

Since a typesetting error on a line caster requires the resetting of an entire line, monotype is sometimes preferable. This dual machine, invented by Tolbert Lanston in 1892, sets and casts individual letters and spaces by keyboard operation. As a result, corrections in columns of figures or other complicated typographical matter can sometimes be more easily made.

Today, two of the major typesetting machine manufacturers bear the names of the inventors: Mergenthaler Linotype Company, and Lanston Monotype Machine Company. Two other important firms in this field are Intertype Company and the Ludlow Typograph Company.

In recent years a number of photographic typesetting machines have been devised to set negative or positive images of type on strips of film. The Fotosetter, for example, manufactured by Intertype Company, is operated in a manner similar to the linotype, but instead of casting metal lines on brass matrices, individual film images of the letters are rapidly photographed by a high-speed camera mechanism, which can be adjusted to enlarge or reduce the type for a variety of point sizes. (See *Photography*) The resulting film strips of type lines can be used for exposing offset lithography printing plates. Linofilm, a machine for photo composition recently developed by the Mergenthaler Linotype Company, combines provision for typesetting, corrections, alterations, and page makeup. A film corrector device automatically cuts out an error line, replacing it with the new one in an operation that requires no hand opaquing or correction. There are also several phototype machines designed to produce single lines of composed type in a wide range of sizes and from a variety of pattern alphabets.

As an industry, typesetting is widely distributed in cities and towns throughout the United States. To serve printers, publishers, and advertising agencies there are hundreds of large and small typesetting firms, sometimes called trade compositors, who specialize in setting by linotype, monotype, and Fotosetter. For many applications, carefully prepared proofs called reproduction proofs or "repro" proofs are furnished to be photographed in the making of printing plates.

PRINTING PROCESSES

From Gutenberg to the days of the Franklin Press in America, letterpress was the fundamental, most widely used printing process, and so it remained throughout most of the nineteenth century. Letterpress is a relief printing process based on the simple principle of inking a raised, or relief, image and pressing it on a piece of paper. Nearly all newspapers and a majority of magazines are printed by this process. It is the method used to print directly from metal type.

The early letterpress was a flatbed class of press, with the type or woodcuts placed on a flat surface. Paper was squeezed between the type form and another flat plane, the platen. But in 1830 the first American cylinder press made a significant change in the concept of printing presses. Made by R. Hoe and Company for an Albany, N.Y. newspaper, it drew sheets of paper around a rotating cylinder which then rolled over the flatbed type form. It was operated by hand until later models were converted to steam power. The Miehle two-revolution flatbed cylinder press of 1889 was a further improvement of the cylinder principle. Modern cylinder presses operate at high speed and are used to print paper in sheets. Vacuum suction cups and mechanical finger-like clamps lift and draw the sheets from a stack as they are fed to the cylinder. As the paper is rolled around the cylinder, it comes in contact with the type form, then is snatched from the cylinder and automatically piled at the foot of the press.

For very long, high-speed runs, rotary presses are generally used. The rotary press prints a continuous roll or "web" of paper which travels through a series of curved printing plates mounted on cylinders. Some block-long newspaper presses can turn out 40 to 50 thousand 52-page newspapers per hour, folding and trimming the papers as they emerge, printed, at the end of the machines. (See *Publishing*) In order to make plates for rotary presses, it was necessary to devise a means of reproducing entire pages of type on single pieces of curved metal. This led to the development of the stereotype and the electrotype.

To make a stereotype, a dampened sheet of papier-mâché is compressed at about 300 lb. pressure per square inch against a type form. Thus an impression of the entire page of type and pictures is formed in the heavy paper, which is then used as a mold for casting a metal plate. Since the paper mat may be used to cast either a flat or curved·plate, it is an inexpensive and versatile mold. Plastics and special rubber compositions are now being used increasingly in place of metal for casting letterpress printing plates.

Another type of letterpress plate, called an "electrotype" is prepared by making a wax or plastic matrix from the type form. This mold is then coated with an electrical conducting substance and placed in an electrolitic bath. As an electrical charge causes copper to be deposited on the mold, a thin copper shell forms. This, when backed with reinforcing metal, provides an exact replica of the original type matter on a single plate. Most books printed by the letterpress process, are produced with electrotype plates. The type itself is rarely used directly in the printing process. As a result, the making of electrotypes is frequently done by typesetting firms or by photoengravers who make plates for printing illustrations.

PHOTOENGRAVING

For centuries, the printing of pictures was largely accomplished by means of hand carved woodcuts. Type-high blocks of wood were used by the craftsmen who tooled the surface with pictorial designs of great intricacy. This wood-engraving craft reached a peak of perfection in America during and shortly after the Civil War period, when thousands of detailed engravings were made for the periodicals and books of that day. During this time, the development of photography led to photographic methods of transferring images to the surfaces of wood blocks. Yet it was many years before a method of mechanical engraving of the photographic image was devised. (See *Photography*)

Another method of reproducing pictures was the steel engraving, created in the manner of a wood engraving, the craftsmen using sharp tools to cut fine lines into the surfaces of steel plates. Steel engravings are still made for certain kinds of quality printing such as engraved letterheads, postage stamps, and currency. Etching is an artist's method of producing a design on an "engraved" copper plate by applying acid to the surface. This art was prac-

A pressman is making final shifts of electrotypes to move them into exact position required for accurate register for four-color process printing. The electros have been mounted on Sterling Toggle Base and Hook System.

ticed by many of the old masters and is used today for making artistic prints. An acid resist (coating) is first spread on a polished copper plate. The artist then scratches fine lines in the soft coating, exposing the metal underneath. When the scratched drawing is complete, the plate is treated with acid, which eats into the copper wherever the coating has been removed. After the lines have been etched to a desired depth, the resist is removed, a heavy bodied ink is rubbed into the depressions, and the surface of the plate is wiped clean. Dampened paper is laid on the plate, which is then forced under a roller with considerable pressure. As the paper is pressed into the ink-filled grooves of the plate, it pulls the image away from the plate, resulting in a fine print of unique quality.

It remained for printers of the late nineteenth century

In the U.S. Government Printing Office, Washington, D.C. eleven-point electrotypes are mounted on Sterling Toggle Hook and Base System. Each plate is held in proper position by small mechanical assemblies called hooks.

to apply the principles of etching and photography to the mechanical reproduction of black-and-white drawings. Photoengraving today is a major industry serving the publishing, printing, and advertising fields.

To make a photoengraving, a metal plate of zinc, copper, or magnesium is coated with a light-sensitive emulsion. This is then exposed to light through a film which bears a negative image of the subject to be reproduced. Light hardens the acid resist, but in all unexposed areas, the coating washes away, leaving only the bare metal. Next the plate is placed in an acid bath. In the case of a zinc plate, nitric acid is used to eat away all uncoated areas of the surface. Thus, nonprinting areas are etched below the surface. The finished plate is generally mounted on a wooden block, making the engraving exactly type-high. When the plate is inked, an exact reproduction of the original picture may be printed.

The two types of photoengravings are known as "line plates" and "halftones." Line plates, or line engravings, are made from pen-and-ink drawings or other artwork with sharp black-and-white definition. Halftones are made by introducing a very fine screen between the subject and the film being exposed; they reproduce subtle tones of gray. The process was perfected by Frederick Ives in 1881. Glass screens for this purpose are made by cementing two thin glass plates with transparent Canadian balsam. On the surface of each glass sheet are fine parallel lines. The lined surfaces are cemented face to face, with the lines on one surface at right angles to those of the other. This forms a mesh of crossed lines, so fine that the individual squares are invisible to the naked eye. The number of lines per inch varies from 65 to 150, with some special screens containing 300 lines to the inch. Today, most of the screens used for halftone work are on

In preparation for making offset printing plates, a "stripper" opaques flaws in film, working over a light table. When film is ready it will be used to expose a sensitized metal-printing plate.

film, rather than on glass, and are known as "contact screens."

When a continuous tone image (one having many gradations of tone from light gray to black) is exposed through a halftone screen, the resulting negative is composed of a myriad of microscopic dots. These dots are thin where the tones are light, thicker where the tones are dark. From such a halftone negative, a photoengraving may be made in the same manner as a line plate.

The photoengraving industry is today suffering from serious competition by the offset lithography segment of printing industries, and for some uses the letterpress process itself has greatly declined in relative importance during the past few years. Most photoengraving still involves a considerable amount of hand craftsmanship and is therefore costly. A few years ago a machine for mechanically etching magnesium plates was introduced by the Dow Chemical Company. Known as the Dow etch process, it etches the metal almost straight down, even at considerable depth, thus conquering "undercutting," the age-old problem of the photoengraver. Ordinarily acid etching tends to eat laterally as well as vertically, thereby destroying some of the finer lines or dots on the printing surface. New methods of electronic engraving, instruments for measuring color and ink, and better photomechanical separation systems have helped to keep the engraving industry in a strongly competitive position.

OFFSET LITHOGRAPHY

As stated earlier in this chapter, the great threat to photoengraving and to letterpress printing is the newer giant of the industry, offset lithography, sometimes known as photo offset or lithography.

The origin of this printing process was the true lithograph, which consisted of making a grease pencil drawing on a smooth stone. Lithographic stone, a fine-grained form of limestone, is still used for making art prints. After a design or picture is drawn on the polished surface, a solution of nitric acid, gum arabic, and water is spread over the stone. The acid etches the bare surfaces but does not affect those areas having a greasy crayon coating. Now the bare surfaces of the stone are receptive to water; when dampened, they will resist a grease-base ink. The stone is alternately dampened and inked, so that ink impressions of the artist's drawing may be transferred to paper.

The principle of lithograph printing was discovered by a Bohemian, Alois Senefelder, in 1796, and it was from his experiments that modern offset lithography was to grow.

Lithography falls under the classification of planographic printing, meaning printing from a flat plane or surface. Because stone is too cumbersome a material for practical printing plates, thin sheets of metal are used. Originally, metal lithography plates were made of zinc, finely grained to simulate the surface of lithographic stone. But today many are bimetal or trimetal plates, smooth and highly polished.

As in the preparation of photoengravings, the first step in offset plate making is the negative. Line or halftone negatives are produced as described earlier. For certain types of offset plates, film positives are used. The negatives or positives are then placed in contact with a metal plate which has been coated with a light-sensitive emulsion. After the image has been exposed and developed on the plate, the printing areas have a chemical attraction for greasy ink and a resistance to water. On the other hand, the bare metal areas will accept water and resist the ink. The plate is now wrapped around a cylinder of the offset press, and when the press is set in motion, it is alternately dampened and inked by sets of rollers designed for this purpose.

The term "offset" is derived from the fact that the printing plate does not come in direct contact with the paper or other material being printed, but first leaves its ink impression on a cylinder covered with a sheet of rubber known as the "blanket." From the blanket, the ink is "offset" to the paper. Due to the fact that the rubber blanket is comparatively soft, offset lithography has the great advantage of being able to print the finest halftone or detailed line work on comparatively rough surfaces. Whereas hard metal letterpress plates cannot impart ink into minute crevices or valleys in textured papers, cloth, and other coarse-grained materials, the soft rubber blanket of an offset press will conform to almost any printing surface. For this reason more and more offset lithography is being used to print books where finely detailed photographs and pictures in full color must be combined with type matter. This makes possible the use of matte-surfaced or textured book papers rather than the high gloss coated papers required for printing halftones by letterpress.

Although offset lithography is being used for every conceivable kind of printing today, most newspapers and

With the negative in contact with sensitized metal, a plate-maker exposes a large offset printing plate in a vacuum frame.

national magazines are still being produced by letterpress. It is in the periodical publishing industry where letterpress and photoengraving have their greatest market. Nevertheless there are few printing establishments today that do not have offset equipment. This was not true prior to World War II. The web offset press prints at high speed on paper in rolls rather than single sheets.

GRAVURE

The third major printing method is gravure or photogravure, which is an intaglio process. In this category are the steel engraving and the copper etching. Literally translated, the word intaglio means "to cut into," which is descriptive of the process. The gravure plate's printing areas are etched *below* the surface, exactly the opposite of the letterpress principle which depends upon raised or relief images for the transfer of ink.

Rotogravure, which is the application of gravure printing to rotary presses, is the familiar method for printing the color sections of many metropolitan Sunday newspapers. Naturally the quality suffers somewhat from such high-speed production, but at its best, gravure produces some of the finest pictorial reproductions of any of the various printing processes.

To make photogravure printing plates, the first step is photography. The subject, a photograph, painting, drawing, or a proof of type, is photographed. A continuous-tone negative is made, retaining all the tone values of the original picture. From this, a continuous-tone positive is exposed and developed. Next, a gelatin-coated sheet of paper, called a carbon tissue, chemically light sensitized, is exposed through a glass photogravure screen. The screen, with 150 to 175 transparent lines per inch, has a pattern of minute opaque squares, so that light penetrates through the crossed lines. Exposed through this mesh, the carbon tissue's gelatin is hardened in the fine lines, but not where the opaque squares block the passage of light. Next the carbon tissue is exposed a second time, this time through the continuous tone positive film of the picture or

An offset printing plate is made on a thin sheet of metal, usually zinc or aluminum. After it is exposed and developed, it is wrapped around a cylinder on the press and locked in position as shown here.

A Harris-Cottrell double five-color web offset press is shown in operation at Haynes Lithograph Company in Washington, D.C. This multicolor press prints a continuous web, or roll of paper at high speed and accommodates plates 22¾ x 38 inches.

image to be reproduced. The effect of this second exposure is to harden the tiny squares of previously unexposed gelatin in varying degrees; it is comparatively soft where the positive film is dark, harder where more light penetrates, and so forth through a full scale of tone values from white to black.

In order to transfer the image to a printing plate, the exposed carbon tissue is spread on the wet surface of a sheet of polished copper and squeezed flat to remove all air bubbles. By means of hot water, the paper backing is washed away, and the softer portions of the gelatin image are dissolved. What remains on the copper plate is a photographic image called the "carbon resist." This is a coating of hardened gelatin of varying depth. Thickest areas of gelatin are those which received the most light when exposed to the positive image. Thinnest areas are those which received little or no light.

The plate is now ready to be acid etched. Thin areas of gelatin are rapidly penetrated by the acid applied to the surface, whereas the heavier gelatin cells hold back the etching process. Thus, dark areas of the picture become composed of microscopic wells where acid has eaten deeply into the copper plate. Lighter tones are formed by shallower depressions.

After the plate is cleaned and polished, it is wrapped around a plate cylinder of the press and as the press turns, the plate is inked by rollers with a special transparent ink; then the plate passes under a flexible steel blade which wipes the surface clean, leaving ink deposits only in the minutely etched wells. Unlike other printing processes, all the dots in a gravure reproduction of a toned picture

are the same size. Their lightness or darkness is entirely controlled by the depth of the wells in the plate, the deeper wells depositing more ink on the paper, the shallow wells printing thin, light tones.

Since the making of photogravure plates is a relatively expensive process, this method of printing is generally practicable only for very long press runs of many thousands of copies, or for printing of such high quality that the cost of plates is not a limiting factor. Gravure is widely used for textile printing, packaging, printing patterns on floor coverings and wallpaper.

SILK-SCREEN PRINTING

For posters, car cards, and for printing on unusual surfaces, the silk-screen or stencil-printing process is widely used. It is often more economical than other printing processes for short runs of color printing where 200 or 300 posters, for example, may be required in several colors. A piece of silk or finely meshed wire is coated with a substance called "film" in all nonprinting areas. The coating may be applied by brush, by cutting a stencil, or by photography, using a light-sensitive gelatin. Wherever the film is applied, it acts to prevent the thick heavy ink from passing through the silk to the paper. Thus the silk screen is a form of stencil. Modern silk screen presses can be operated at comparatively high speed and can print a great variety of complex designs.

One of the special advantages of silk-screen printing is the ability to apply thick, opaque ink to dark surfaces so that bright colors or pure white can be printed on black paper or on other deep colors with excellent effect. It is used for printing on glass, ceramics, fabrics, and many other special surfaces.

FLEXOGRAPHY

Another process in wide use today is flexography, a form of relief printing which employs rubber plates and a volatile, quick-drying ink. (See *Printing Ink*) It is used primarily in printing on foils and transparent film, such as cellophane, polyethylene, and other packaging materials. Flexographic presses are operated at very high speeds and are fed continuous rolls or "webs" of the material to be printed. Since the rubber plates can be molded in varying degrees of hardness, or "durometer," they can be custom-made to perform well on a great variety of printing surfaces. At the same time, the comparative softness of even the harder rubber makes it difficult to retain very fine lines or the fine dots of halftones. As a result, simple designs and line plates dominate this field of printing.

The rubber flexographic plates are made from standard letterpress engravings, generally deeply etched zinc or copper. First a negative plastic mold is made from the engraving. Into this a soft, gummy rubber, or "raw stock," is molded under pressure and heat. Vulcanizing produces a semihard rubber plate, suitable for printing.

COLOR REPRODUCTION

One of the most fascinating phases of printing is the reproduction of color photography or multicolored artwork. Many special art techniques and photographic processes have been devised for this purpose.

For most of the color work in books, magazines, and advertising brochures, full color or four-color halftones are made. This is done by photographing the painting, drawing, or transparent color film, such as a Kodachrome or Ektachrome, through a series of color filters, thus

This simply designed unit is the keyboard for operating the Linofilm typesetting machine. Typesetting on film is becoming more and more prevalent with the increasing importance of offset lithography.

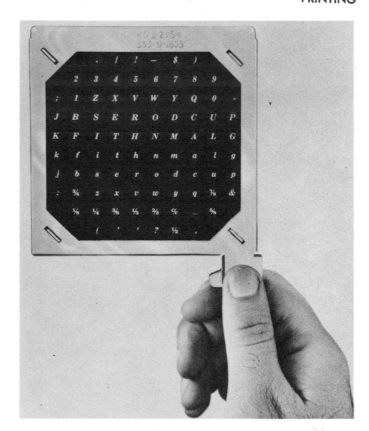

A compact film negative "grid font" contains a complete font of type for use in the Linofilm machine. This single unit provides type sizes from 6- through 36-point by means of keyboard focusing adjustments.

breaking down the image into its primary colors. An orange-red filter is used for the primary "blue" negative; a blue-violet filter, for the "yellow" negative; and a green filter, for the "magenta" negative. In most printing, a fourth negative is made for black. This provides strength of color in the darkest shadow areas. (See *Photography*)

After the separation negatives have been made, they are used to produce four separate halftone printing plates (for letterpress, offset, or whatever printing process is being employed) in the manner described in other sections of this chapter. These plates are inked in the primary blue, yellow, and magenta colors plus black and printed in exact register to produce a faithful reproduction of the original subject. In gravure printing, the black plate is not usually needed, full black tones being produced by the heavy buildup of primary colored inks.

To achieve the best printed results, great skill is required on the part of the camera technician and the plate maker. Due to shortcomings in film and photography, most color separations require hand correction, which can be done by chemically bleaching negatives or by working on the printing plates themselves. Letterpress engravings can be reetched with acid locally to open up certain areas, or they can be burnished to darken some tones. Offset plates can also be burnished to *remove* printing areas, although correction on these plates is greatly limited. Skillful burnishing of gravure plates will serve to lighten tones by making the printing wells shallower.

Special color presses are made for all processes by putting several plate cylinder units in tandem. A two-color press has two plate units; a four-color press, four units, and so on. Color printing today has reached such a high point of perfection that superb full-color reproductions are produced at very high speeds. Newer presses have electric eyes to control register and to stop the mechanism automatically if anything gets seriously out of adjustment.

SCOPE OF THE INDUSTRY

The vast and complex printing industry is one of the largest in America today. Yet big as it is, it has not fallen into the hands of a few giant concerns as has been the case with some other major industries. The need for printing is so universal that there are large and small printing shops in almost every community in the United States and Canada. Printing establishments may be highly specialized, as are those which cater solely to the printing of certain types of labels; or they may be versatile, general shops with both letterpress and offset presses of various sizes for single color, two-color, and four-color printing. There are, of course, some huge printing concerns with giant branch plants in major cities. Nevertheless, almost 1,000 firms are needed to handle 50% of U. S. printing. More than 13,000 individually owned and operated printing shops are engaged in this amazing industry, in addition to at least 25,000 shops using some type of duplicating or small printing equipment.

Production of printing machinery, which continues to increase year after year, has been amounting to more than three-hundred-fifty-million dollars annually during the 1960's. This equipment, consisting of typesetting machines, printing presses, and engraving equipment, is used in the production of books, magazines, newspapers, maps, advertising matter, checks, stamps, stationery, greeting cards, labels, boxes, business forms, catalogs, pamphlets, instructions, games, and thousands of other items. Every business and profession, virtually every person in the nation uses printing in many forms.

The trend today is for higher speed with improved quality, particularly in color printing. Web offset is being used for the production of books in modern plants. On presses that print 25,000 copies per hour, rolls of paper speed over plate cylinders to receive the impressions of 64 two-color book pages at a time (32 pages on each side of the sheet). Electronic steering rollers and center-line scanners insure perfect register of colors. Printing pressures, ink flow, heating, and cooling are also electronically controlled.

Printing, like publishing, has been tradition bound for many years, but it is suddenly breaking free with a host of technological advances. The next 10 to 20 years will unquestionably mark one of the most exciting eras in the history of this great industry.

A giant of the printing world, this double, five-color, Harris-Cottrell, 43- by 64-inch web offset press is the pride of Western Printing and Lithographing Company's Poughkeepsie, New York, plant.

By contrast, the Davidson Dualith 500 is one of the offset printing "compacts" available for high-quality office printing and duplicating. It will handle 11- by 17-inch sheets at speeds up to 8,000 impressions per hour.

33 Publishing

Most books today are bound by elaborate machinery. Shown here is a Sheridan machine for rounding, backing, lining up, and putting on headbands at a large book-manufacturing plant in Kingsport, Tennessee.

The dictionary defines publishing as the act of making public, of announcing or proclaiming; it further states that to publish is to print and offer for sale, especially a book or magazine. Taking the more general definition of the term, it might be said that the first publishers were story-tellers or minstrels who strolled about from village to village reporting events of the day and entertaining groups of listeners with tales of heroic exploits. How far back in history the art of storytelling may be traced is a matter of speculation, for men doubtlessly began to entertain audiences with real or imaginary tales almost as soon as they learned to communicate with speech.

But from the standpoint of a modern industry, publishing history is directly tied to the story of printing (See *Printing*) for it was with the printing of books that mankind began to disseminate information and knowledge to large groups of people at the same time.

Although Johann Gutenberg is popularly credited with inventing printing from movable type and with printing the first book, the Chinese had printed books more than 500 years earlier. A printed Chinese work produced in A.D. 868 still exists, and there is evidence that some works were printed as much as 100 years earlier than that. However, the beginning of publishing in the Western world may be marked with the great Gutenberg Bible, which was printed in 1452. In 1477, William Caxton published a Bible in England, and before the turn of the next century, printing and publishing had spread to all parts of Europe. Thus, the development of printing gave birth to publishing, one of the most fascinating industries of the modern world. With the advent of the printed word, European emergence from the Dark Ages was assured. Superstition, feudal government, religious and political tyranny, technical and scientific ignorance all began to crumble under the impact of printed books.

While book publishing was the first use to which letterpress printing was put, and although it is still the cornerstone of all publishing, it cannot be said that it is the principal segment of the industry. Today, publishing is divided into three major fields: books, magazines, and newspapers. In addition there are a number of other printing activities which come under the heading of publishing. These include maps, greeting cards, prints, music, catalogs, directories, and a vast variety of pamphlets. However, in general, when we speak of the modern publishing industry we think first of books and periodicals.

BOOK PUBLISHING

The creating and publishing of books remains one of the vital activities of our civilization. Without books, our technology would be at a standstill, and would not, indeed, ever have reached its present high state of development. In books we find all the wisdom, knowledge and philosophy of the ages; we find all of man's foolishness and vanity, as well. In most large cities, a single central library could be used to build or rebuild an entire civilization, assuming there were people able to read the language.

Oddly enough this oldest and most highly respected of publishing activities is at the same time the despair of many who are engaged in it. Book publishing in America today has been variously described as antiquated, a dangerous gamble, a leisurely business, a formidable and complex operation, and a sure way of achieving insanity if you aren't already in that lamentable state before you enter the field.

Actually it is an industry with so many facets that there is some truth in all of these statements, but the only one describing it adequately is "a formidable and complex operation."

Book publishing involves the writing and creation of literary works and the marketing of them by authors and literary agents; the editing, designing, and planning handled by publishers; the typesetting, making of paper, the printing and binding carried out by compositors, paper manufacturers, printers, and binderies; the promotion, sale, and distribution of books by advertising agencies, publishers' sales representatives, and shipping departments; the local warehousing and retail selling of books by book "jobbers," or wholesalers, and the bookstores; the library services offered by public, school, and college libraries; and the sale of "subsidiary" publication rights to book clubs, magazines, newspapers, TV and radio, syndicates, and motion-picture producers.

Contrary to popular notions, most book publishers are not printers. Their functions are primarily editing, directing and financing production and marketing the finished product. Usually they buy their typesetting, paper, printing, and binding from other companies which specialize in those services. Only a few large book publishers, such as Doubleday and Company, have their own printing and binding plants.

THE PUBLISHING DILEMMA

Despite its great importance, book publishing in America faces serious difficulties. Recent surveys have indicated that only 17% to 18% of U.S. adults are reading books at any given time. This compares with about 55% in Great Britain. Although U.S. book production amounts to some eight hundred to nine hundred million volumes a year, book publishing accounts for less than one five-hundredth of the nation's business and uses less than one percent of the total United States paper consumption.

A major part of the book publisher's difficulty lies in an antiquated and inadequate system of distribution and marketing. In the United States there are less than 1,000 active retail book outlets which can qualify as bookstores, and about 650 book departments of department stores. Of this total (approximately 1,500) only 400 or 500 are considered worthy of calls by book salesmen. Worst of all, the number of these outlets is *decreasing* in proportion to the population. About 65% of all bookstores are located in 25 major cities where only 20% of the population resides. Even so, these few outlets annually sell over one hundred fifty million books with a retail value of four hundred million dollars.

Compared with the distribution of other national products this picture is a sorry one. Magazines, for example, may be on sale simultaneously in as many as one hundred fifty thousand newsstands, drugstores, candy, variety and food outlets throughout the country. Paperback books come closer to achieving modern mass market distribution. A dozen or more national distributors ship paperbacks to about 800 regional news and magazine wholesalers who, in turn, place the low-priced books in some one hundred twenty-five thousand outlets.

Another effective means of achieving wide book distribution is the book club, which offers its subscribers selections of books from a number of publishers. Some 75 to 80 book clubs conduct a large volume of business and make books available to people in communities where book stores are nonexistent. The idea is credited to Harry Scherman, a founder of Book-of-the-Month Club, who

Covers, or "cases," for books are made on specialized machines. This is a Dexter casemaker in operation at Kingsport Press, Kingsport, Tenn.

established a successful mail-order book business in 1916, offering inexpensive editions of well-known classics called The Little Leather Library. In 1926, with a group of eminent authorities making selections of the best new books, BOMC began mailing books to 5,000 subscribers.

Inadequate retailing has contributed to the phenomenal success of book club operations in America. There are now, in addition to the two major clubs (BOMC and the Literary Guild), dozens of specialized clubs which make selections of religious books, sport books, children's books, and other limited categories for their members.

Upon joining, book club subscribers agree to purchase a stated minimum number of titles during a period of a year. In return, most clubs offer free premium books and produce their own reprint editions at generally lower prices than the publishers' original editions. When a publisher sells one of its titles to a book club it will usually furnish plates for the complete text, illustrations, and jacket. The club pays royalties to the publisher. These payments may range from three or four cents a copy to ten percent of the club's selling price. As the larger clubs may distribute as many as one-half million copies of a popular title, royalties can amount to thousands of dollars. In most cases, the royalties are divided equally between author and publisher.

CLASSIFICATIONS OF BOOKS

There are many different kinds of books, and they come in every imaginable size, thickness, and shape. The chief categories are adult "trade" books, such as novels and nonfiction titles, accounting for about 14% of dollar volume; children's books (generally known as "juveniles"), 16%; paperbound books, 18%; school and college textbooks, 25%; subscription reference books, such as encyclopedias, 17%; and all others, 10%.

HOW BOOKS ARE PRODUCED

For a publisher to be successful he must be able to find and attract authors of the highest caliber and to choose works which will appeal to a wide market. It is in the editorial selection of material where the book publishing industry stands or falls, and it is for this reason that it is often looked upon as a commercial gamble. However, in addition to publishing new works, every major book publisher has a long list of staple books (classic and standard) which are sold in substantial quantities year after year, and which form the "backbone" of the publisher's profits.

The trend in the publication of new books is today moving more and more in the direction of planned projects. In years past, the majority of books were written and submitted to publishers by authors who knew little or nothing about the market for books. Publishers would then sift through scores of manuscripts in the hope of finding a few which they would consider worthy of production. While writers still send thousands of unsolicited manuscripts to book publishers, and while some small percentage of these do find their way into print, editorial staffs are endeavoring to study the book market, to ascertain its needs, and to assign specific projects to writers who are considered experts or authorities in various fields. Even many fiction works are created by cooperative planning between editors and writers.

One of the newest devices in modern textbooks is the use of colored diagrams printed on acetate pages. This anatomical drawing is one of the recent "maps" of the human body produced by C. S. Hammond and Co.

As the writing of any book is a laborious work, requiring months and sometimes years, few professional writers are able to derive all their income from books. Most are engaged in some other full-time business or profession, or they gain the greater portion of their writing income from other publishing fields, primarily magazines.

When the typewritten manuscript is turned over to the editor of a publishing house, it is read, criticized, and accepted or rejected by a staff of "readers." Once it has been approved for publication, a contract is signed by author and publisher, and the manuscript is given to a "copy editor," whose job is to prepare it for the typesetter. Copy editing is an exacting operation involving detailed checking of spelling, punctuation, and grammar as well as verification of facts and the accuracy of the author's statements. After the manuscript has been marked with numerous corrections and queries (the traditional "blue-penciling"), it is either returned to the author for final corrections, or it may go directly to the typesetter, together with layout and design sheets prepared by the publisher's art or production department.

Modern typesetting is done on keyboard-operated machines which can set and cast metal type at a rapid rate. Two kinds of typesetting machines are used for setting most books: the linotype and the monotype. (See *Printing*) In recent years, several photographic typesetting machines have come into use due to the increasing importance of offset printing, the plates for which are made from film negatives or positives. The Fotosetter and other

Skilled operators sit at banks of linotype machines and set copy for books, magazines, or newspapers. Development of tape-operated linecasters has reduced but by no means eliminated the need for human operators.

similar machines are operated from a keyboard, as is the linotype, but they record the letters on film instead of casting them on metal slugs. (See *Photography*)

Whatever method is used for setting type, proofs in the form of long paper strips are returned from the typesetter to the publisher's editorial office. These are known as "galley proofs," a name derived from the fact that columns of metal type are stored in long trays, or drawers known as galleys. Usually one set of galley proofs is sent to the author who reads and corrects it, while the editor corrects another set. Finally all corrections are made on a master set of proofs which are also marked off into pages. Corrected and "paged" proofs are then returned to the typesetter who, following the editor's markings, resets all lines needing corrections and physically divides the type columns into page lengths. He then pulls "page proofs" and returns them to the publisher's offices.

Page proofs are again read and corrected. This is, or should be, the final editorial check, although corrections are sometimes made even after printing plates are ready for press. Upon the approval of page proofs, metal type is locked into forms and cast into plates, if the book is to be printed by the letterpress process. If offset lithography is to be used, perfect proofs are carefully printed on a smooth paper. These are called "reproduction" or "repro" proofs and are photographed by the offset printer to produce film negatives or positives of the complete pages.

Whenever there is a number of pictures to be combined with the text of a book, another editorial operation, known as "dummying" is carried out by the publisher's staff. The dummy is made by cutting and by pasting type and illus-

tration proofs on blank pages, making up a complete book with everything in position, as a guide for the printer. Next the book is printed, the pages being run in large forms of eight to as many as sixty-four pages on a sheet. These large printed sheets are delivered to a book bindery where they are folded into units known as signatures. These signatures are "gathered" or arranged in proper sequence and bound.

BOOKBINDING

Bookbinding, or "edition" binding, is a highly specialized business requiring special equipment and skills. For years it was a slow process involving many hand operations, and even today the best quality books are bound by methods similar to the old-time handicrafts. For most modern books, however, machines have been designed to fold the pages, sew and glue the backs, make the "cases" or cloth covers, and attach the covers to the books. Before being joined to a book, the cover may be printed or stamped with ink or gold leaf.

Most books are sewn with cotton or nylon thread on a machine which puts several stitches through the inside fold of each signature. The threads are hooked to the next signature, which is stitched in its turn, and so on until the entire book of several signatures is sewn together. A signature generally consists of 16 or 32 pages. Special inserts can be pasted in place by the machine, though often this operation is still done by hand. Some books which require extra strength are side-sewn, with the thread running through the entire signature, close to the back.

Next the sewn books are "smashed" in a powerful press which forces all air from between the pages. Another ma-

With this stamping press, book covers are stamped with gold leaf or colored foil titles and decorative designs.

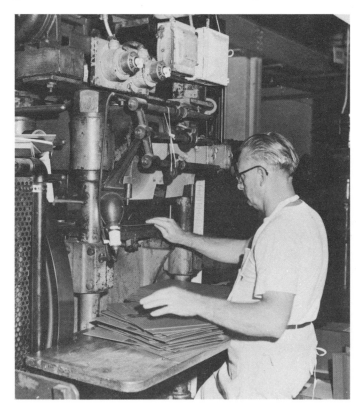

chine rounds the back, applies glue, gauze-reinforcing strips and paper linings. While the sewed book is held in clamps, with the trim edges pressed against a rounding "iron," rollers shape the back. Another set of irons flares the two back edges where the hinge of the cover will later be fitted.

Covers are put together on casemaking machines which glue the cloth, leatherette, or other cover material to pieces of stiff cardboard. The machine turns the edges of the covering material over the two side boards, and over a heavy paper strip which is attached as a lining for the back. Finished covers are then stamped with titles and other decorations before they are attached to the sewed books.

With the development of offset lithography, which has made possible the printing of highly detailed pictures on a variety of surfaces, the printing of full-color art or photographs on the bookcloth itself has come into wide use, especially for school textbooks. In this case the cover designs are printed, several at a time, on large sheets of bookcloth. The printed sheets are lacquered, trimmed, and glued to boards on the casemaking machine.

Several textile mills make special cloth for bookbinding. The cloth is generally a lightweight cotton fabric, specially sized with starch or pyroxylin and dyed in various colors. Foremost in this field are Columbia Mills, Holliston Mills, and Joseph Bancroft & Sons.

Most trade books (those sold to the general public through bookstores) have colorful, printed paper jackets which serve as a protection to the binding as well as a display piece to attract buyers. As a rule, jackets present the publisher's advertising copy, describing the book's contents on the "flaps" which are turned over the front and back covers of the binding. In order to make the package as attractive as possible, the publisher sometimes spends almost as much in the production of the book jacket as he does on printing the entire text of the book.

CHILDREN'S BOOKS

Traditionally books for children have been filled with more pictures and color than any other trade books. In recent years the use of color illustrations in juveniles has greatly increased. Many are made with magnificent printed covers, laminated with clear plastic film to give them a sparkling brilliance and great durability. Some of the finest contemporary commercial art is printed within the pages of modern children's books.

Shortly before World War II, Simon and Schuster brought about a revolution in American children's book publishing by introducing the gaily colored little twenty-five-cent "Golden Books." These have been successfully marketed in the same types of mass outlets as those used for paperbound adult books and magazines. To compete, other publishers brought out equally attractive books, and several lines of low-priced picture books are now on the market. At the same time, the high-priced handsome editions of thicker volumes, beautifully illustrated children's classics and oversized picture books are published in comparatively large quantities. Contemporary American children's books are unsurpassed for technical excellence and lavish use of color in illustrations.

191

Sewing machines in a large book bindery where folded signatures are sewed together with thread prior to being glued and cased-in.

After being sewed, books are glued in this section of a modern bindery.

Some simple designs are printed on cloth book covers by small presses, hand fed by individual operators.

Printing of books is still largely done on sheet-fed presses such as this one, although for large quantities, web presses printing continuous rolls of paper are coming more and more into use.

Large sheets of binder's board are cut to exact size for making book covers.

Fork lifts are used to raise stacks of finished books to the storage shelves in the stock room of a book-publishing firm.

TEXTBOOKS

Although the planning and production details of school textbooks are carried out in much the same way as for other types of books, they require highly specialized editorial knowledge and skills, and the marketing of textbooks is accomplished through entirely different channels. Most of the authors and editors are educators or former educators. Manuscripts on such subjects as mathematics, social studies, English and other languages, history, health, and hygiene must follow certain prescribed curricula for the various grades. Publishers attempt to acquire authors who are recognized authorities on their subjects, for the competition between the textbook publishers is very keen.

Even the physical makeup of textbooks must adhere to certain minimum standards. Because they must withstand hard wear, cloth covers must be of good, durable quality, and bindings are generally reinforced. Due to the great cost of producing a new textbook, publishers of this type of material require large financial resources. For example, more than a million dollars and five or six years of work may be invested in a single series of "readers," before they can be offered to school systems throughout the country.

Sales of textbooks are not made through bookstores or other trade book outlets, but by publishers' representatives, who visit teachers and school administrators in prescribed territories. These specialists must be familiar with the rules and procedures of the school systems. Textbook purchases are subject to local and state laws which establish boards of reviews, set up machinery for making purchases at certain times of the year, regulate amounts of money to be spent on books, and so forth. An adoption committee will often select a textbook for an entire system. Adoptions call for publishers to supply books at a specified price for a period of five or more years.

In recent years the single basic adoption method of making purchases has been largely abandoned in favor of multiple list adoptions. This provides the individual schools with recommended lists, giving each school a choice of two or more books on a subject. Despite strict government regulations controlling school book purchases, textbook publishing in the United States has maintained its status as private enterprise, along with all other commercial publishing.

BIBLES AND RELIGIOUS BOOKS

Another highly specialized field is religious book publishing. Most of the large religious sects in the United States have their own publishing operations for producing books and periodicals. There are also a number of commercial publishing firms which specialize in Bibles and in religious works.

The Holy Bible, still the world's best-selling book, involves special production problems. In the United States, three separate editions are in wide use: the Authorized King James version; the Revised Standard version; and the Douay, Roman Catholic version. Bibles are made in many different styles and bindings, from small, pocket editions and pocket Testaments, to the massive pulpit Bibles. Bindings are generally more complex and more expensive than the bindings of other types of books. Many Bibles are bound in genuine leather. Usually ribbon markers are included, and the better editions are printed on a special thin paper so that the bulk of the volume may be held to a minimum. Edges may be stained red or may be gilded with gold leaf.

Publishers of Bibles compete by offering a list of what is known in the trade as "helps." Helps are special sections of reference material, maps, illustrated features, indexes, and concordances which are added to the text of the Old and New Testaments.

CAREERS IN BOOK PUBLISHING

While it cannot be said that book publishing offers the highest-paid jobs in industry, most publishers today offer good salaries and benefits. There are opportunities for editors, artists, sales and promotion personnel, and particularly for printing production experts. In marketing and distribution there is a great need for new, imaginative thinking. At the same time, book publishing as an industry is founded on a historical background of conservative tradition. Changes come about slowly as a rule, often against stiff opposition of old-guard management. But within the past 10 years, a younger, fresher viewpoint has made itself felt among book publishers who are beginning to recognize that modern marketing and distribution methods are greatly needed. There is a definite trend toward publishing more new books in paperback form and toward distributing low-priced editions through mass outlets. At the same time, publishers have come to recognize the importance of libraries to their business. Many publishers have established departments which specialize in cooperating with libraries, seeking books to fill certain needs, supplying materials which help librarians to promote reading, and making books in durable library bindings.

With all its shortcomings, the book industry is steadily growing, both in dollar volume and number of titles produced. There is every reason to believe that this trend will continue for years to come.

MAGAZINE PUBLISHING

Since the days of Benjamin Franklin's publishing ventures, American periodical publishing has been an exciting, dynamic, and constantly changing industry. As a matter of fact, Ben Franklin not only ranks as America's first great magazine publisher, but he started a publication which grew to be one of today's greatest magazines, more than two centuries later. For the *Saturday Evening Post*, published by Curtis Publishing Company in Philadelphia, traces its ancestry to Franklin's *Pennsylvania Gazette*, founded in 1728.

In the words of Robert E. Kenyon, Jr., 1960 President of the Magazine Publishers Association, magazine publishing "is creating a medium of information, of ideas, of communication, where the intangible content vastly exceeds the tangible product in value. The word for it is publishing. Magazine publishing, moreover, is a creative vocation that offers stimulating challenges in every area of its operation."

One of the presses at the Curtis Park Plant, Sharon Hill, Pa. Each press prints more than 600,000 pages of a magazine in four or five colors every hour.

Of all the types of periodicals, magazines come closest to the category of books. Actually, there are some magazines made almost in the format of books; a notable example being *American Heritage,* which is bound in hard covers and is issued without advertising.

However, unlike books, a magazine has a kind of continuity from issue to issue, an editorial policy, even a theme, by which it is identified. It must establish itself in the minds of readers as an institution; it must build traditions, and when those traditions become outworn, it must either break with the past, or die.

As a result, the editorial staff of a great magazine must operate as a cohesive and compatible team. The editor bears a tremendous responsibility; he wields a significant influence, and it is his direction which gives the magazine its identity. Naturally in such large and complex publishing organizations as the *Post, Life, McCall's, Ladies' Home Journal, Time, Newsweek, Look* and *Good Housekeeping,* there are many writers and department editors contributing to their magazine's composite image, but unless a certain consistent editorial approach is maintained, the publication will literally fall apart and fail.

THE EDITORIAL OFFICES

Whatever a magazine's basic policy or purpose, whether it be to give readers the best of current fiction, weekly news summaries, timely articles on current events, or combinations of these, a general plan and format must be laid out in advance. Art directors and editors plan the layouts of pages to conform with the nature of the articles or stories. As in the making of books, type is set, galley proofs are received and read, dummy pages are made up, and artists or photographers are assigned the task of furnishing illustrations.

The primary difference between magazine and book preparation is the matter of deadlines. While books are produced in accordance with fairly loose schedules, the magazine must be ready to go to press at a certain specified time. There can be no exception to this, and no excuse for delay is acceptable. Whether the magazine is issued weekly, monthly, or at longer intervals, the closing time, when pages are finally turned over to the printer, is absolute. To miss an issue or even to be late on the news-

stands would be almost certain suicide for a magazine of any importance.

In order to meet these deadlines, magazine editorial staffs prepare as much of the material for a given issue as far in advance as possible. Cover paintings, for example, may be bought several months in advance. Articles, stories, or other features which are general in nature and are not dependent upon timeliness are set in type, and pages are completely made up well ahead of the issue date. Even advertising is usually reserved far ahead, and most ad copy is ready long before an issue goes to press. Only the most timely features are written and set up at the last minute.

In the case of a weekly news magazine, the deadline problem is much more urgent. Every issue must be largely made up during the week preceding its release. Even here, the publishers have "filler" material on hand to take care of unfilled pages in case of emergencies. Fillers usually consist of articles and features of general interest which can be printed at any time.

As in modern book publishing, most magazine material is planned or assigned. The editors, sensitive to what is in popular demand, seek writers who will furnish pieces on specific subjects and even with specific editorial points of view. In this, the role of the literary agent can be an important one. Active agents who represent a number of topflight writers, check constantly with editors to ascertain the type of material needed by the various publications. They will then inform the writer or writers who, in their opinion, can do the best job of writing what the magazines want. Sometimes editors will send out a call to agents for good articles on specific subjects.

The larger magazines have their own staff writers who are sent on assignments much as newspaper reporters are sent to get news items. The only difference is that magazine articles must necessarily be more comprehensive, and of more sustained interest than the average daily newspaper story. News magazines, such as *Time, Newsweek, Life, Look,* and *U.S. News and World Report,* have correspondents in many parts of the United States and in most of the world's capitals. Their articles are often wired or cabled in the manner of daily newspaper stories. One of the magazine's functions is to express an editorial view-

(Left) The editor of a weekly news magazine and members of his staff discuss questions on the coming issue. **(Right)** The Teletypesetter Room at "Newsweek's" New York office, where final editorial text is transmitted to the printing plant in Dayton, Ohio.

The editorial makeup room of a large weekly magazine is a hive of activity. Here, upcoming stories are analysed, cut, and fitted into the issue.

point on current news and events. Most national magazines carry regular editorials, written by the editors; the articles, even fiction stories, will reflect in some degree the magazine's editorial policy. Of the various forms of publishing, it is only the magazine which can report in depth, giving analyses of current events in perspective.

ADVERTISING

A large proportion of space in most magazines is devoted to advertising, and it is from the ads that the publishers derive the lion's share of their revenue. The price paid on the newsstand for a national weekly is only a fraction of the production cost per copy. Magazine advertising rates are governed by circulation figures; the larger the circulation, the higher the rates as a general rule. However, specialized magazines with small, select audiences may sometimes command proportionately higher advertising rates than publications with a broad, general circulation.

Because of the tight schedules and deadlines of most national magazines, advertising agencies must reserve space well in advance for their clients. (See *Advertising*) Each magazine has its advertising deadlines for reserving space, for submitting copy, and a later, final deadline for receiving plates. Most magazines have editorial policies concerning the quality and nature of advertising which they will accept. *The Saturday Evening Post,* for example, long refused to accept advertising for alcoholic beverages. All major magazines are careful to police ads to guard against misrepresentation and indecency.

Despite the upsurge of network radio and television, U.S. magazine advertising has increased steadily, with few setbacks, from one hundred million dollars in 1920 to nearly nine hundred million dollars annually in the 1960's.

BUILDING CIRCULATION

The importance and success of a magazine are measured by its circulation. Periodicals are sold in two ways: by subscriptions, and on newsstands and in other outlets which furnish point-of-sale display. Some specialized magazines are sold only by subscription; most are distributed by both ways.

Subscription departments of large magazines must be efficiently organized operations, since they handle thousands of new subscriptions, cancellations, and renewals daily; in addition, they must see that notices are sent to subscribers a few weeks before their subscriptions expire. Most of these operations are now handled by automatic machines. A coded card is made up for each subscription, and a system of punched holes makes it possible to sort the cards automatically by geographical location, expiration dates, and so forth. Though the proportion of subscriptions to newsstand circulation varies with different publications, most national magazines sell more single copies on newsstands than they distribute by subscription.

To maintain a high newsstand circulation, a complex system of checking and scientifically controlled shipping has been developed. Through several hundred wholesalers, bulk shipments of each issue of a magazine are broken up and redistributed to the thousands of food outlets, newsstands, drug and variety stores throughout the country. Each wholesaler keeps careful records showing the number of copies delivered to every retail outlet, the number sold and the number returned for credit. Since all magazines are placed on sale on consignment, publishers must absorb the losses resulting from returns. Because old magazines have virtually no resale value, they are baled and disposed of as scrap paper. Obviously, a magazine cannot long endure if its returns are consistently too heavy.

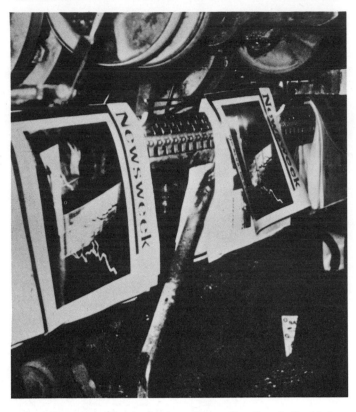

Copies of "Newsweek" magazines are shown going through the bindery. From six A.M. Sunday to early Tuesday morning each week, these magazines are printed, bound, and distributed to all parts of the United States.

To avoid disastrous losses, constant checks are made by the publisher's circulation men, who frequently visit the wholesalers to double check the sales records. The record of each retail outlet is studied. If its returns are high, the number of copies of subsequent issues is cut back; if the record shows it has been selling out all copies, the weekly or monthly deliveries are increased. A good wholesaler will exercise his own judgment in increasing or decreasing the number of magazines delivered to his various outlets. Sometimes he will shift copies from a poor outlet to a more active one while the issue is still current.

Back at the publisher's main circulation office, reports on newsstand sales from all parts of the country are tabulated and analysed, and print orders for new issues are set in accordance with the figures sent in from the field, added to the number of subscriptions in force at that time. A circulation manager must use a combination of science and intuition born of long experience in setting print orders. Even when field reports indicate a decline of sales, he may sometimes increase the next printing, basing his decision on some important feature in the forthcoming issue or on any of numerous other factors.

One of the important recent trends in magazine publishing has been the emergence of regional issues and the sale of regional advertising. Several of the large national magazines have offered local advertisers the opportunity to buy regional space at a considerably lower rate than would be possible on a national basis. This is accomplished by printing special sections of the magazine that will appear only in copies distributed in certain geographical areas. Thus, smaller firms, whose business is regional, are able to afford ads in major periodicals which were formerly beyond their reach. At the same time, large companies can pinpoint their ads to appeal to sectional interest. A tire company, for example, can advertise snow tires in the north and regular tires in the south in the same issue.

Regional advertising is now offered by more than 125 magazines. The magazine largely responsible for this trend is the industry's amazing newcomer, *TV Guide*. Because of its chief feature, the local television weekly program, this magazine must be published in a number of regional editions. Its phenomenal success has led other magazines to study its operations and to imitate some of its unique features.

AMERICA'S GREAT MAGAZINES

One of the newest of U.S. National magazines, *TV Guide* boasted the largest weekly circulation, over eight million copies in the early 1960's. Of this total, about five and one-half million were single copy sales and two million were subscriptions. Located outside of Philadelphia, in Radnor, Pa., *TV Guide*'s main offices are in an ultramodern building completed in 1957. The publication itself was started in April, 1953, with ten regional editions and an initial circulation of a million and one-half copies. In 1961 it had mushroomed to a gigantic organization producing 63 regional editions serving markets in the United States and Canada. The staff of *TV Guide* is composed of more than 850 people in 32 offices; 500 of these persons are employed at the Radnor headquarters.

Compilation of the numerous TV programs throughout the United States and Canada is one of the most complex editorial operations in magazine publishing. With a vast teletypewriter network connecting all of *TV Guide*'s offices and some printing plants, the latest programing information is made available at all times. Occasionally the magazine gathers information that even the major television networks do not have available. In 11 regional offices located at Radnor, Atlanta, Miami, Minneapolis, Detroit, Kansas City, Houston, Los Angeles, San Francisco, Seattle, and Wilkes-Barre, editors are assigned the makeup of programs for various cities. In Radnor, program sections for 13 editions are made up, covering areas from New England to Washington, Detroit, and Chicago. The 32-page national feature section of *TV Guide* is common to all editions and is prepared by the Radnor editorial staff from material sent in by staffs in other parts of the country, including New York and Hollywood. Printing the 63 editions each week consumes 950 tons of paper, enough to fill 32 railroad box cars.

Another great Philadelphia magazine operation is Curtis Publishing Company, publishers of *The Saturday Evening Post* with approximately six and one-half million readers weekly; *The Ladies' Home Journal* with five and one-half million readers; *Jack and Jill,* a children's magazine, with a circulation close to one million; *Holiday* with nine hundred thousand circulation; and *The American Home* with three and one-half million readers—in the early 1960's.

The *Post* maintains a top position as a general magazine of fiction stories, articles on every conceivable subject in the fields of science, sport, politics, and international

Benjamin Franklin's first issue of "The Pennsylvania Gazette" came from the press of B. Franklin, Printer, on October 2, 1729. "The Saturday Evening Post" traces its descent from Franklin's sheet.

Another nostalgic cover representing an era in magazine publishing is this one from the March, 1924, issue of "The Ladies' Home Journal." (©"Ladies' Home Journal." The Curtis Publishing Company.)

An issue of the "Post" at the turn of the century featured a colorful cover which was a pacesetter for magazines of the twentieth century. This one is dated January 27, 1900. (©"The Saturday Evening Post." The Curtis Publishing Company.)

(Left) The Curtis Park Plant at Sharon Hill, Pa., where more than a million and one-half magazines are manufactured and shipped every working day. (Right) The magnificent home of "The Reader's Digest" in Pleasantville, N.Y.

affairs. Its editorial policy has always been marked by a forthright brand of conservatism, and it has endeavored to appeal to all members of the family. In addition to publishing the work of some of America's most brilliant authors over the years, such as Booth Tarkington, Joseph Conrad, O. Henry, Mary Roberts Rinehart, P. G. Wodehouse, Stephen Vincent Benét and Irvin Cobb, the *Post* pages have glittered with the magnificent reproductions of paintings of N. C. Wyeth, J. C. Leyendecker, Maxfield Parrish, Dean Cornwell, Norman Rockwell, and many other great names of American illustrators. *Post* covers have become an American tradition; many by famous artists are classics in their field.

Evidence of the perspicacity of *Post* writers and editors is revealed by an amazing incident of World War II, when federal agents impounded all existing copies of the September 7, 1940 issue and demanded the names and addresses of all persons who requested that issue. The reason for this security measure was an article by William Laurence entitled *The Atom Gives Up*. Written five years before the explosion of the first bomb, it told of the discovery of Uranium 235 and the possibility of a new super weapon. Laurence himself was later forced to surrender his only copy of the issue when he was assigned by the government to prepare releases on the A bomb at Oak Ridge. He had to obtain permission from special guards whenever he wanted to consult his own article.

One of the foremost women's magazines is *Good Housekeeping,* which has developed along with its editorial features a unique service of testing household products. The well-known Good Housekeeping seal of approval is widely recognized as a reliable measure of excellence.

Other important women's magazines include *McCall's* and *The Ladies' Home Journal.* In 1959 and 1960, *McCall's* highly original format set the pace for the entire magazine industry.

NEWS MAGAZINES

The two leading news-picture magazines are *Life,* with a weekly circulation in excess of six million, and *Look,*

with about five and one-half to six million. The main offices of both publications are in New York City.

Life, which was organized by Time, Inc. in 1936, was the first major magazine of this type. Its policy is to present world events primarily through pictures, with a minimum of accompanying text. To make captions and text as interesting and illuminating as possible, as much as five pages of research material may be gathered for the preparation of a single three-line caption. Pictures for a given issue are selected from as many as 10,000 photographs as well as from the magazine's permanent collection of over a million and one-half photos.

Look entered the picture magazine field a few months later, in February, 1937, has grown steadily, and has developed a distinct style and format. Its editorial creed is this: *"Look*—the exciting story of people . . . what they do, what they feel, what they want, what they think . . . an ever changing story told with warmth, understanding, and wonder."

Possibly the most dynamic and exciting of the popular weekly periodicals are the regular news magazines, and for timely coverage of world events, *Newsweek* is outstanding in its field. First published in the depth of the depression, in February, 1933, *Newsweek* has gained a reputation throughout the world for integrity and perception. Its main executive and editorial offices are in New York, but its printing operations are in Dayton, Ohio; Dunellen, N.J.; Los Angeles; London; and Tokyo. It has 17 news bureaus in the United States and abroad and more than 500 writers, researchers, correspondents and editors. The U.S. bureaus of *Newsweek* are located in Atlanta, Chicago, Detroit, Los Angeles, San Francisco, Washington, and the United Nations, and it maintains foreign bureaus in Moscow, Mexico City, Nairobi, London, Paris, Bonn-Berlin, Rome, Beirut, Tokyo and Hong Kong. From these offices, a steady flow of information comes to New York, where editors decide which stories should be prepared for the current issue. When specific stories are assigned, instructions and queries are cabled to the field correspondents; a research staff in the *Newsweek* home office studies its extensive files for background information. As the teletypes begin to click, rattling off a welter of fact and opinion, New York editors prepare orderly and concise accounts, select pictures, maps, and charts to accompany the stories.

Typewritten stories are then accurately copyfitted to precise space allocations and are transmitted to the Dayton, Ohio, printing plant by a teletypesetter. This amazing machine records the words on punched paper tapes which are later fed to the typesetting machines. Instructions at the head of each story give the printer information as to size and style of type, width of lines, and so forth. Each issue closes at midnight Saturday. By six A.M., Sunday, presses are rolling and, by Tuesday morning, *Newsweek* is on sale all over the United States. Simultaneously it is appearing in England and Japan for, at 6:30 A.M. on Sunday, film negatives of the complete issue were put on planes for London and Tokyo. Press plates were also flown to Los Angeles and Dunellen.

Similar in format, but with a strikingly different editorial approach, *Time* is another of the great weekly news magazines. *Time*'s unique style of news writing has been much admired and severely criticized. In any event, it has achieved a distinct identity, differing from *Newsweek*'s handling of news in its editorial "slant," and in the way it injects opinion into its reporting of fact.

Time was organized in 1923 and is now one of seven divisions of Time, Inc., which publishes *Life, Fortune, Sports Illustrated, Architectural Forum, House and Home,* and *Time-Life International.*

For its news-gathering operations *Time* employs about 20 full-time correspondents in its Washington bureau alone; more than 80 in other parts of the United States and Canada. The foreign staff numbers about 70 correspondents, researchers, and photographers.

OTHER WELL-KNOWN MAGAZINES

Other important magazine publishing firms include The New Yorker Magazine, Inc. which publishes *The New Yorker;* Street & Smith Publications, Inc., which produce *Mademoiselle* and *Charm;* Parents' Institute, Inc., which publishes *Parents' Magazine;* Macfadden Publications, Inc., publishers of *True Story, True Romance, True Experience* and others; and McGraw-Hill Publishing Company.

Another great magazine which stands alone in the field is *The Reader's Digest.* This pocket-sized monthly is made up largely of shortened reprints of factual articles, features, and fiction stories selected from other magazines, books, and newspapers. Although its original idea was to digest material from various publications, it now occasionally uses original stories. It also carries advertising, although for years it was one of the few national periodicals which succeeded without revenue from ads. The *Digest* publishes British, Japanese, Latin American, Middle East, Overseas Military, Scandinavian, Swiss, and Western European editions. Total U.S. paid circulation of this magazine exceeds thirteen million copies, of which subscriptions account for more than eleven million. Its global circulation of 40 editions printed in 13 languages has reached the staggering total of over 21 million copies.

This is the largest circulation of all American magazines.

Religious magazines such as the *Christian Herald, Catholic Digest,* and *Presbyterian Life* have large circulations, some well over a million. Nearly all of the major religious sects and denominations sponsor their own periodical publications, some with controlled, non-paid distribution, but many with commercial circulation and paid advertising.

Standard Rate & Data Service, Inc. publishes a periodical catalog of magazine rates and data. This compilation, requiring 476 pages of fine print, lists nearly 100 American magazines with average circulations over a million copies and includes information on about 1,000 periodicals and magazine publishing firms.

In addition to the large popular magazines, American publishers turn out hundreds of specialized publications such as hobby magazines, magazines for fish fanciers, hunting and fishing enthusiasts, railroad men and women, photographers, writers, stock brokers, advertising people, and artists. Nearly every major industry has its trade magazine. Notable among these are *Iron Age; Inland Printer,* and *Western Printer and Lithographer; Modern Packaging; American Druggist;* and the major magazine for the book publishing industry, *Publisher's Weekly.*

MAGAZINE PRODUCTION

National magazines, printed in huge quantities, are run at very high speeds on giant rotary presses which can print, fold, bind, and trim entire issues at rates up to 75,000 an hour. Many of these are color presses which have separate plate cylinders for four, five, or six colors, and which can turn out color illustrations, advertisements, and covers almost as fast as the black-and-white pages are produced.

As fast as the binding sections of the machines turn out finished copies, the magazines are stacked and loaded on waiting trucks, to be transported to distributors and newsstands around the country.

Of all the vast publishing industry, the magazine segment appears to offer the most opportunities for the future. Despite inroads made by television on American reading habits, circulation and magazine advertising figures show no sign of diminishing, rather they have been exhibiting a steady and healthy growth year after year.

NEWSPAPER PUBLISHING

While most people think of newspapers as a modern publishing phenomenon, their history can be traced as far back as Julius Caesar's ancient Rome. It was there in 60 B.C. that the earliest written news publication, the *Acta Diurna* was distributed. Tablets were issued reporting market transactions and prices, the progress of Caesar's legions, and the actions of the Senate. Throughout human history, people's hunger for news has been satisfied by couriers, minstrels, books, magazines, and finally the modern daily newspapers.

In their original form, newspapers were known as "news letters," the first regularly published newsletter appearing in Germany in 1609. It was in England that the term "newspaper" originated, probably with the *Oxford Gazette* about 1665.

American newspaper publishing has a long tradition of fearless presentation of facts and a continuous search for truth, beginning with the *Boston Publick Occurrences, Both Forreign and Domestick* on September 25, 1690. This two-column, three-page newsletter, which measured only six by ten inches, was suppressed after its first and only issue by the British Colonial Governor Simon Bradstreet, who objected to its criticism of the government. Nevertheless, only a few years later, in 1704, another Boston publisher produced *The Boston News-Letter*. This is believed to be the first regularly issued American newspaper. In 1775, there were 37 newspapers flourishing in the colonies, despite the fact that all their type had to be set by hand and that they were laboriously printed on hand-operated presses at a top speed of about 100 copies per hour!

By the Civil War period, illustrated weeklies such as *Harper's* and *Leslie's* were in wide circulation. As there was still no way to reproduce photographs, hand-cut wood engravings were used. For a period of about 25 years, American wood engravers were among the highest-paid craftsmen in the publishing industry. Their detailed illustrations, cut into the end grain of Turkish boxwood blocks, represent a lost art which disappeared with the invention of photoengraving. The introduction of halftone screens to reproduce photographs and the development of typesetting machines, in the latter half of the nineteenth century, made possible the publication of daily, illustrated newspapers.

Today about sixty million daily newspapers are sold in the United States together with some twenty-one million copies of weeklies. There are roughly 1,800 English language dailies, more than 500 Sunday papers, and 9,000 weeklies. In addition, there are eighty foreign language dailies with a combined circulation close to two million.

PUTTING A NEWSPAPER TOGETHER

The ultimate in high-speed publishing is the daily newspaper with its thousands of words, many pages of elaborate advertising, news photos, comic strips, editorial columns, stock market reports, weather data, women's pages, and dozens of other special features. Just to set the type for a single issue of a large metropolitan daily requires a whole battery of linecasting machines, each of which costs from ten to twelve thousand dollars. Presses with ten or more plate cylinders, or units, may cost from one-half a million to three million dollars.

However, before the massive, block-long presses can roll, printing the continuous webs of "newsprint" paper at speeds of many thousands of copies per hour, reporters and editors must gather the news, write the stories, take the pictures, and make up the pages. All this is done in much the same manner as for the makeup of books or the more nearly comparable weekly news magazines, except the entire production must take place in a 24-hour period.

Reporters are assigned to certain "beats," or sources of news. On a city daily, one of the most active of these is the police beat, since the police stations are the focal points for a great variety of events, from robberies, murders, fires, and other disasters to births in taxicabs, missing persons, and a host of tips that can lead an astute reporter to the scenes of important news. Other sources of news are the hospitals and the city hall. Meanwhile the larger newspapers have correspondents in Washington to cover national political events, in the United Nations, and in several of the major capitals such as London, Paris, Moscow, Berlin, Bonn, and Tokyo.

Since no single newspaper is able to cover all the complex activities of the world, wire services have been established to serve newspapers in all parts of the country. The major services, Associated Press, United Press, and International News Service, have correspondents in all parts of the world. Their stories are cabled to central offices which, in turn, send the material out by teletypewriter to all newspapers subscribing to the service. Articles from these services are identified by the datelines leading off the first paragraphs, which carry the initials AP (Associated Press), UP (United Press) or UPI (United Press International), and INS (International News Service). There are also a number of newspaper syndicates whose business is to supply editorial features, comic strips, and cartoons to papers in all parts of the country.

Local and wire-service stories are given to the copy desk, where they are edited and shortened if necessary to fit an allotted space. Next, a headline writer makes up the headlines which must tell all the essentials of the stories in two or three lines. Important stories carry additional subheadlines. If there are to be photographs, captions or "cutlines" must be written and the photos are marked for size and cropping. On layout sheets, which are ruled out in columns corresponding with the standard newspaper pages, areas are marked off for pictures, headlines, and stories. Copy then goes to the composing room where type is set and proofed on galley strips. After editors have read and corrected proofs, dummy pages are pasted up and returned to the composing room. There the type and cuts for pictures are locked up in metal frames so that mats can be pulled. The matrix, or mat, is made from a sheet of fiberboard which, when it is rolled over the type under heavy pressure, receives a female impression of an entire newspaper page. This serves as a mold which can be used for casting a curved metal plate. Curved plates are made to fit the cylinders of the rotary press on which the newspaper is printed.

Last minute stories of important news breaks may be set in type within a few minutes by having a dozen or more linotype operators each assigned to setting up a single paragraph. In extreme cases, an order to stop the presses may be given while a major front-page story is being written, set in type, and cast into a new plate. Stories have been known to appear in newspapers which "hit the street" within an hour after the actual events.

A rotary newspaper press takes paper rolls each weighing about one ton. At a rate of 30,000 to 50,000 copies an hour, the continuous "web" speeds over a maze of cylinders, each of which prints a page of the newspaper. Folding and cutting is done as part of the continuous operation so that finished newspapers emerge at the end of the huge press, ready to be loaded on waiting delivery trucks.

FREEDOM OF THE PRESS

American newspapers, their editors, publishers, and reporters are traditionally unswerving in their quest for facts, and their constant battle to preserve the free press as guaranteed by the United States Constitution is one of the great chapters in American history. In the face of pressure from special interests they have continued to print the truth as they see it. Newspaper reporters have been beaten and jailed, editors have been persecuted, publishing headquarters have been looted and destroyed, but they go on printing the news.

Despite the absolute assurances of freedom under U.S. law, some unscrupulous politicians, gangsters, and many misguided pressure groups try ceaselessly to gag the newspapers. The danger of incurring the displeasure of powerful interests is by no means the only hazard of newspaper publishing. Many correspondents have lost their lives covering such dangerous events as wars, fires, floods, and other disasters.

While there is bound to be some "yellow journalism" and abuse of free speech in a free society, the vast majority of newspapers are noted for their integrity. Even in advertising, publishers exercise their own self-imposed censorship. When a Broadway producer of a musical show tried to place a misleading full-page advertisement in the *New York Herald Tribune,* it was not only taken out of that paper but rejected by other New York newspapers as soon as its false statements were discovered.

NEWSPAPER INDUSTRY, PRESENT AND FUTURE

During the past quarter century, newspapers have undergone some notable changes, particularly in format and typography. Column width has become narrower and average body type larger, making for easier reading. More pictures are better reproduced on an improved quality of newsprint. "Magazine" sections, feature pages, and even some front pages of daily papers are beginning to use color.

Newspapers are still the largest medium for advertising, which furnishes about 70% of their revenue. Annual newspaper advertising expenditures amount to about three and one-half billion dollars. Still, many individual newspapers are facing financial difficulties partly due to the greatly increased costs of labor and machinery. Mechanical equipment in many plants is becoming obsolete; yet with high taxes they cannot accumulate enough reserve capital from earnings to modernize.

Very few new newspapers are being founded; virtually no sizable dailies have been started in the last 25 years, whereas a large number have closed their doors. An internal tug of war between management and labor has not helped the situation. Publishers have been slow to take up technological innovations or to sponsor research and development studies. By the same token, unions have resisted labor-saving devices and machinery.

The industry is in need of production engineers and imaginative management who will make quick and effective use of technological advances. Not only are more and more tape-operated linecasters coming into use, but electronic scanners can reproduce and automatically engrave photographs on a printing plate. Better color presses

Workmen swarm over a giant newspaper press as it is made ready to run the first of a day's editions.

Checking one of the color pages of a daily paper while it is still on the press, these "Philadelphia Evening Bulletin" pressmen can make corrections directly on the curved plates if flaws are not too serious.

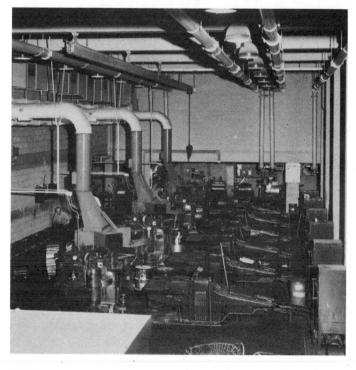

In stereo presses, curved newspaper plates are cast from fiberboard mats.

As daily newspapers emerge from the monstrous rotary presses at a rate of 30,000 to 50,000 copies per hour, delivery trucks wait at the loading platform to speed the papers to newsstands and dealers in all parts of a great city.

are offering advertisers more effective ads which in turn will bring more revenue to the newspapers.

Meanwhile there are hints of things to come which may completely revolutionize newspaper publishing. The Russians claim to have an electronic machine that can set type from copy at a rate of 8,000 characters (about 2,300 words) per second. Meanwhile a Swiss scientist has designed a "typosonograph" which can type words spelled phonetically directly from voice dictation. There are experiments being made in printing newspapers with photo-offset presses, instead of the traditional letterpress, at great cost savings in equipment and plates.

Whatever the problems and whatever the new technological innovations, the newspaper industry remains a vital factor in American life, for without it a free society could not long endure.

MAP PUBLISHING

Cartography, the art of making maps, has been practiced for at least 4,500 years, the oldest known maps having been inscribed on clay tablets about 2500 B.C. On the renowned Turin Papyrus, which dates back to 1320 B.C., is a map locating an Egyptian gold mine.

However, the mapping of large areas of the earth's surface did not begin until the development of mathematically precise surveying instruments. It was the Greek, Claudius Ptolemaeus, living in Alexandria about A.D. 150, who established some of the first sound principles for map making. It is believed that Columbus used a Ptolemaic map when he set forth on his first voyage. As exploration pushed the world's unknown frontiers farther and farther back, knowledge of geography increased. Accurate charts of the Mediterranean Sea were produced in Renaissance Italy, and by the fifteenth century, Spanish and Portuguese maps were in wide use. In 1568, Gerhardus Mercator, a Dutch cartographer, devised a projection of the world to aid navigators.

Modern production of accurate, minutely detailed maps

began only about 200 years ago. It was made possible by the accumulated knowledge of centuries, the development of trigonometry, and the perfection of surveying instruments.

Nevertheless, no map is ever completed or final for all time. Because the earth's land and water areas are constantly shifting, and because political boundaries are even less permanent, map publishing is a process of perpetual revision.

Maps fall broadly under four classifications: *Physical* or *Topographical* maps showing the earth's mountains, valleys, forests, deserts, rivers, and lakes; *Political* maps giving the arbitrary, man-made divisions of nations, states, counties, cities, and so forth; *Geological* maps indicating rock, soil, and some subsurface features; and *Hydrographic* maps dealing primarily with water areas and the depths of various parts of the seas, as well as lighthouses, buoys, fisheries, shipping channels, and coastal markings. Most maps combine the features of two or more of these general classifications. In addition there are many types of specialized maps such as weather maps and those dealing with statistics.

MAP PREPARATION

The map publisher's art department must be well equipped with drafting instruments and staffed with skilled specialists. Map making requires the skills of mathematicians, surveyors, historians, artists, mechanical draftsmen, photographers, and printers. One of the most interesting art processes involved is that of portraying topography to give the effect of mountains and valleys in relief. Most of the drawings for this are made on acetate sheets placed in position over master outlines of the maps. Artists painstakingly render the peaks and valleys with fine pencil- or crayon-shading strokes. There are only a handful of specialists in the United States who are capable of this exacting work.

To label various geographical units, cities, towns, and rivers, different typefaces are selected. Roman, italics, capital letters or lower case, bold- and light-faced types are employed to make a variety of classifications easily identifiable. Most of this type must be set by hand and carefully proofed on small presses. It is essential that each name or title shall fit its space on the finished map. Often the names must be arranged in curved lines, as along the courses of rivers and streams. Proofs of the type are photographed, made in the form of film positives, and then burnished into the film positives of the map drawings.

Meanwhile areas of color are painted in by hand on acetate overlays. Many maps are printed in five or more colors, and a separate drawing is made for each color.

The map publisher is aided by a number of official geographical and geological agencies. Among these are the U.S. Geological Survey which maps land areas, the Hydrographic Office for charting foreign seas, Canada's Department of Mines and Technical Surveys, and the U.S. Government's Army Map Service.

GATHERING DATA

One of the most fascinating aspects of modern map publishing is the constant search for up-to-date statistical and geographical data. In a world politically divided, information is sometimes hard to obtain, but every effort is made to penetrate behind the iron curtain as well as into remote and inaccessible areas of the world. A map publisher obtains the latest atlases from Russia and other European Communist countries through dealers in West Germany. Meanwhile, contacts in Hong Kong provide information on Communist China. As there is no way to be certain of the accuracy of Iron Curtain publications, every effort is made to check new data against past information and to compare it with that which other sources have uncovered. The U.S. Government assists map publishers by furnishing translations of various foreign publications.

A veteran typesetter carefully compares a piece of type with his specimen chart for map preparation. Dozens of different type faces must be used on a single map to designate various geographical units.

Sometimes the quest for map and atlas information smacks of high adventure. To obtain facts concerning population figures, changes in political boundaries, and other pertinent data from remote sections of Asia, a lone operator makes regular journeys from India into the Himalayan states. These hazardous research trips may require six to eight months, during which time no contact can be made with the publisher.

Map accuracy has been greatly improved by aerial photography. Recently detailed Canadian maps of the Arctic regions revealed a huge island never previously recorded, but which was clearly shown by aerial photographs. Among the more difficult regions for up-to-date

(Left) Maps are used to create new maps, and the map publisher is aided by a number of official geographical and geological agencies. This is a scene in the map division of C. S. Hammond and Company. (Right) A cameraman prepares to expose a map negative in Hammond Company's massive 42-inch camera.

and accurate cartography are Latin America and Africa. In both continents, political upheavals and disputed boundaries present constant problems to the map publishers. Important sources of census statistics and information on geographic boundaries are the U. S. consulates and embassies in the various countries.

Map compilation has its humorous aspects, particularly when it comes to names. Some of the smaller communities have a disconcerting habit of picking bizarre titles and voting to rename their towns. When Hot Springs, New Mexico received some sudden publicity on a popular radio show, its excited residents changed the name to Truth or Consequences, which was the show's title. Probably one of history's best examples of making a mountain out of a molehill occurred when citizens of Molehill, West Virginia decided they might have a better chance of "putting their town on the map" by calling it Mountain. It is of such things that map publishers' gray hairs are made. But it also keeps map sales active, as last year's maps quickly become obsolete.

PRINTING MAPS AND ATLASES

Map publishers produce a great assortment of folded maps, globes, and atlases. Road maps, maps of cities, states, and other geographical areas are in constant demand. They must be revised and reprinted continually to be kept up to date.

In addition to preparing dozens of complex maps, making the plates and printing them in several colors, the publishing of an atlas requires tabulation of all sorts of statistics and indexes. So extensive is the index in a world atlas that a modern publisher uses tabulating machines for the compilation.

Though it is an exacting and highly technical aspect of publishing, map making is a rewarding and stimulating field. With the continuing increase of land, sea, and air travel, and with the never ending changes in world geography, this is an industry that must continue to grow in this space age. What do the stars foretell of its future? One thing is certain, there will be maps of the heavens, the planets, and of the stars themselves!

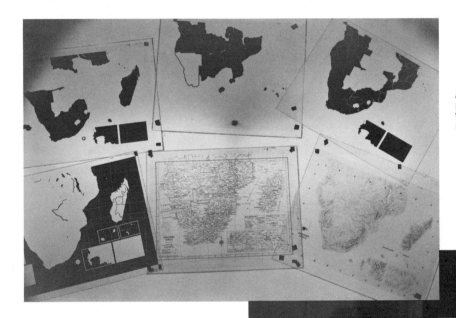

Art preparation for a map includes detailed overlays, painted by hand on acetate sheets, for various colors, as well as for carefully delineated mountains and surface contours, as shown at lower right.

Painstaking handwork is required to prepare a map negative prior to exposing a plate. Dust-caused pinholes in black areas and rough edges must be corrected by a master craftsman.

The live show in close proximity to an applauding audience will probably persist as the ultimate in entertainment, and the stage is still the core, the heart, and the soul of the entertainment world. Above is a scene from "My Fair Lady," one of the greatest Broadway musical hits of all time.

34 Stage

The curtain is going up! In a darkened theater, the audience is hushed, the orchestra is playing the last strains of the overture, while a glow of footlights illuminates the stage. A little world is about to envelope us with its magic, and for an hour or two we live the hopes, the fears, the laughter, and the tragedy created by a handful of actors on a small platform.

Since ancient Greece, when the theater reached a rare peak of dramatic art, the stage has been the focal point of all entertainment industries, and even in an age of movies, radio, and television, actors still find that the stage play, or "legitimate theater," is the best training ground and in many ways the most satisfying of entertainment media. Early in the development of radio, performers found that they could do a far better job in front of a live audience than by merely talking into a cold, lifeless microphone. As a result, most of the important radio and TV shows are enacted before live audiences, whose laughter and applause are important ingredients for a successful production. (See *Radio and Television*) Motion pictures, on the other hand, are produced under very different circumstances and with special techniques which make it impossible to have theater audiences during filming. (See *Motion Pictures*) Still, most movie actors and actresses find it necessary to return to the stage occasionally to get the "feel" of an audience.

THEATER AS AN INDUSTRY

The creation of a major stage production, whether it is a play, a musical, an opera, or a ballet, requires all the management, direction, finance, labor, and skill of a major industry, and although it is seldom thought of as an industrial enterprise, it is big business in the strictest sense. A producer of a dramatic play on Broadway will require from fifty to a hundred thousand dollars in order to put the production together. For an elaborate musical comedy he may need close to half a million dollars. He must first select a play, which he may buy from the playwright outright, or on some sort of royalty basis. He then engages a director, scenery and costume designers, stage hands, electricians, business and publicity managers, actors, actresses, "extras," and musicians, and procures a theater and a hall for rehearsals. Rental of a Broadway theater may cost from $3,000 to $7,500 per month. This is a major item in the budget of the producer. Also, in his

At first rehearsal of "My Fair Lady," on January 2, 1956, Julie Andrews and Rex Harrison talk over the musical score with author Alan Jay Lerner, and composer Frederick Loewe. In the background is the late Moss Hart, director.

budget will be such items as insurance, costs of transporting large pieces of scenery, newspaper advertising and publicity, to say nothing of salaries for the cast, stage hands, and clerical help. Legal fees can be a considerable budget figure, since a lawyer is engaged to draw up contracts with a number of guilds and labor unions, including the Actors' Equity, American Federation of Musicians, Dramatists Guild, United Scenic Artists of America, International Alliance of Theatrical Stage Employees, and the Association of Theatrical Agents and Managers.

PREPARATION AND CASTING

Before any production can get under way, the producer, director, and sometimes the playwright supervise selection of the cast. Casting and talent agencies are notified that performers are needed and that casting and auditions will take place at a certain time and place. Each actor selected for a part is given an Equity contract, drawn up to conform with rules of Actors' Equity, the bargaining agent for the acting profession.

Artists who "try out" for the play are given copies of the script and are asked to read some scenes to the director and producer. Established stars may not be asked to audition, since their style and talents are well-known. Frequently, the male and female leads are selected by reputation and all that remains is bargaining over the salaries they will be paid.

Meanwhile, artists are submitting their sketches for costumes and scenes. Design of stage settings requires full knowledge of mechanical requirements of the theater, and of the particular stage or stages on which the play will be performed. The designer must plan for lighting effects, special properties called for by the script, efficient and rapid scenery changes. When his sketches have been approved by the producer and his director, blueprints are prepared and are turned over to a scene builder who constructs the various sections. Where special designs are

required, costumes are likewise made to order, or are rented from a costumer for classical or established plays, such as Shakespeare or Gilbert and Sullivan productions, which may call for stock outfits. In all cases, the costumes must be fitted to each member of the cast.

REHEARSALS

Ranking with the most grueling and exhausting work in the world, rehearsing for a play or musical production may go on for three to four weeks before the first performance. Beginning with informal rehearsal of lines, without scenery or "props" (properties), the actors go through motions, reading from "sides" or individual actors' parts extracted from the book and with special cues and directions typed in.

The director follows every line and action, instructing each performer how to gesture, where to stand, how to move across the stage, how to produce the proper tone and inflection of voice. Within two weeks, performers have their parts fully memorized and during the third week begin to run through the complete play. After a full dress rehearsal, complete with scenery and costumes, the play is ready for its first public performance.

OPENING NIGHTS

Most Broadway productions are tried out first in other cities where audience reactions can be tested and weak spots can be corrected before the Broadway opening. A typical opening circuit would start in New Haven, Conn., move to Boston for a week, then to Philadelphia for a week, and finally to the Broadway theater.

An opening is always a time of great excitement; it will probably be attended by critics, playbrokers, ticket brokers, important directors and producers, talent scouts from movie studios and from television networks. The future of the play and its actors is greatly affected by the reaction of this first-night audience.

While actors apply stage makeup and get into costumes, carpenters and electricians rehearse cues for changes of

Rex Harrison and Julie Andrews enact a scene from "My Fair Lady," the musical comedy based upon George Bernard Shaw's play, "Pygmalion."

In the heart of Manhattan's garment district, the Metropolitan Opera House is a drab brick structure occupying an entire city square.

scenery, for lighting effects and for having properties in the right places at the right times.

As the curtain time approaches, usually 8:30 P.M., tension mounts. The stage manager who is in charge of the performance, sees that prompters are ready with "prompt books" to help any player who may forget a line or miss a cue. Meanwhile a "callboy" knocks on dressing room doors, calling the actors to the stage. When everything is ready, the curtain goes up and the drama begins.

Assuming that all goes well and the show is ready for its important New York opening, the producer and his cast must now pass another critical test. Attending a Broadway premier will be the drama critics from the leading New York newspapers and a large number of "first-nighters" whose approval or disapproval can make or break a new play. Some plays and musicals survive only a few poorly attended performances, but the smash hits have been known to enjoy Broadway runs lasting for years.

STOCK COMPANIES AND ROAD SHOWS

Although stock companies which perform an established list of plays, or a repertory, have almost died out in America, a few semiprofessional and amateur repertory groups still keep the practice alive in smaller towns and cities around the country. But in many sections of the United States good stage productions are rarely seen. Occasionally, the cast of a hit show will tour the country after completing a long Broadway run. In other cases, a separate road company will take the show on tour while the original cast is giving performances in New York.

Summer theaters, usually near vacation resorts, present plays and musicals by having some well-known star acting the lead, while the rest of the cast is filled by young actors and actresses who are thus afforded an opportunity to gain professional experience.

OPERA

A highly specialized form of theater is the opera which requires the most highly trained musical and singing talent. As with symphony orchestras (See *Music and Re-*

cording), opera companies are heavily supported by patrons whose contributions help to make up operating deficits. However, increased interest in the opera in recent years has resulted in greater support by the general public.

Modern opera as an art form first appeared during the sixteenth century in Renaissance Italy, and for some of the spectacular scenic effects used in early operatic productions, the great Leonardo da Vinci contributed his talents. The revolving stage was one of his innovations.

From its beginning, opera symbolized the glitter and wealth of a select circle of aristocratic patrons. Consequently, most European opera halls were magnificent, palatial structures, and performances were attended by royalty and other elite. To some extent, this tradition is still reflected in the great operatic productions in the United States, but as might be expected, American audiences are composed of music lovers from all walks of life.

The first operatic performance in America was given in Charleston, S.C., in 1735, where *Flora, or Hob in the Well,* a comic opera by Cibber, was produced. From that time to the present, American cities have supported a number of distinguished opera companies, and performances are popularly attended in Chicago, Boston, New York, and Philadelphia. Since its founding in 1883, the Metropolitan Opera has been America's foremost opera company and one of the leading theatrical companies in the world. In the heart of Manhattan's bustling garment district, the Metropolitan Opera House is a drab brick structure occupying an entire city square. Inside, it is luxuriously appointed with wine colored, upholstered seats on five balcony levels.

Now known as the Metropolitan Opera Association, Inc., the company has built up an outstanding repertory of famous operas and has developed or starred most of the world's greatest singers. During a typical opera season of twenty-four to twenty-six weeks nearly six hundred thousand people attend the regular performances, while it is estimated that some fifteen million listeners tune in on Saturday afternoon radio broadcasts. Television performances are further expanding the national audience.

The famed "Diamond Horseshoe" inside the Metropolitan Opera House on the night of a performance. The interior is luxuriously appointed.

On the Metropolitan's payroll are some 800 people, about 300 of whom are performers. There are nearly 100 members of the orchestra, a chorus of 78 singers and a ballet troup of 36 dancers. Major operatic productions require the following techniques and talents of the theater: costume and scenery design, stage direction, acting, singing, dancing, and musical direction.

CIRCUSES

Spectacle of spectacles, aptly termed by P. T. Barnum as "the greatest show on earth," the circus remains one of the most amazing productions in show business. Sadly, the day of the "big top" or giant tent seems to have waned, and the great Ringling Brothers Barnum and Bailey circus no longer moves into town behind the tent crews and the fabulous tent city which they used to erect like magic in the night.

Nevertheless, the smaller tent circuses still exist, and the big ones still put on their great shows, complete with sawdust rings, elephants, horses, and acrobats in indoor halls and arenas.

The term *circus* is a Latin word meaning ring, or circle, and it was used in ancient Rome to designate the large circular arenas in which spectacular sports' events and entertainments were held. The modern circus show can trace its origin to traveling bands of jugglers, clowns, and acrobats who entertained the populace at country fairs during the Middle Ages. Then, in the late eighteenth century, an Englishman by the name of Philip Astley organized a circus featuring equestrian tricks. It was he who originated the custom of advertising the coming of his show with flamboyant posters stating that his acts would amaze and astonish his audiences. Those audiences were not disappointed.

During the nineteenth century, circuses reached a peak of popularity in the United States, where people in isolated rural areas turned out *en masse* to see the shows. As their following increased, circuses grew in size and became major business enterprises. The big three-ring circuses erected tents 90 ft. high with seating capacity for 5,000 people. Circus caravans of gaudily painted wagons stretched for the better part of a mile, and the circus parade preceding the opening show was a holiday event.

Today's circus is still big business in the show world, but modern traffic and the disappearance of open lots for the erection of tents has transformed it into a more conventional type of indoor entertainment. Nevertheless, as a traveling organization, it is still a miracle of efficient planning. Wild animals, horses, tons of complicated equipment, performers, blacksmiths, animal trainers, veterinarians, musicians, technicians, and stage hands all must be packed up and transported on a tight schedule from town to town; and the paraphernalia must be set up, ready for the opening show in a new location in record time.

Most circus people spend their lives traveling with their companies and know no other homes, though between seasons, many of them go to Florida where they practice their acts or originate new ones.

Where tents are used, the procedure for setting them up is in itself a wonder to behold. While a boss canvasman gives directions, sections of canvas are rolled out and laced together. The tall center pole is raised, by means of a power-driven crane, or by elephant power and block and tackle. Guy wires are stretched and staked, then other poles are raised and large stakes are driven, either by sledgehammer crews or mechanical pile drivers. So efficient are circus crews that it is said German military leaders during World War I sent spies to study the operations of the Barnum and Bailey circus as a model for moving large bodies of men and equipment.

With all the technological changes in modern living, and despite the advances of electronics and television, the live show in close proximity to a cheering, applauding audience will probably persist as the ultimate in entertainment. The stage is still the core, the heart, and the soul of the entertainment world.

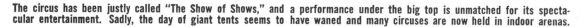

The circus has been justly called "The Show of Shows," and a performance under the big top is unmatched for its spectacular entertainment. Sadly, the day of giant tents seems to have waned and many circuses are now held in indoor arenas.

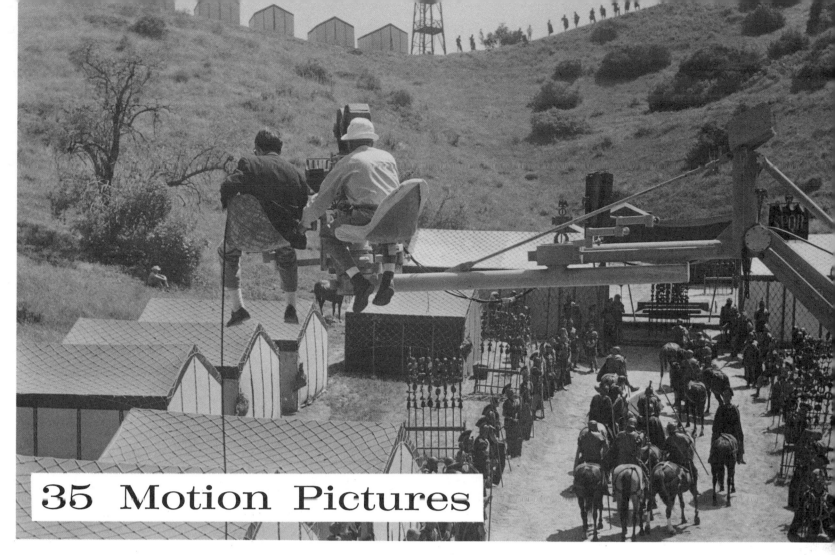

A camera boom, with the director sitting next to the camera operator, goes up high to film a scene in the movie, "Spartacus," a twelve-million-dollar production of Universal-International.

35 Motion Pictures

Let's go to the movies! Even in this era of television, that invitation is an appealing one, for the spectacular color and scope of the modern motion-picture production is unmatched by any other form of entertainment. Indeed the motion-picture industry plays an important role in television itself.

With all its size, wealth, and glamor, the industry has a brief history. In 1900 there was no such thing as a movie theater. By 1910, a few vacant stores and warehouses were being used to show nickelodeon films, and in 1920 a wildly disorganized, but exciting, new giant of the entertainment world was just beginning to hit its stride. Today it is estimated that the weekly world audience for motion pictures is about one hundred fifty million people.

Movies began with two inventions. Thomas Edison first created a practical motion-picture camera, but to accomplish this he needed George Eastman's flexible film. (See *Photography*) Edison was actually combining a number of previous developments and experiments when, in 1888, he made a revolving cylinder for taking a series of pictures to create the illusion of motion. The machine utilized the features of the popular "magic lantern," and a toy called the magic wheel, or zoetrope, which whirled a series of painted figures past an opening. However, Edison's first results were unsatisfactory. The introduction of cellulose nitrate film solved his problem.

The first peep show using Edison's kinetoscope was unveiled to the public in New York in 1894, but since it could be viewed by only one person at a time, its commercial possibilities were limited. Two years later another machine, designed by Thomas Armat and called the Armat Vitascope projector, made possible the showing of movies on a screen.

Still, movies did not graduate from the novelty category until 1905, when John P. Harris and Harry Davis, two Pittsburgh real estate men, put 99 seats, a movie projector, and a piano into a vacant storeroom and charged the public a nickel to view *The Great Train Robbery*. Made two years earlier, this was the first complete story to be recorded on a reel of motion picture film. Soon nickelodeons were opening everywhere. Among the early promoters were some of the industry's greatest names. Adolph Zukor, William Fox, Marcus Loew, and Carl Laemmle all started their movie careers with penny arcade kinetoscopes and nickelodeons.

A legal battle now developed between Edison's firm and the Biograph Company over the control of motion-picture patents. When the two groups pooled their processes in 1908 to form the Motion Picture Patents Company, they began licensing their machines to nickelodeon operators. Still, the day of the nickelodeon was rapidly waning. Men with greater vision soon put the Patents Company out of

(Left) Nickelodeons got their start in 1905 by showing the first full-length feature picture, entitled 'The Great Train Robbery." A rare scene is shown here. (Right) Among the great motion pictures of all time was Charlie Chaplin's "The Gold Rush," a top box office attraction in 1925.

business, as the "big picture" concept began to sweep the industry. In 1915, D. W. Griffith produced one of the first great spectaculars, *Birth of a Nation,* which ran on Broadway and then throughout the United States for several years.

When producers and promoters began to realize that fabulous amounts of money were to be made on movies, a mad scramble for distributor franchises, popular stars, dramatic stories, and all types of talent ensued with a resulting chaos that nearly wrecked the industry. But in 1922, Motion Picture Producers and Distributors of America, Inc. was established with Will H. Hays at its head. This organization, later to become Motion Picture Association of America, Inc., brought stability and direction to the situation by setting up codes and standards for the industry.

INTRODUCTION OF SOUND

Although as early as 1894 Edison had experimented with sound movies by combining his phonograph with the kinetoscope, successful amplification and synchronization systems did not come until 1921. After a period of testing and improvement, the first sound pictures were tried on the public in 1926, but it was another two years before sound production was in full swing.

Though the modern sound movie is a great improvement over the early efforts, it is merely a refinement of the same basic principles. As the film passes before the projector's lens, a rapid succession of still pictures is flashed on the screen at a speed of 24 frames per second. Each picture is stopped for a brief fraction of a second, and the human eye tends to retain the image for about a tenth of a second after it is removed. This "persistence of vision" results in a kind of blending of images, so that the impression is of continuous motion. Meanwhile, a shutter in the projector is so synchronized that it shuts off the light while one picture frame is being replaced by the next. This prevents blurring as a picture moves out of position and a new one slides into view. It was the rotary shutter, a spinning disk with openings at correct intervals for proper synchronization, that made good motion-picture projection possible.

On the talking film is a sound track consisting of a narrow band at the left. While a movie is being filmed, microphones pick up voices and all other sounds, and an electronic tube converts the sound into electrical impulses whose variations correspond to the varying sound vibrations. The electrical impulses produce light of varying intensity; this light, in its turn, is photographed on the film's sound track. When the film is run through the projector, the light and dark changes on the sound track fall on a photoelectric cell and another electronic tube reconverts the light to its corresponding sound vibrations.

VISIT TO A STUDIO

Because of its amazing diversity of scenery, California was an inevitable geographical center for America's movie world. Within a comparatively small area are deserts, large modern cities, tropical forests, snow (in the high elevations), and prairies. Although New York City is the financial and distribution capital of the motion-picture industry, it is in Hollywood where we find the color and glamor of cinema production.

Each major Hollywood studio is in itself a small city, complete with streets, industries, retail stores, offices, theaters, and projection rooms, as well as elaborate sets for actual filming operations. Within the confines of a large movie studio, more than 275 trades and professions are represented. Among them are artists, writers, carpenters, electricians, painters, cameramen, sound men, directors, producers, actors and actresses, laboratory and research personnel, stenographers, makeup specialists, barbers, manicurists, seamstresses, and tailors.

The sets are found on numbered "stages," but these

stages are not small platforms like those in ordinary theaters. "Stage 6," for example, may be a tremendous shed, constructed like a Quonset hut. Inside, hundreds of people are at work in an atmosphere of seeming confusion where carpenters are hammering, electricians are arranging mazes of wire, banks of overhead lights glare brilliantly from different angles, and performers in costume seem to be wandering aimlessly.

All this is preliminary to shooting a scene. In one corner of the huge building, workmen have set up two interior walls of a room in an ancient castle. Furnishings, tapestries, candelabra—everything is being put in place to achieve an effect of utmost realism. Yet at the edges of the set are clutters of mechanical equipment, wires, lights, reflectors and unused properties which give the appearance of some curiosity shop or junkyard. In two or three groups, actors and directors are rehearsing lines, while script men or women, carrying bound portfolios, give speech or action cues by referring to the pages of the script.

When at last the scene is ready to be filmed, the "extras" move onto the set. In this case they are a group of armored castle-guards; there is to be some sword fighting; and the hero of the story will engage the guards on a flight of steps at the right side of the set. The director and his assistants give the extras their final instructions while cameramen and sound men move into position.

Modern cameras move on dollies and on huge overhead booms so that scenes can be filmed from all sorts of angles, and the cameras can be moved in for close-ups with smooth precision. Cameras are now trained on "stand-ins." These are a man and a woman about the same build as the two stars of the picture. Their job is to go through some of the action on the set while cameramen adjust their focuses, and sound men check sound levels.

The director, who is in charge of the entire operation, is having the light crew adjust some spotlights to his satisfaction. A moment later, the rehearsal is under way. The principals, or stars, take their places on the set; extras are ready; lights are turned on; and the shouted order, "camera" is the signal to begin filming.

Instantly all clatter and activity of work crews cease. Red lights go on in various parts of the shed, warning everybody to silence. The hero and heroine speak a few lines; they embrace; then from a wing of the set, another actor in costume strides onto the scene. He and the hero draw swords. After a brief clash, the director stops the action. This short sequence is filmed three or four times before the next part of the action is begun.

Few people realize how much preparation, time and money must be expended to produce a few feet of film for a movie. Average production in the big Hollywood studios has been calculated to be three minutes of finished film in an eight-hour workday. Some feature pictures are a full year in production.

Outdoor sequences may be filmed on sets at a studio ranch, many of which are in the San Fernando Valley. Of course, where special scenery is required, casts and production crews are often transported to locations where authentic backgrounds are available. Occasionally, this may be thousands of miles from the studio.

Many American motion pictures are noted for mammoth spectaculars and lavish scenes such as this one from "Cleopatra," which was filmed in Rome by Twentieth Century-Fox in 1961.

THE WORD IS "BIG"

The motion-picture business, even with the advent of television, remains one of the world's major industries. Although it is almost entirely an entertainment medium, except for a small percentage of educational film production, it was nevertheless considered an essential service during World War II. Like publishing, radio, and television, it requires the investment of large sums of money on ideas, stories, acting talent, and so on without any assurance of public acceptance. It is the producer's responsibility to gauge his public and to turn out pictures

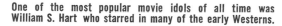

One of the most popular movie idols of all time was William S. Hart who starred in many of the early Westerns.

that will be popular at the box office. Failures are far too costly for a movie studio to absorb many and still survive.

About a quarter of a million people depend on the motion-picture industry for their income. With an invested capital of some two and three-quarter billion dollars, the major movie companies, which include Warner Brothers, Twentieth Century-Fox, Paramount, RKO, United Artists, Metro-Goldwyn-Mayer, Universal Pictures, and Walt Disney Studios, consume over two billion feet of film a year and spend fifty to sixty million dollars annually on newspaper advertising alone.

After movies are filmed and edited, from 250 to 400 prints of the finished pictures are made for distribution to theaters throughout the United States and the world. Distribution is made by the studio sales department or by an independent distributor who has a contract for handling the company's productions. Some years ago, motion pictures were sold under a system called "block booking" whereby an exhibitor contracted for all or a large percentage of a producer's output in a given year.

However, a Federal court ruling in 1940 resulted in limiting the sale of blocks to five pictures and in giving exhibitors the right to see them at trade showings in their respective territories before agreeing to take them. Again, in 1946, the court ruled that no exhibitor may be forced to take other films as a condition for being allowed to show an important feature film.

Exhibiting theaters are of many types. There are the deluxe "first-run" city theaters which specialize in premier showings of features films at high prices. After these showings, the pictures move on to the suburban, or neighborhood theaters, and to the open-air, drive-in theaters which have become increasingly popular in recent years. Rental fees vary according to the number and quality of the audiences. The same picture may bring the producer several thousand dollars in rental fees from a Broadway theater and only fifteen or twenty dollars in a small town. Generally these rentals are determined as a percentage of box office receipts.

The foreign market for American movies is very large, accounting for from 40% to 50% of the producers' total revenue.

With the impact of TV, the motion-picture industry has undergone important changes since World War II. Despite many technical improvements, such as the wide-angle screen, Cinerama, CinemaScope and various three-dimensional viewing and stereophonic sound techniques, moviegoers began to stay home in front of their TV sets. In their efforts to shock or impress the public with bigness and startling effects, the movie producers seemed to forget that depth of emotion, character, and drama are more important elements of their art than depth of screen dimension, color or sound.

Inevitably a large proportion of motion-picture production has become devoted to films for televiewing. Producers are also deriving considerable income from repeated telecasting of old movies. Yet the local theater remains the greatest source of motion-picture revenue.

The industry appears due for a renaissance of superb acting and photography. As the early novelty of television has worn off, there has been a noticeably increased attendance in theaters. With better quality productions, the motion-picture industry has a golden opportunity to reach greater heights than ever before as America's number one source of entertainment and dramatic art, although it will have to go far to surpass the great performances of Hollywood's most glamorous era, which produced such stars as John and Lionel Barrymore, Will Rogers, Gary Cooper, Charles Boyer, Charlie Chaplin, Cary Grant, Errol Flynn, Douglas Fairbanks, Jr., Olivia de Haviland, Myrna Loy, William Powell, Irene Dunne, Katharine Hepburn, Ronald Colman, Clark Gable, Charles Laughton, Norma Shearer, Marlene Dietrich, Leslie Howard, George Arliss, Paul Muni, Greta Garbo, Bette Davis, James Stewart, Spencer Tracy, and Clifton Webb.

Still the challenge remains and the opportunity is there, for the magic of the movie screen has lost none of its fascination nor any of its capacity for spellbinding audiences with pathos, drama, humor, or vivid action.

(Left) During the production of a Hollywood movie, directors give film star Jean Simmons off-stage cues. **(Right)** A Technirama camera captures a dramatic scene in "Spartacus" when Laurence Olivier takes command of Roman armies.

36 Radio and Television

An NBC-TV color camera mounted on auto wheels picks up an approaching float in the Macy's Thanksgiving Day Parade which is broadcast nationally from New York each year.

While world communities were being linked by millions of miles of wire for telegraphic and telephonic communication, a few scientists were experimenting with another, revolutionary form of sound transmission. The first practical experiments in radio communication were performed by the German physicist, Heinrich Hertz, in 1888. But the idea was conceived long before that. As early as 1842, Joseph Henry at Princeton University discovered the nature of electromagnetic radiation, and in 1875, Thomas A. Edison further explored this field of science.

The successful Hertz experiments were a direct result of the theoretical writings of an English scientist, Clerk Maxwell. Maxwell's mathematical theory, published in 1865, had excited scientists in other countries. Three separate groups in England, Germany, and Italy began to seek means of transmitting energy through free space. In 1896, Guglielmo Marconi of the Italian group developed an antenna and ground system which represented one of the great advances in developing radio communication, and it was Marconi who built the first wireless telegraphy receivers by which he transmitted the initial transatlantic radio message in 1901.

WHAT IS RADIO?

A radio transmitter sends out electrical signals that are carried through the atmosphere on electromagnetic waves. In the broadcasting studio sound waves are changed to radio waves and amplified in a series of high-voltage tubes. The radio waves are of too low a frequency to be seen as light, yet are too high to be audible. A receiver must, therefore, be made to pick up the waves and transform them to "audio frequency," and to further change this audio frequency into air waves, or sound. Three basic devices are employed to perform these functions: the antenna, the detector or radio tube, and the amplifier. In the early days of popular radio, simple "crystal detector" sets were easily built by youngsters at a cost of only two or three dollars. These crystal sets were much the same as Marconi's first wireless telegraphy receivers.

The antenna is basically a wire which is connected with the receiver. The Marconi antenna consisted of a 50-ft. length of wire suspended horizontally about 30 ft. above ground. Modern tube and transistor sets are so sensitive that outside antennae are no longer necessary, though superior reception results when an antenna is used.

In the simple crystal set, the detector generally consists of a galena crystal, placed in a metal mounting and connected by wire to a terminal post. The other terminal is connected with a metal rod which may be manually pivoted by means of a dial. At the end of the rod is a fine wire, called the "cat's whisker." By manipulation of the rod, the operator can make contact with the cat's whisker on a sensitive spot of the crystal.

Waves sent out by a radio transmitter are oscillating bursts of alternating current, to which the galena crystal is sensitive. However, the crystal conducts current well only in one direction, thus rectifying the alternating current to a pulse of direct current in the audio frequency range. Now the waves must be amplified. In the primitive radio set, headphones, working on the same principle as the telephone receiver, were used, and the DC pulsations actuated an electromagnet which in turn caused a mica diaphragm to vibrate and produce sound waves. (See *Telephone*)

The next problem is to select a particular group or pattern of radio waves. The atmosphere is jammed with a variety of waves caused by radiation from the sun, atmospheric stresses, high-voltage power lines, as well as by the many broadcasting stations and privately operated transmitters. While the crystal is able to select two or three stations, it is not adequate for a broad range of radio reception. The first device to solve this problem was the wire tuning coil which, when slid back and forth over a contact point, picks up different frequencies. These frequencies are determined by the length of the coil wire from its point of contact to its terminal connection with the antenna.

From such comparatively simple instruments grew all the complex modern radio and television receivers and the vast broadcasting networks which now make up a mighty industry. Condensers, audion tubes, resistors, rectifiers and transformers have all been added as refinements of the three basic elements in any radio receiver, and with the invention of the transistor (See *Machinery*), the simplification of many formerly complex parts became possible, as well as smaller, more compact equipment.

CBS foreign correspondents return to the U.S. at year's end for an annual "Years of Crisis" broadcast on which they analyse the news.

TELEVISION

The newest of electronic communication marvels, television is now a mammoth industry that in the course of a few short years has superseded radio as America's popular home entertainment medium. Very few people were privileged to see the first regularly scheduled telecast in 1936, as the commercial production of TV receivers had not yet begun. Only ten years later, in 1946 there were nine television broadcasting stations operating in New York, Philadelphia, Schenectady, Chicago, and Los Angeles. Now it is the rare household in the United States which does not have at least one black-and-white TV set; some homes have two or more, while many possess color sets.

Dozens of inventors contributed to the development of this miraculous device. In 1817, J. J. F. Berzelius discovered a metallic substance, known as selenium, which could convert light rays into electrical energy. This was the first major step toward the creation of television, yet it was not until 1875 that G. R. Carey, an American, constructed a mosaic arrangement of selenium cells to operate a series of individual shutters. When this selenium mosaic was placed before a beam of light, a coarse image of small black-and-white squares resulted, for the metallic element's resistance to the flow of electricity decreases as the intensity of light striking it is increased.

A few years later scanning devices were being tested. The first of these were revolving disks, perforated with a series of holes. As they rotated, the disks exposed different parts of an image in quick succession, but even if the disks were turned at a very high speed, the resulting image appeared to flicker. Nevertheless, using an improved disk scanner, a Scottish inventor named John L. Baird publicly demonstrated television in 1925. Baird's scanner contained a series of lenses instead of simple perforations.

Meanwhile, electrical scanners were being tried with much greater success by Vladimir K. Zworykin and Philo T. Farnsworth. These were cathode-ray tubes, the first of which were introduced in 1925. The Zworykin tube was developed and refined to become the iconoscope, in which the cathode beam sweeps across the electric eye mosaic in parallel lines. Farnsworth's "image dissector" moved the mosaic across the path of a stationary beam. The principle and the end result of both devices were the same; both translated an image into a series of electric impulses which could then be transmitted, or broadcast to a distant receiver. When sound and picture transmitters send high-frequency signals simultaneously from the broadcasting station, both sets of signals are picked up by the receiving antenna of the home television set.

Scanning in a modern TV camera is done at the incredible speed of 30 complete images every second. To do this, the cathode beam must travel across more than 500 lines on the mosaic, so that it scans a total of over 15,000 lines per second. The electrical impulses, varying in strength as the light and shade varies in the image being transmitted, are picked up in the kinescope of the receiving set where another cathode beam "paints" 30 complete pictures each second, much too fast for the human eye to detect as separate images.

High-frequency radio waves needed for the transmission of television signals limit the broadcasting range to an area about 30 to 40 miles in diameter. To extend this range to national coverage, coaxial cables connect networks of TV stations all over the country. These underground wires are used to carry both telephone and television signals. Worldwide television broadcasting and reception will become possible when relay satellites are placed in orbit for bouncing microwave signals halfway around the earth. (See *Telegraph, Telephone*)

COLOR TELEVISION

The Columbia Broadcasting System demonstrated color television in 1940 and again, after World War II. In 1946, Radio Corporation of America introduced a different technique which started a controversy as to which system should be adopted nationally. The CBS method required a special receiving set containing whirling disks. It could be used only for color reception. On the other hand, RCA's system was "compatible," meaning that a single receiving set could be used for both black-and-white and color broadcasts. After two years of investigation, the Federal Communications Commission ruled in favor of the CBS system. But public apathy to expensive, limited color sets, plus the interruption of production during the Korean War, led to a reevaluation of the problem. Engineers at RCA, Philco, Dumont, and a number of other manufacturers had worked jointly on an improvement of the rejected RCA system and had developed what was termed the "dot sequential" method.

After a demonstration of the new color system, CBS joined RCA in applying for and gaining the approval of the Federal Communications Commission.

To transmit color images, it is necessary to break up the light vibrations into primary colors by filtering, as in color photography and color printing. (See *Photography, Printing*) A rapid succession of primary-colored images are traced on the TV screen, giving the eye the impression of full color.

Within six years, from 1954 to 1960, color television became a hundred-million-dollar business in the United States, including the sale of home receivers, cameras, servicing, parts, and equipment. A recently developed camera tube has made possible the broadcasting of color with no more intense lighting than is used for black and white. This has greatly accelerated the shift of programs from black and white to color, so that the promise of the next decade is that color may replace nearly all black-and-white broadcasting and reception.

BROADCASTING

When the miracle of radio captured popular imagination in the 1920's, an industry grew up so rapidly that manufacturers could scarcely meet the demand for radio receivers, and the newly organized broadcasting companies had to improvise programs without any knowledge or experience of the broadcaster's art. Broadcasting studios were often little more than crude, soundproof compartments in rented offices, where local talent was employed to report news, put on musical programs and, occasion-

A rainbow of color is produced on RCA's new 21-inch color TV picture tube which provides bright pictures with greater sharpness and contrast through the use of improved phosphors.

ally, to enact a skit or play. The airways were crowded with signals from dozens of small stations. Even improved receivers had difficulty selecting a given station without interference. Inevitably, radio networking was developed to consolidate what might have become a chaotic situation. In 1926, Radio Corporation of America bought the New York station WEAF from the American Telephone and Telegraph Company and organized the National Broadcasting Company. On November 15, 1926, the first NBC radio program was broadcast from the old Waldorf Astoria Hotel in New York. This was a four-and-a-half hour production with top stage and concert stars, and it went on the air over a network of 25 stations covering most of the eastern half of the United States, from Maine to Washington, D.C. and from New York to Milwaukee. On New Year's Day in 1927, the first coast-to-coast broadcast reported the Rose Bowl game at Pasadena, California. In a period of ten years, from 1920 to 1930, radio grew from amateur experimentation to a billion dollar industry with 600 U.S. broadcasting stations and employing over three hundred thousand people.

Today, the three major broadcasting networks, National Broadcasting Company (NBC), Columbia Broadcasting System (CBS), and American Broadcasting Company (ABC) are on the air day and night with radio and television programs in all parts of the United States. In addition there are dozens of local, independent stations and hundreds of private or closed-circuit systems.

INSIDE THE BROADCASTING STUDIO

The modern broadcasting studio is a highly efficient and complex organization. Radio and TV shows begin in the program departments, where program directors and their staffs decide what talent will be hired and what type of show will be put on the air at different times of the day. Since the station derives most of its income from sponsors, or advertisers, who want to buy only the most popular programs, new shows are often tested for audience reaction. These unsponsored broadcasts are called "sustaining programs." Usually they are limited to local reception and are not broadcast over an entire network. If a sustaining show proves to be popular with local audiences, it will then be offered to advertisers; if it becomes sponsored, advertising "spots" will be included at intervals during the program. For these spot announcements the advertisers pay varying rates based upon the amount of coverage (local or national) and upon the time of day. "Prime time" on a national network is, of course, the most costly time to buy; it is that time which broadcasters have found to be most popular with listeners. Radio prime time used to be the evening, after-dinner hours, but now that this time has been taken over by television, the largest radio audiences are captured during morning and evening commuter rush hours, due to the great number of automobile radios in operation.

What goes out over the airways is indirectly controlled by the Federal Communications Commission, which insists that broadcasting stations must be operated "for the public interest, convenience, and necessity." As the FCC has the power to grant, withhold, or cancel station franchises, all commercial broadcasters are careful to include a good proportion of public service programs such as news, weather and crop reports, and religious and educational features.

When a program has been planned, the next step is to hire or assign talent. In the case of news programs, staff announcers usually handle the broadcasts. For musical and other entertainment programs, outside artists are employed. Sometimes auditions are held to try out new talent. Well established stars can command large fees for their performances and are in constant demand. But whether a show is composed of new or seasoned talent, it must be rehearsed before going on the air.

It is now the producer's turn to get the program ready for broadcasting. One of his chief duties is to see that the show exactly fills its allotted time. In all radio and TV broadcasting, timing is of the utmost importance. No show is permitted to run over its time by a single second, and if it runs short, the performers or station personnel must improvise something to fill the remaining interval. During rehearsal, the timing of each section of the program is carefully checked, parts of the script may be cut out or lengthened, and performers are cautioned to speed up or slow down their delivery. If, during an actual performance, the show seems to be slowing down or moving at too fast a pace, directors are on hand to signal the announcers and performers accordingly. In the case of a large, "spectacular" TV show, the timing and direction become an intricate matter requiring the most expert

A TV color camera, shooting a play on the field at Yankee Stadium, New York, during 1961 World Series. Five such cameras were used to transmit play-by-play action to millions of viewers across the country.

handling. Amid the apparent chaos of wires, microphone booms, powerful overhead lights, and TV cameras, the directors assign actors, dancers, singing stars, and comedians to precise locations on the set. Markings are painted or chalked on the floor to indicate positions for performers, "props," and scenery. Even the cameramen rehearse the precise timing of moving in for close-ups, for fading in or out, and for various special effects. In the course of the actual performance, the director continues to tell his camera crew when to pick up the scene, when to move in, and so forth.

Meanwhile, in a control room, the rehearsal is being "monitored." The director watches everything on his monitor television screen and gives directions over an intercom. His voice is also heard by cameramen through earphones. Sound levels of all microphones are tested and are adjusted to pick up voices with high or low register and with varied timbre. The director may ask a performer to speak more loudly, to lower his voice, or to move back from a microphone a few inches, depending upon the quality of his voice production. With the increasing use of small compact microphones which can be suspended from wires placed around a speaker's neck, or concealed in clothing, the problem of microphone distance has become minimized. Volume is adjusted by technicians in the control room, where the entire technical operation is managed by the engineer. It is the engineer's responsibility to see that power decibels going through the tubes do not overload the circuit. When a peak sound volume is reached, he turns down the volume control to avoid burning out parts of the mechanism. This is called "riding gain."

Cards with instructions for announcers or actors are held up within view of the speakers during a performance. Another system to aid performers is the "teleprompter," a device for flashing the words of a script or speech in large letters on a viewing screen which the speaker can read easily from his vantage point.

Telecasters have become remarkably adept at broadcasting on-the-spot news from places where the action originates. Mobile broadcasting units for "remotes" follow parades, political conventions, sports events, and many other live activities. Individual newscasters carry portable transmitters which can send signals through a mobile unit or temporary control room and thence to the local broadcasting station. If the broadcast is to be picked up by the network, it is relayed over telephone coaxial cables to the master control room of the network, where it is simultaneously sent out to subscribing stations in other cities.

A great many television shows are video-taped: that is, recorded on movie film before they are broadcast. This makes possible the broadcasting of the identical show at different times in different cities. It also gives the producer an opportunity to edit the show by cutting or retaking rough spots in the performance.

STATE OF THE TV INDUSTRY

It would appear that the television industry, like any enterprise that grows so large in so short a time, is due

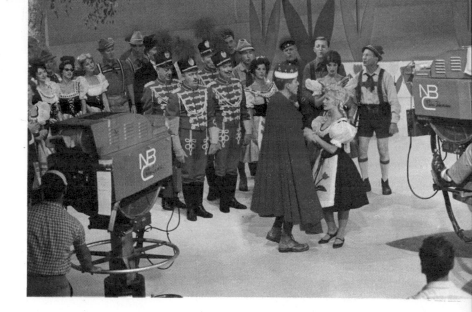

Two colorful scenes from NBC-TV's "Sing Along With Mitch" program as the show is taped for color broadcasting. In the lower picture, a color camera goes high in the air for an angle shot. Called a "boom" camera, it may be automatically raised or lowered. At right is a "pedestal" camera.

to undergo great changes. For one thing, public taste changes. From its earliest days, TV has seen numbers of bright stars reach peak popularity and then "nova," or burn out as popular tastes shifted. Increasing criticism, aimed at the poor quality of many programs, has come from government officials and educators, and the FCC has been taking an ever tougher stand regarding the broadcaster's responsibility to the public.

So vast is the audience and such influence does the TV screen wield on American opinion and taste that the industry is bound to be under severe and constant surveillance. At the same time, broadcasting companies and networks argue that freedom of thought and expression must be preserved on the airways and that censorship by government agencies is unthinkable. Still, advertisers cater to popular demand for blood and thunder Westerns,

On set during a performance of "The Scarlet Pimpernel," an elaborate production starring Michael Rennie, Maureen O'Hara, and Zachary Scott.

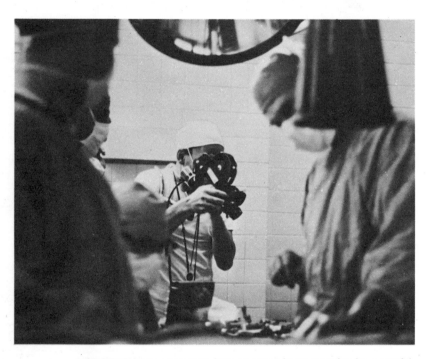

WBBM-TV Chicago cameraman films an actual heart operation for a special one-hour documentary "Four Seasons," which traced the effect of recent medical advances upon infancy, adolescence, maturity, and senescence.

Correspondents and couriers at CBS news election headquarters in Studio 65 for an election night report on voting in the 1960 presidential contest.

lurid mysteries, family comedies, and cartoons. But while such shows get high ratings in popularity polls conducted by the networks and by independent surveys, some critics maintain that no adequate testing has been made of more sophisticated programs, as the public has had comparatively little opportunity to pass judgment on superior fare.

Trends toward multiple sponsorship, when several advertisers sponsor a single network show, have helped broadcasters to regain more direct control of their programming, for the simple reason that no one of five or six sponsors can, alone, threaten to discontinue the show by canceling his support. This has led to what the industry calls the "magazine concept" of broadcasting, whereby the network provides the editorial content of its programs, while sponsors buy a certain amount of commercial time, like the ads in a magazine, to be spotted at intervals throughout an entire evening of news and entertainment. The plan has not been generally adopted because advertisers, under this system, have no guarantee of the size of audiences which they might reach.

As the range of television wavelengths is limited, licenses to use certain channels are controlled and restricted by the Federal Communications Commission, which in turn is responsible to Congress. Wavelength channels are numbered. From channel 2 through 82, assignments may be made to commercial TV stations. Below channel 2, wavelengths are reserved for military use. Actually, most home sets will receive channels only up to 12 or 13, the VHF (very high-frequency) stations; above 13 is the range known as UHF, (ultrahigh-frequency). Efforts are being made to open up the higher-frequency channels.

Meanwhile, one of the industry's major controversies is over the possibilities of pay-TV, whereby subscribers would pay for programs on the basis of use. Through community antennas, programs can be delivered only to customers whose sets are connected with the central system. Public resistance and doubt on the part of networks that pay-TV can be profitable have slowed progress in this field. Nevertheless experimental pay programs and stations continue to raise the question as to whether television's future points in this direction.

THE ROLE OF RADIO

Of all the popular entertainment and news media, radio has undergone the most drastic changes since the introduction of TV. No longer are dramatic and comedy shows considered top radio fare. Television has monopolized this type of entertainment, while radio, both AM and FM, has gravitated into regions of pure sound, particularly popular and classical music. News and weather reports are still widely heard, as are sportscasts of important baseball, football, and other contests not carried on television.

Curiously, while television has moved with giant strides into a field once monopolized by radio, the number of radiobroadcasting stations has increased to some 3,500 in the United States—seven times the number of TV stations. This appears to be the result of specialization, forced upon the radio industry by television. Stations have been created to serve special groups, such as farmers, foreign language, racial and religious groups. Many of the newer stations cater to small, suburban communities within an eight or ten mile radius. Such stations can broadcast local high school sports, parent-teacher meetings, and social events while advertising local stores and business firms which could neither afford nor benefit by a national network audience.

By the same token, network radio has steadily declined since pre-television days, though it is still an industry of greater size and importance than might have been expected. Radio programs are widely heard by workers who can listen but are unable to watch TV, by the customers in barber shops and beauty parlors, by vacationers at beaches and on the water, by drivers of trucks and automobiles, and by many other people who cannot sit and watch the magic screen.

A MULTI-PRONGED INDUSTRY

Radio and television as an industry may be broadly divided into several segments: the manufacture of home receiving sets by electronics firms such as RCA, Westinghouse, General Electric, Philco, and Zenith; retail sales and service handled mostly by local merchants; radiobroadcasting and television broadcasting. In every segment of this vast and complex industry there are opportunities for a variety of skills and talents. Advanced technology requires highly trained electronics experts. In the field of color television particularly there is still great opportunity for discovery and invention.

Demand for performers of many kinds, and the public's interest in top television stars is reminiscent of Hollywood's golden era (See *Motion Pictures*), when popular idols commanded fabulous salaries and when young singers, dancers, and actors could sometimes skyrocket to fame overnight.

But generally speaking the caliber of television stars has not been as high as that of the great actors and actresses of motion pictures. It would appear that a glittering future awaits the broadcasting studios and the performers who can achieve a level of artistry comparable to that attained by the motion picture industry in the years just prior to television's debut.

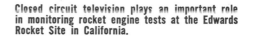

Closed circuit television plays an important role in monitoring rocket engine tests at the Edwards Rocket Site in California.

A scientist at the David Sarnoff Research Center in Princeton measures color characteristics of experimental red, green, and blue phosphors similar to those used in color TV picture tubes. Phosphors are mounted on panels in tube at right and illuminated by electron bombardment.

219

37 Music and Recording

As the recording engineer adjusts his controls to achieve proper balance before the sound is recorded on tape, an orchestra rehearses. Soon a new record will be in production.

Without music, the human race would find life to be a pretty dreary business. The most primitive peoples are strangely stirred by the rhythm of drums and by the melodious sounds of crude musical instruments. So fundamental is man's desire for music that throughout history, it has been an integral part of the most important rites and ceremonies observed by peoples in every region of the earth.

In the modern, civilized world, the performance of music by professional bands and orchestras has become an important business activity, and with the invention of the phonograph, mass reproduction of music has brought a major industry into being.

The first phonograph was an invention of Thomas A. Edison, who wrapped a sheet of tinfoil around a cylinder and traced a pattern of sound vibrations by means of a needle. This was in 1877. Although German experimenters had managed to record sound on foil a few years earlier, Edison's invention was the earliest practical application of the idea. His first recording was *Mary Had a Little Lamb*. Improving on the Edison machine in 1885, Chichester A. Bell and Charles S. Tainter coated the recording cylinder with wax. The inventors called their device the graphophone. Two years later Emile Berliner's gramophone produced sounds by having the needle vi-

brate laterally instead of vertically. This lateral cut method, combined with the electrical systems introduced in the 1920's, is still used for the making of disc recordings. No major changes occurred until the 1950's, when high fidelity (hi-fi) and stereophonic records appeared.

MAKING A JOYFUL NOISE

The great recording industry depends for its existence upon the singers, instrumentalists, and composers who produce songs and symphonies which people want to hear. As in all the arts, there are good, bad, and indifferent musical artists, and (rarely) geniuses. In modern times, serious musicians have been heavily subsidized by royal families in nineteenth century Europe, and by wealthy patrons of the arts in America. Every section of the United States contributes to our musical heritage. Such cities as Detroit, Houston, Louisville, Minneapolis, New Orleans, Seattle, and San Francisco have enthusiastic musical organizations. Most of the major American cities have their symphony orchestras which, like opera companies, operate at deficits largely made up by wealthy subscribers. Nevertheless, some of the world-famous U.S. orchestras have immense followings. Such symphonic groups, as the Philadelphia Orchestra, the New York Philharmonic Society, the Boston Pops, the Boston Symphony, the Cleveland

Symphony, and the Chicago Symphony, are known throughout the world for their fine recordings of great music and are heard on radio and television in all parts of North America. Most of these great orchestras go on tours of other U.S. cities, and occasionally to foreign countries. A great part of their income is derived from royalties on recordings.

In the popular field, most successful musical groups devote their talents to performing at formal dances or in night clubs and other places of popular entertainment. Some of America's leading dance bands, with their singing stars, are highly successful as commercial enterprises. They perform for TV shows, musical programs, radio, and of course for recording companies.

An important segment of the music industry is the manufacture of musical instruments. While it is by no means a large industry, it is made up of specialized manufacturers whose production requires the work of highly skilled technicians. Particularly interesting is the making of pianos. Building a fine piano is essentially a handcraft, and although the many intricate parts making up the cabinet and key action may be machine made, all piano manufacturers employ skilled experts for the final assembly. Among the best-known names in this field are Steinway, Baldwin, Lester, Hardman, Wurlitzer and Knabe. Wurlitzer manufactures many types of musical instruments, including organs and various wind and percussion instruments. They are also major producers of jukeboxes.

THE MAKING OF MODERN RECORDINGS

The biggest business in American music is in popular recordings, some of which achieve sales of more than a million "platters." In addition, the hit tunes are heard millions of times over from the gaudy, blaring jukeboxes found in nearly every roadside tavern, diner, and snack bar across the country.

When a recording is to be made, whether it is to be a classical symphonic composition or a rock 'n' roll number, the musicians assemble in a recording studio where, as in radio or TV broadcasting (See *Radio and Television*), microphones are set up, sound technicians operate electronic controls, and timing is carefully rehearsed before a tape is made. The musical director leads the orchestra or band, but he is in turn directed by a sound engineer who may even interrupt the performance to make changes in sound levels, positions of microphones, and other technical details. Some recordings requiring voices and sound effects must have an overall director who puts all the elements together into a coordinated unit.

The initial recording is on magnetic tape which may be edited by erasing unwanted sections. Next, the sounds on the tape are transferred to an acetate disc, as the sounds produce electrical vibrations which are cut into the record's surface by a recording needle. This disc goes to the record factory where it is sprayed with a fine coating of silver. When the silvered disc is immersed in electroplating tanks, a thin coating of nickel is deposited on the surface, followed by a heavier coating of copper. The comparatively rigid copper is stripped from the original disc. This provides a negative "master," with all vibration grooves re-

221

Plastic sheets are cut into preforms, called "biscuits," or ground into small granules. Here, biscuits are ready for delivery to the press for the final record-molding operation.

A newly recorded acetate disc is given a thin coating of silver, then immersed in a plating tank to make a metal master record.

After a nickel stamper is made from the mold, an operator uses a microscope to locate the true center of the stamper.

When the stamper is mounted in an automatic hydraulic press, a label is placed on each side of the press, a hot plastic "biscuit" is inserted, and the press forms the plastic into a molded record.

produced as protruding ridges on the metal. Now a nickel positive, or "mother" record, is produced by the electroplating process, and from this, a final negative disc called the "stamper" is made of solid nickel. Through all of these complex operations, the minute, microscopic irregularities in the grooves, representing the sound vibrations, must be preserved without a flaw.

To manufacture thousands of duplicate records, two stampers, one for each side of the record, are mounted in a special press. A plastic compound, usually a form of vinylite, is melted in a heated mixer, and the resulting plastic mass is passed between steel rollers which press the material into a continuous ribbon. As it is cooled, the plastic sheet is cut into "biscuits" which will be used in the final molding operation. These biscuits are preheated, sandwiched between two labels, and inserted by an operator between the stampers in a hydraulic press. As the press is closed, the biscuit is flattened and molded, taking on the grooves and vibration contours of the finished record.

After a pressman removes the pressed record and trims off excess plastic, the disc moves down an inspection and packaging line. A record from each stamper is periodically checked on sensitive electronic equipment. If a stamper is found to be defective, it is immediately discarded and all records pressed from it after the last check are scrapped.

TYPES OF RECORDINGS

In the field of electronics, such firms as R.C.A., Westinghouse, General Electric, and Columbia Records do a large volume of business in recorders, players, and various types of amplifying systems. Other well-known names are Emerson, Magnavox, and Webcor. There are three principal types of recordings: *optical,* which is the method used for putting a sound track on motion-picture film; *mechanical,* by which sounds are reproduced with a needle traveling along modulated grooves, as on disc recordings; and *magnetic,* the tape or wire recording method.

The magnetic system was introduced in 1896 by a Danish physicist named Valdemar Poulsen. A magnetized metal wire or a tape coated with a powdered metal paste is used as the recording medium. As the tape or wire comes in contact with the poles of an electromagnet called the recording head, electric current of varying intensity corresponding with sound waves produces what amounts to a series of small magnets in the tape. The strength of these magnets is proportional to the amplitude of the sound waves being reproduced. The recording is then played by passing the tape in front of a reproducing head similar to the recording head. Magnetic variations cause varied voltage to induce the desired electrical signals for the amplified production of sound. Tape recorders are becoming increasingly popular for home use in the United States.

In the past few years, the entire recording industry has been shaken by a series of technical innovations. Foremost of these are hi-fi and stereophonic sound. High fidelity reproduces sound almost exactly as it sounded originally, and record players today are compact, highly refined units consisting of automatic changers and almost perfect amplifying systems, usually containing at least two speakers for high and low vibrations. In 1958, stereophonic records were introduced by the leading manufacturers. By making two simultaneous sound tracks from separately placed microphones, then reproducing the sound through two amplifiers placed at different locations in a room, the resulting sound emanates from two directions as in the original performance.

PHONOGRAPH RECORDS ARE BIG BUSINESS

The phonograph record industry in America is a five hundred million dollar a year activity that involves the sale, through retail outlets, of some two hundred million records, almost equally divided between 33 1/3 rpm and 45 rpm speeds. While a majority of these recordings, both popular and classical, are sold for use on home record players, the use of jukeboxes, as mentioned earlier, produces huge income in royalties to musicians and manufacturers. Radio stations also give records thousands of playings on popular music programs, hence the name "disc jockeys" for the radio announcers who handle these recorded sessions. (See *Radio and Television*)

The sale and use of records has been growing steadily over the years. From an all-time low of five and a half million dollars' worth of records in the depression year of 1933, the record business has shown a constant, rapid increase year after year. There appears to be no surfeiting of the American appetite for music.

This compact RCA Victor tape cartridge recorder weighs slightly more than 13 pounds and provides an optional adapter for reel-to-reel playing.

38 Sports

No professional sport is more packed with thrills and fast action than ice hockey. Here the Boston Bruins play the New York Rangers at Madison Square Garden before a sell-out crowd.

When crowds gather at a huge sports stadium, when bands are playing, bright pennants are whipped by a pleasant breeze, the vendors are hawking their wares up and down the aisles in the packed stands; and when the teams sprint out onto the playing field to the thunderous cheers of excited rooters, it is difficult to think of the game to be played as a major business enterprise. Yet today's professional baseball, football, basketball, ice hockey, boxing, and other sports spectacles are so well organized and have reached such proportions that they rank with other major entertainment industries. Baseball, particularly, is a huge activity involving millions of dollars, gigantic business organizations and costly stadiums in all parts of the United States.

THE STORY OF BASEBALL

Baseball is America's national game. It is the number one sport in the United States and is almost equally popular in Canada, Cuba, and Mexico. Yet, oddly enough, the only other country to adopt the game on a scale of any importance, is Japan. While there are several plausible accounts of how, when, and where baseball was developed, its origin has never been clearly documented. Certainly English cricket, played with a ball and bat and with a single base, was the forerunner of the American game, but why and under what circumstances the play was modified and transformed no one seems to know. A game called "rounders," which was popular during the eighteenth century, had a batsman running a circuit of several bases instead of the single base of cricket. Then, shortly after 1800, the game of "old cat" appeared. This early form of baseball could be played with one or two bases. The single-base variation was known as "one old cat"; the two-base game, "two old cat." Generally the decision as to number of bases rested upon how many players could be mustered to make up opposing teams. Because there were rarely enough players available for a three-base game outside of the larger towns, "three old cat" acquired the name of Town Ball. Later, this was changed to baseball.

About the 1850's amateur teams began to organize leagues and to establish official rules. By this time, baseball had captured public interest sufficiently so that professional teams could be assured of a following. The first "pro" organization was the Cincinnati Red Stockings, founded in 1868 and still going strong as a major league team. By 1871 other professionals formed a league and organized baseball was on its way.

Today there are a great many professional leagues whose public following is so large that their overall game attendance exceeds forty million persons each year. The major leagues alone draw from twenty-five to thirty million fans in a season. Since many of these are repeat customers it is impossible to estimate the total number of baseball fans in the United States, but it is safe to assume that more than ten million people pay to watch professional baseball at least once in a season. Other millions watch major league games on television or follow their favorite teams via radio broadcast.

STRUCTURE OF ORGANIZED BASEBALL

Until 1961, the American and National major leagues consisted of eight teams each, and they played 154 games in a season which runs from April to October. A given team played 22 games against each of the seven other league members. Now the leagues are composed of ten teams who play 18 games against each of nine opponents, or 162 games per season. At the end of a season the top-ranking teams in each league play each other for the "world championship" in a best-out-of-seven series of games known as the World Series.

In addition to the two so-called major leagues representing the larger cities, there are more than 150 minor league teams in towns and cities all over the United States, Puerto Rico, Mexico, and Canada. Minors are classified in ranks by the letter designations AAA (highest ranking), AA, A, BB, B, C and D. Usually the lowest ranking teams are composed of younger and less experienced players than may be found in the triple-A and double-A circuits.

When players in the 1919 World Series were proved to have accepted bribes to lose games intentionally, the resulting scandal shook the professional sports world and the nation generally. Worried over loss of public confidence, the big league teams agreed to set up a Commissioner who would establish, administer, and enforce strict regulations. First of the Baseball Commissioners was Federal Judge Kenesaw Mountain Landis. Fines and other harsh penalties, including banishment from the professional leagues, were established by the Commissioner's office for violations of rules.

The major leagues operate under the Commissioner, a Secretary-Treasurer, and an executive council with headquarters in New York. There is also a National Association of Professional Baseball Leagues in Columbus, Ohio, whose members include both the major and minor leagues.

HOW PLAYERS BECOME "PROS"

All of the major league teams employ scouts whose job it is to observe promising young players on college teams and even on high school squads. When an unusually good pitcher or hitter is found, a scout will talk to him and to his family about the possibility of playing professional ball. If everybody agrees, the youngster will sign a contract with

A high point in the 1960 World Series, Pittsburgh Pirates versus New York Yankees, at Yankee Stadium. The underdog Pirates won the series.

the scout's team, stating that he will not join any other club. After the young player starts training, his team may sell his contract, but the player himself is never permitted to change teams or to negotiate with other ball clubs for higher pay.

Salaries of average big league players are not as high as many people suppose; they compare with average living wages in other industries. It is only the stars—the great pitchers and the heavy hitters—who command five-figure salaries. Of course, not every young baseball player is fortunate or talented enough to start his professional career on a major league team. Many begin with Class D teams in small towns; then endeavor to work up through the minors as their skill increases. Only about 600 players participate in big league games during a given season.

One of the great sports events of the year, the annual World Series is a big business venture in itself. Gate receipts from these championship games have been as high as five and one-half million dollars. Games are often attended by two hundred fifty thousand to four hundred thousand people. The individual players on World Series teams receive substantial shares of the gate receipts on a percentage basis established by the Baseball Commissioner's office. Players of a winning team receive greater shares than do those of the loser, thus discouraging any dishonest efforts to "throw" the games, or to lose intentionally.

At the Baseball Hall of Fame in Cooperstown, N.Y., are relics and mementos of great stars of the game, including George Herman Ruth (Babe Ruth), affectionately known as the "Sultan of Swat"; Ty Cobb, Tris Speaker, Honus Wagner, Walter Johnson, Rogers Hornsby, Christy Mathewson, and Cy Young. Babe Ruth's incredible record of 60 home run hits in a single season was passed in 1961 by Roger Maris of the New York Yankees, but Maris required 162 games to hit 61, whereas Ruth's record was achieved in only 154 games. Such statistics are typical highlights of a game that lives and breathes statistics. Professional sports writers, newscasters, and official team and league statisticians are kept busy recording a veritable mass of figures for teams and individual players on hits, pitching records, errors, strikeouts, and all the other aspects of this amazing game.

FOOTBALL

Of three principal types of football played in various parts of the world, the American brand is in many respects the most spectacular. In England and in most of the Commonwealth countries the popular game is rugby; soccer is widely played in Europe; and variants of rugby called Canadian and Australian football are found in those countries. When autumn comes to the United States, college and professional football games draw huge crowds, and on weekends the crisp air is filled with the music of bands and the roar of wildly cheering spectators.

Unlike baseball, a great portion of the public interest in this sport is centered on college and high school games. But since the 1940's, professional football leagues have steadily gained attendance, largely due to their spectacular play and their highly developed aerial attack, or forward

In the last game of the 1961 season, Roger Maris of the New York Yankees is shown hitting his 61st home run against the Red Sox in Yankee Stadium.

passing, which consists of throwing the elliptical ball from one player to another of the same team in order to advance down the playing field toward the goal.

As this is a game of hard bodily contact, most professional players must be heavy and solidly built. Before he is accepted for the squad of one of the major league teams, he must undergo gruelling tests and practice periods. Members of the teams lead a Spartan existence, observe strict rules of diet and sleeping habits, and train continuously with the roughest kind of exercise and practice play.

Largest of the professional leagues is the National Football League, which is divided into Eastern and Western Conferences. The teams, which draw huge crowds in all sections of the country, are the Chicago Bears, Cleveland Browns, Chicago Cardinals, Baltimore Colts, Philadelphia Eagles, San Francisco 49ers, New York Giants, Detroit Lions, Green Bay (Wisconsin) Packers, Los Angeles Rams, Washington (D.C.) Redskins, and the Pittsburgh Steelers. Organized much along the lines of professional baseball, these football teams are major business enterprises each doing an annual volume of millions of dollars. Crowds of 50,000 to 100,000 are usual at most of their games.

BASKETBALL

Invented by Dr. James A. Naismith, a physical director of the Y.M.C.A. College at Springfield, Mass., in 1891, basketball is strictly an American sport. Since its inception it has grown to become the greatest of indoor sports for the winter season in the United States and is becoming increasingly popular in Canada. Seeking an active sport that could be played in gymnasiums, Naismith first nailed a peach basket to a wall and organized a contest to see which of two teams could throw a soccer ball into the basket more often. Luther Gulick contributed to extending the action of the game and to enlarging the rules. Now, this fast-moving, action-packed game, played in all parts of North America during a season from November to early April, attracts more spectators than any other U.S. sport, although the professional following is by no means as large as that for organized baseball.

Nevertheless, professional basketball has been gaining importance, especially since the advent of televised games.

ICE HOCKEY

No more exciting spectacle is offered by the sports world than professional ice hockey, a game similar to field hockey but played on ice, the players wearing ice skates. While it is seen largely in Canada and in the northern sections of the United States, interest in the game has spread with the development of artificially frozen, indoor ice rinks. The first ice hockey games were played at McGill University in Canada about 1875, and in 1908 a number of professional teams were organized.

The National Hockey League, founded in 1917, was composed solely of Canadian teams until 1925 when teams from American cities, including New York, Boston, and Chicago, were added to the circuit. Other professional leagues represent such cities as Baltimore, Philadelphia, and New Haven, Conn.

OTHER SPORTS AND SUPPLIERS

Professional teams and players have built up large followings in nearly every major sport. Among the most popular are boxing, golf, tennis, wrestling, horse racing, and automobile racing. In every case, champions play for high stakes, and some of the major events in each category draw crowds exceeding those for any other type of local entertainment.

Supplying both professional and amateur sportsmen is a large industry, which manufactures sporting goods and equipment. Leaders in this field are A. G. Spalding and Bros., the largest makers of baseballs and manufacturers of gear for virtually every outdoor and indoor sport; Rawlings Sporting Goods Company, Wilson Sporting Goods Company, and The MacGregor Company. Hundreds of specialized sporting goods stores, as well as the large department stores and mail-order houses, handle retail sales of their products to the general public. (See *Marketing*) Manufacture of sport clothes, shoes, and caps makes up a specialized segment of the apparel industry. (See *Wearing Apparel*)

OUTLOOK FOR THE FUTURE

As skills in spectacular sports increase and as more sports events are shown on television, it seems probable that professional sports and related industries will continue to gain importance in the United States. It will be essential, however, for the professional leagues to maintain strict discipline over players in order to avoid any taint of "fixing" the outcomes of games, races, or other sporting events. In the long run, the American public will not support organized sports unless they are assured of seeing genuinely competitive contests. This was amply demonstrated by the near collapse of organized baseball following the 1919 World Series scandal, and the great resurgence of public interest when a strong central control was established to insure the game's integrity.

Basketball, rated the greatest of indoor sports for the winter season in the United States, attracts more spectators than any other U.S. sport. This picture shows a game between Los Angeles Lakers and Philadelphia Warriors at Philadelphia.

39 Ceramics

A member of the Lenox design staff works on minute pattern detail for a fine piece of dinnerware. Hundreds of such sketches will be made and many hundreds of hours spent before a design concept will emerge on actual dinner plates.

Probably the making of clay pottery can lay claim to being the first of the plastics industries, for clay is a natural thermosetting plastic that has been molded into useful shapes since prehistoric times. The history of pottery is so old that no records exist to indicate how men first discovered that heat-baked clay made serviceable vessels for holding food and various liquids. One of man's most ingenious inventions, the potter's wheel, is known to have been used by ancient Egyptians as early as 2000 B.C. Egyptians also found a way to put metallic glazes on their pottery, while the Chinese, about 87 B.C., were using fine white clays to produce some high-quality vases and dinnerware. Because Marco Polo brought fine Chinese ceramics back to Europe in the thirteenth century, it acquired the name of chinaware, or china, and this term has been applied since then to many types of dinnerware.

TYPES OF CERAMICS

In correct modern terminology, only porcelain dinnerware should be referred to as china. Basically, there are two types of ceramic dinnerware: china and earthenware.

CHINA or PORCELAIN is fired at an extremely high temperature which results in the clay becoming glassy or vitrified. This gives it a distinctive translucent quality not found in earthenware. Its smooth, hard glaze is virtually impervious to scratches, and despite its comparatively light weight, it is actually less subject to breakage or chipping than thicker, heavier earthenware objects. Bone china is a term applied to a type of fine porcelain which contains a percentage of bone ash. This imparts pure whiteness to the finished pieces.

EARTHENWARE, or semivitreous ware, is heat treated at lower temperatures than china and is opaque, heavier, and less expensive than porcelain. For everyday use it is serviceable and can be handsomely styled and decorated.

Although the term POTTERY itself actually includes any clay objects made by the potter, it has acquired some special meanings. Certain types of crude earthenware, such as the handmade native ware from Mexico, are called pottery. Generally speaking this kind of pottery is made from coarse clays, is thinly glazed, and is fired at low temperatures. For this reason it is porous and easily chipped. Many people refer incorrectly to semivitreous ware as pottery, particularly when it is gayly decorated and styled in the manner of early American folk art.

AMERICAN DINNERWARE MANUFACTURE

Virtually all American dinnerware is made from formulations of clay, flint, feldspar, and water. After the raw materials have been mixed, the resulting fluid is known as "slip." This clay mix has reached a high state of perfection and is the product of careful laboratory testing by ceramic specialists. Clays are imported from many parts of the world; balanced "blends" of a variety of clays are used to produce the best quality china.

In the making of fine porcelain, such ingredients as powdered quartz and marble are sometimes added to the mixture. After being ground for hours to extreme fineness in huge ball mill tumblers, the slip passes through a filter press which squeezes out some of the water, leaving a creamy, malleable substance. To eliminate all air from the clay, the mixture next goes through a vacuum "pug mill." The resulting "pug clay" is now ready for forming, or "jiggering."

Jiggering is a refinement of the ancient potter's wheel. When the pug clay is thrown on a mold which shapes the front of the object, the jiggerman places it on a wheel, then lowers the jiggerarm with its back-contour die until it comes in contact with the clay. The wheel is then revolved to shape and smooth the clay, which is left on the face-contour die to dry.

For hollow ware, such as teapots and sugar bowls, slip clay is retained in its more liquid form and is poured into plaster molds. Water is absorbed into the mold. At the proper time, excess slip is poured off and the piece is

After "slip," the raw material of fine china, is poured into a mold, excess slip is poured off, leaving a thin coating to dry.

With infinite care and control, a craftsman removes excess slip with a "trimmer" stick. Marks left by molds are erased with a soft brush dipped in water, giving a satin smoothness to the "green" or unfired ware.

A designer shown "throwing" or forming the shape of a vase, using a revolving potter's wheel. Later a mold will be made from this model.

allowed to dry. This process is known as casting. The smaller pieces, such as knobs, cup handles, and other extraneous embellishments, are formed and skillfully joined to the main object by hand. They are then dipped in slip which acts as the adhesive to seal the joints.

FIRING

When the pieces are ready for firing they are placed in kiln cars which carry them through the "bisque kilns." The cars travel on rails at varying speeds, depending on the firing time required. The kiln is a firebrick oven in which graduated temperatures are accurately controlled. The cars advance through increasing temperatures until the maximum intense heat is reached, then move through progressively lowered temperatures. After this first firing, the china is at a stage called bisquit ware, or bisque. It is fairly hard, but dull surfaced.

The bisque is next subjected to a coating of liquid glaze. Complex shapes are dipped by hand and placed on drying racks, while flatware, such as platters and saucers, are coated by an automatic spraying machine. The plates, mounted on continuously turning spindles, move through spray jets which coat all surfaces uniformly.

After application of the glaze, the pieces are ready for second firing, sometimes known as the "glost" firing. Once more the ware travels on kiln cars, this time into a glost kiln. At a somewhat lower temperature than used for the first firing, the glaze is melted and fused into the bisque pottery, sealing all pores. The ware now emerges as fine, translucent china.

Other firings are required in the production of the best decorated china, since various colors must be treated to individual temperature requirements. Strict firing timetables and temperature controls must be maintained at all times. Frequently, high-quality dinnerware requires four or five days in kiln-firing processes.

A jewel-like effect is created by hand-applied raised enamel dots. A great deal of hand craftsmanship is employed in making fine china.

DECORATION

Decoration is applied to ceramic ware by means of prints, decalcomanias or by hand painting. Underglaze designs are added at the bisque stage after the first firing. Colored rim patterns are often applied at this stage.

Overglaze decorations, which can be decalcomanias or hand painting, are applied after the glaze has been fired. Gold and silver rims are added as overglaze applications. The ware is then subjected to a decorating fire to fuse the colors into the glaze.

Other methods of decoration include *incising* with sharp tools, and *impressing* with design molds before the unglazed clay has dried. By means of *slip coating* and *slip tracing,* raised ornaments may be added to the basic piece. Coloring may be mixed into the wet slip, called "engobe," which is thin enough to flow easily. When the coating has become nearly dry, part of it may be scraped away from the base, leaving a two-tone pattern or decoration. Scratch decorations called "sgraffito" are etched with a stylus in the wet coating of engobe.

Expert designers are employed by dinnerware manufacturers to design both the shapes and the decorative applications of their china and earthenware products. Patterns for a style may require hundreds of sketches before the final design is accepted for production.

Since the early 1900's the American ceramics industry has made great strides. Today it competes in quality with the best of European products. Among the top ranking U.S. firms are Castleton China Inc. in New Castle, Pa.; Lenox Inc., Trenton, N.J.; Syracuse China Co., Syracuse, N.Y.; and Theodore Haviland & Co. Inc., New York, N.Y.

Though the industry is not large in comparison to giants like the chemicals, metals and plastics industries, it is growing and improving its products at a steady rate. It is one of the few modern industries where handcraft still plays a major role and where artistic workmanship is in demand.

The potter's wheel and skilled hands are required to shape a ceramic piece. At the precise moment, the potter must exert the proper pressure.

A decorative piece of china is first sculptured in clay by an expert craftsman, after which a master mold is made from the model.

229

40 Glass

Although many mass-produced jars and bottles are machine molded, special shapes are still formed by the ancient craft of glassblowing, as shown in this scene at the Corning Glass Works. Powerful lungs are required for this work.

According to the Roman naturalist, Pliny, writing in the first century, glassmaking was discovered accidentally by a group of Phoenician sailors about 5000 B.C. The legend, unsupported by any definite evidence, tells how the sailors had landed on a sandy Mediterranean shore and were preparing to cook a meal. As supports for their cook pot, they used blocks of soda ash taken from their ship's cargo. The heat from the fire caused a fusion of the soda ash and beach sand. After they had finished their meal, they were amazed to see a strange molten material flowing from their fire. The material hardened into lumps of glass which the sailors took with them to Syria. Whether or not there is any truth to this story, Syria was the region where some of the earliest known glassmaking was done.

Millions of years before men found a means of manufacturing glass, nature had formed lumps of obsidian in the heat of volcanoes. This natural glass looks like shiny stone, and bears little resemblance to the clear crystal glass made by modern manufacturers. Primitive men, who found lumps of obsidian, polished and chipped it to make crude articles of jewelry.

In the tombs at Memphis and Beni Hassen in Egypt are wall paintings depicting glassblowing. One picture clearly illustrates a type of circular furnace, about three feet high and twelve inches in diameter. The glassmakers appear to be drawing molten glass through a small opening at the base of the furnace.

One of the oldest glass objects known to have been made for a practical use is a pale green cylindrical container which was made in Mesopotamia about 5000 B.C. Beads, ornaments, and imitations of gemstones were made of polished glass in nearly all the early Mediterranean civilizations. About 3500 B.C. the Egyptian glassmakers learned to wind softened strips of glass around a sand mold. When the mold was heated, the glass fused to form bottles, vases, and other containers.

The Romans were the first to use window glass, and a large windowpane 44 by 32 in. was found in Pompeii.

Although the Roman windows were by no means transparent, they did admit light and at the same time kept out the elements. They were formed by dropping molten glass on a stone slab dusted with sand. Several workers with pincers pulled the mass from all sides until a flattened sheet of glass was formed.

After the fall of Rome, glassmaking techniques were lost to Europe until about the fifth century. Meanwhile Byzantine artisans produced a great variety of glass art objects. In 1266, Roger Bacon described the first practical magnifying glass. However, the microscope and telescope were not invented until late in the sixteenth century.

Some of the world's finest glass was Venetian cristallo made in the fifteenth century on the Island of Murano, where the famous Glass Colony of 300 glass works had grown up. This was the first colorless, clear glass which could be made extremely thin and formed into innumerable shapes. The Venetians also made excellent mirrors.

GLASS INDUSTRY IN THE UNITED STATES

Not until the latter part of the nineteenth century could glassmaking be considered successfully established in the United States, despite the fact that it was one of the first industries brought from Europe to the North American continent. A glasshouse was built near Jamestown, Va., in 1609, to make windowpanes, bottles, and glass beads for trade with the Indians. A replica of this first glassmaking plant is now operated by the Jamestown Glass Foundation, the glassblowers wearing colonial costumes and using implements exactly as they were used more than 300 years ago.

Unfortunately there were not enough skilled workers in America to develop the industry on a large scale. Foreign competition seriously curtailed attempts to establish American factories. Probably the oldest glassworks in the United States still in commercial operation is one at Glassboro, N.J., which was founded in 1765. An effort to establish a glass operation completely staffed by natives resulted in the formation of the Boston and Sandwich Glass Co. on Cape Cod, Mass. The firm was organized in 1825 by Deming Jarvis and produced some creditable glassware which became known as Sandwich glass. This company continued its operations until 1887.

INDUSTRY FAILURES

Almost every effort to create a full-fledged glass industry in the United States seemed doomed to failure. A company was established in Cheshire, Mass. in 1853. European patents were obtained but after five years the enterprise failed. Another group in Lenox, Mass. struggled to get a plate glass venture under way, but it failed to overcome foreign competition and went out of business in 1871.

In the meantime, a Captain John B. Ford built a plate glass factory at New Albany, Ind. When his company failed in 1880, he persisted in studying glass processes and manufacturing methods. Convinced that there was a future for the industry in the United States, he joined with John Pitcairn, an official of the Pennsylvania Railroad, to form the New York City Plate Glass Co. This firm built its factory at Creighton, Pa. in 1881. Although it,

too, very nearly failed, it was reorganized in 1883 as the Pittsburgh Plate Glass Co.—now one of the great names in American glass.

Today glassmaking is big business. It is largely a machine process, although high-grade glass is still blown by hand.

TYPES OF GLASS

Basically, all glass results from the melting of pure sand, or silica, and fusing it with chemicals. Under intense heat, the glassmaking ingredients become gradually soft and pliable, liquify, then flow freely as temperature is increased. Because it does not turn to liquid at a definite temperature, glass is not classed as a true solid. It has the same molecular structure as a liquid, even in its so-called solid state.

There are four primary types of glass resulting from manufacturing methods:

Flat glass comprises plate and sheet glass. Though it is made flat initially, it can be converted into many complex forms and shapes.

Pressed glass comprises blocks, lenses, flameware, ornaments, or other molded products. It is produced with molds to form the molten material into desired shapes.

Blown glass includes such articles as jars, bottles, light bulbs, and stemware. These objects are blown into the desired shapes.

Specialty glass includes tubing and laboratory glassware such as retorts, test tubes, fiber glass, and materials that require special processing.

These categories are descriptive largely of the forming or shaping of the glass. But in glassmaking processes are a number of different formulations which give varying degrees of hardness, clarity, heat resistance and other qualities to the glass itself. Chemically, glass is classified as quartz, water, soda-lime, borosilicate, and lead glass.

Quartz glass is produced from silica without any added ingredient. It requires a very high temperature of 3,100° F. to liquify the sand sufficiently to allow bubbles to es-

231

Molten glass is drawn by hand. Made by melting pure sand or silica and fusing it with chemicals, glass becomes soft and pliable under intense heat and it can then be molded, flattened, or drawn into a variety of shapes.

cape. Though it is expensive, it is important for certain specialized uses, such as lamps, lenses, and prisms, due to its ability to transmit ultraviolet light.

When soda is added to the silica, the mixture will melt at a temperature of 1,450° F. This produces *water glass,* so named because it will dissolve in water. Among the limited uses of this material are the fireproofing of wood and textiles, and the coating of eggs to preserve them.

Soda-lime glass results from the addition of lime. This produces a glass that is water-resistant and harder than water glass. A large percentage of the glass made for windows, jars, bottles, and tumblers is of this type. The raw materials are plentiful and inexpensive. In order to give added brilliance to the finished product, potash may be substituted for the soda. This is the formula used in making glass for most lenses and tableware.

For the best grade of optical and decorative glassware, *lead glass* is used. It is produced by substituting lead for lime, or by using a combination of both raw materials. Being comparatively soft, lead glass is easily ground. Also, the lead adds weight and contributes to the brilliance of the polished glass. As it has the appearance of natural rock crystal it is often called "crystal," and it is employed in the production of high-grade tableware and artistic glass creations.

Both soda-lime and lead glass tend to crack when subjected to sudden temperature change. By using boric acid or borax instead of lime, a strong, heat-resistant glass, called *borosilicate glass,* is produced. It is used for glass cooking utensils, windows, and laboratory equipment and is sold under the trade name of pyrex.

Colored glasses are made by adding various metal oxides to the raw materials.

MODERN GLASS MANUFACTURING

In large, automated factories, tremendous quantities of glass are manufactured for every conceivable purpose. The production of plate and window glass is now carried out in a continuous operation from raw materials to the finished sheets. Originally, the four fundamental operations of mixing raw materials, melting them, rolling the molten glass and "annealing," or slow-cooling the hardening sheet were handled as separate procedures. Now glass ingredients feed automatically into a melting tank and are melted at about 2,800° F., after which the molten mass flows through steel rollers which squeeze it into an unbroken ribbon of glass. This ribbon moves on through an annealing "lehr" or oven. By adjusting the rollers, glass of varying thicknesses can be produced in widths up to several feet.

After the annealing, the glass ribbon travels through a cooling system, then is passed through a battery of grinders which, by means of fine silica sand, smooths the surface of the glass almost to perfect uniformity. Next, plates several feet in length are cut from the continuous ribbon and are conveyed to polishing units of the machine.

On cast-iron tables, covered with cloth to hold the glass plates in place, rotating polishing blocks give the glass a beautiful, transparent finish. The polishing agents are solutions of copperas, water, and rouge. As soon as one surface is polished and washed, the plate is lifted by a vacuum crane, automatically turned and sent on its way through a second polishing line. Final cleaning, cutting, and packing in special crates complete the operations.

One of the most up-to-date glass factories in the United States is the mile-long plant of the Pittsburgh Plate Glass Co. in Cumberland, Md. There, every phase of glassmaking is automatic, from the weighing and mixing of raw materials to the cutting and packing operations.

Some of the most spectacular developments in glassmaking have come from the Corning Glass Works in Corning, N.Y. It was there that the famous 200-in. reflector of the giant telescope at Mount Palomar Observatory was made. In addition to manufacturing many commercial and optical glasses, Corning operates the Steuben factory where expert craftsmen turn out some of the world's finest crystal art pieces and tableware. The intricate operations of blowing and shaping this handmade glass may be watched from a spectator's gallery. Some of the fine Steuben pieces are engraved with elaborate designs by highly skilled artists.

SPECIAL GLASS PROCESSES

Because glass softens gradually and becomes more or less malleable at different temperatures, it can be pressed, formed, rolled, or cast into a great variety of shapes. Blowing glass is still done by individual craftsmen for many products such as electronic tubes and specially designed containers. For most commercial bottles, light bulbs, and other hollow glass forms, blowing machines do the work. Feeder pipes connected with a tank furnace drop the correct amounts of molten glass into molds, which revolve on a turntable. Compressed air is blown into the molds, forcing the glass into its basic shape; a second set of molds and charge of air finish the shaping operation.

Cups, dishes, various types of insulators, and thick glass objects are usually formed by pressure when hot glass is forced into molds.

Safety glass is made by bonding a layer of transparent plastic between two sheets of plate glass. Since the inner plastic layer prevents shattering, this type of laminated glass is used for automobile windows and windshields. Another method of reinforcing glass is by molding wire mesh in sheet glass.

By injecting thousands of tiny gas bubbles into molten glass, "foam glass" is produced. Foam glass is a dark, spongy product used for insulating and fireproofing.

OPTICAL GLASS

In the field of optics, glass plays a role of such vital importance that a highly specialized segment of the industry is devoted to this phase of glass manufacture. One of the best-known optical firms is the Bausch and Lomb Optical Co. in Rochester, N.Y. There, every conceivable type of lens and optical glass is produced. Special formulas include an aluminized glass on which perfectly uniform grooves can be etched at intervals of one-thirty-thousandth of an inch. This is used in scientific spectro analysis. Polaroid glass which prevents glare; glasses that will block, pass, detect or measure various types of radiation; and specially formulated glass for tiny lenses or lenses several feet in diameter are made in this amazing plant.

Machine glass blowing rapidly produces the small glass vials seen on the conveyor belt in the foreground.

Workers prepare to press a glowing mass of molten glass, using a hand-operated mold.

Glass for automobile headlamps is pressed into shape by machine-operated molds at the Corning Glass Works in Corning, N.Y.

233

Today's optics demand the ultimate in precision. Ruling engines, with diamond points, can cut as many as two hundred eleven thousand parallel and equidistant grooves on a three-inch by seven-inch glass that has a coating of aluminum only twenty-millionths of an inch thick.

The grinding of lens edges, which used to be done by hand and then by hand-operated machines, is now accomplished by a complex mechanism using hydraulic, mechanical, pneumatic, and electronic systems to give lenses exact diameters yet retain perfect coincidence of optical and mechanical axes. As a result, this exacting job is done three times as rapidly as it could be handled by traditional methods, at the same time working in tolerances measured in hundred-thousandths of an inch. Spherical generators are used to mill microscopically accurate lens curves in a matter of seconds.

HOW BIG IS THE GLASS INDUSTRY?

Figures released by the United States Department of Commerce indicate that American flat glass production has been amounting to some two billion square feet a year. This represents an annual dollar volume of about one-half billion dollars. Although production of flat glass had fallen off slightly in the early '60's, this seemed to be due more to a generally declining business index than to any major change in the uses of glass.

One of the largest industries in the United States is the production of glass containers. The industry, made up of about 50 manufacturers operating more than 100 plants, turns out glass jars and bottles for foods, beverages, medicines, chemicals and many other products at an annual rate of one hundred fifty million gross units valued at close to a billion dollars. In the field of optical glass, Bausch & Lomb, Inc. reported net sales of more than sixty-six million dollars in 1960. These figures serve to give some idea of the scope of the U.S. glass industry, but they by no means tell the story of the importance of glass to our modern world.

USES OF GLASS

So many of the things we use, so many miracles of modern invention depend upon glass that we could scarcely exist in the twentieth century without this versatile material. Window glass is, of course, the most easily recognizable application. Of still greater significance, however, is the use of glass in lighting. In our modern windowless plants and office buildings no work could bo done without the glass of which light bulbs and tubes are made. Without glass, the progress in science would have been impossible. Lenses in cameras, in telescopes, and in microscopes have given us the means to explore outer and inner space and to learn the composition of matter. Other instruments which depend on glass parts or glass construction include spectroscopes, thermometers, barometers, X-ray machines, electronic tubes and other electrical devices, and chemical laboratory apparatus. Medicine would be at a loss without glass hypodermic syringes, glass slides, and the tiny glass electric lamp which glows at the end of the bronchoscope.

Glass piping is used in many manufacturing operations for conveying everything from magnesium to tomato juice and milk. Mirrors, glass bricks, spectacles, electrical insulators, television tubes, neon signs, cooking utensils, and decorative art objects are only a few of the thousands of uses for glass.

Chemists, physicists, and engineers are working constantly to find new ways of making glass and new kinds of glass. Today, the American glass industry is able to make glass that is as fragile as a moth's wing or as tough as a block of granite. Glass thread is being drawn for the weaving of fireproof glass textiles. Glass ribbons one-thousandth of an inch thick and as flexible as cellophane can be made for fabricating electrical capacitors for a variety of electronic devices. Glass ribbon is an excellent substitute for mica as an electrical insulating material.

Glass technicians are now working on a "variable transmission" window, which can be adjusted to admit more or less heat and light. Another sensational breakthrough is in the development of electroluminescent glass panels for interior lighting. Treated with an electrically conductive coating, such glass will emit a soft glow and will not only revolutionize our concepts of interior design but will also provide a new source of heat.

Unbreakable glass as tough as steel has yet to be successfully produced, but scientists believe they are not far from achieving this seemingly impossible product.

With this and other challenging prospects, the future of the glass industry in America is limited only by the ingenuity of its technicians.

A long strand of glass is drawn by machine. Such drawn glass may be used to make glass tubes and piping.

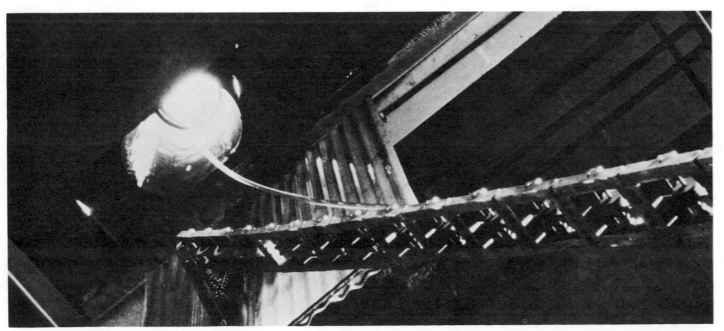

41 Plastics

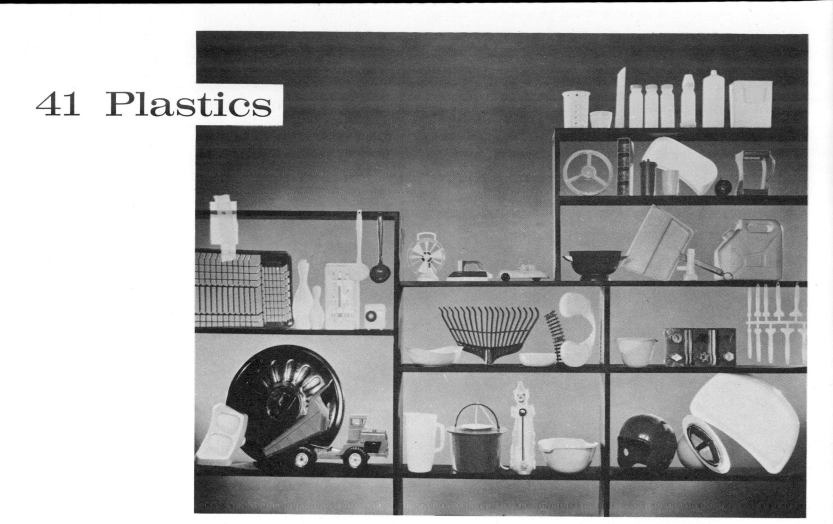

Plastics are used for a great variety of products as demonstrated by this diversified display, which includes bottles and other containers, toys, industrial components, appliance parts, and monofilaments which are made into marine ropes. The products illustrated are made of Fortiflex high-density polyethylene.

Few industries have come such a long way in so short a time as the plastics industry. Less than 100 years ago, the manufacture of artificial materials and substances was unheard of, yet today this is one of a handful of multi-billion-dollar industries in the United States. With all its current marvels, the industry has by no means reached a peak of development. It is just beginning to grow.

Here is further evidence that the world of today and tomorrow is spinning and will continue to spin excitingly in an age of chemicals. Within a span of four decades, nearly all industry has come to rely on laboratory science for its progress, and from miracles of the test tube and the microscope a number of entirely new industries have sprung into being. Plastics manufacturing is one of the foremost of these. (See *Chemicals*)

BILLIARD BALLS AND ELEPHANTS

It all began in the 1860's when the popularity of the game of billiards brought about a scarcity of African elephants. The quest for the ivory, of which early billiard balls were made, so decimated the elephant population that American manufacturers offered a 10,000-dollar prize for a practical substitute for ivory. Spurred by this incentive, an Albany printer by the name of John Wesley Hyatt began experimenting with mixtures of ground wood, paper and rags, which he combined with shellac and glue. His first concoctions were unsuccessful. Next he turned to cotton fibers, a pure form of cellulose, which he treated

with nitric acid. It was known at the time that the acid-treated cotton fibers, dissolved in alcohol and ether, dried as a hard, transparent substance called collodion. But collodion was too brittle to be of much practical use. Seeking a way to toughen the material, Hyatt hit upon what turned out to be the first practical plasticizer—solid camphor. Since camphor is an oil, it dries slowly. Mixed with pyroxylin, made from cotton and nitric acid, it served to keep the resulting film pliable for years. The inventor called his new material "celluloid."

Though it was of little value for billiard balls, celluloid rapidly made its appearance in a host of products. Colored pink, celluloid replaced hard rubber in the making of dental plates. Toys, combs, men's shirt collars, picture frames, and photographic film were produced with the new plastic material, and it was partly Hyatt's invention that made possible the early development of the motion-picture industry (which see). For many years, movie films were referred to as "the celluloids," but the inflammable nature of this type of film spurred the development of safer substitutes. The company which Hyatt formed to make celluloid was the basis for the great Celanese Corporation of America, one of the leaders in the plastics industry today.

In 1889, a Belgian named Leo Hendrik Baekeland was seeking a way to produce synthetic shellac. (See *Paints and Varnishes*) In his New York laboratory, he discovered that the mixture of carbolic acid and formaldehyde

PLASTICS

resulted in a thick, syrupy substance. When he tried to soften this liquid by applying heat, he found to his amazement that it hardened into a mass that was impervious to any solvents he applied. After long, often frustrating experimentation, Dr. Baekeland obtained a controllable reaction between phenol and formaldehyde, and at last, in 1909, he introduced his patented material, "Bakelite," the world's second major plastic compound.

Soon bakelite was in wide use for the making of telephone instruments, electric insulators, marbleized clock bases, handles, tabletops, and many other commercial products. Cold molded plastics also appeared in 1909. Ten years later, in 1919, casein was invented; then, beginning in 1926, the march of plastics advanced at double time, new materials appearing with bewildering rapidity.

WHAT ARE PLASTICS?

Actually, plastics may be classified as those substances, natural or artificial, which can be molded into any desired shape. In this frame of reference, glass is a plastic, as are clay and rubber. Asphalt, especially the form called gilsonite which is mined in Utah, is another natural plastic. By modern definition, however, plastics are artificially created materials, which can be shaped by the application of heat and pressure. They fall into two main classifications: thermoplastic plastics, which soften when heated sufficiently, can be molded, remelted and molded again

Many plastics are derived from cellulose. Here, wood pulp stock goes from the digester through a washing process where impurities and acid are removed. This is one step in the production of purified cellulose.

and again (cellulosics, for example); and thermosetting plastics which undergo a drastic change during the process of their first molding and which cannot then be returned to their original forms (polyesters, for example).

MILESTONES IN PLASTICS

A partial list of important plastics shows how rapidly these products have been developed over a comparatively few years. Alkyds, used for molding electrical bases, appeared in 1926, along with aniline-formaldehyde. The following year saw the introduction of cellulose acetate, the transparent and translucent material which revolutionized packaging and which gave us attractive combs, toothbrushes, spectacle frames, and many kinds of toys. Then followed a whole series of developments: polyvinyl chloride, 1927; urea-formaldehyde, 1929; ethyl cellulose, 1935; acrylic and polyvinyl acetate, 1936; polystyrene or styrene, nylon and polyvinyl acetals, 1938; melamine formaldehyde and polyvinylidene chloride, 1939; polyesters and polyethylene, 1942; silicones and fluorocarbons, 1943; cellulose propionate, 1945; epoxy, 1947; acetal resin, 1956; polypropylene, 1957; and chlorinated polyether, 1959.

BASIC MATERIALS

A great many plastics are derived from cellulose. This vegetable substance composes the cell walls of a variety of plants. Because the length of fibers affects the physical properties of cellulose products, manufacturers use different types of cellulose for various purposes. Wood cellulose, for example, provides short fibers. It is inexpensive but does not have as great tensile strength as the costlier and longer-fibered cotton cellulose. At the same time short fibers result in fast drying which is desirable for certain uses.

Cellulosics are among the most durable plastics, and though abrasives will scratch their surfaces, they will not break under normal use. Made in a variety of brilliant colors, they can be clear, translucent, or opaque.

Cellulose Acetate is resistant to oil, gasoline, and cleaning fluids but should not come in contact with alcohol or alkalies. It is odorless and tasteless. This plastic is furnished to fabricators in pellets, film, sheets, rods tubes, strips, and coated cord; it can be molded by injection, extrusion, blow molding (as with glass), compression, vacuum (forming of sheets); it can be laminated, or coated, or machined.

Cellulose Acetate Butyrate is especially valuable where weather resistance and outdoor use is required, as it can be made to withstand temperatures from sub-zero to near boiling. However, like ordinary cellulose acetate, it is attacked by alcohol and alkalies, as well as by acetone and most paint removers. It is available in the same forms and can be fabricated or molded in the same manner as cellulose acetate.

Cellulose Nitrate is resistant to most acids and alkalies but is flammable. As a result it cannot be heat molded. This colorful material can be obtained in sheets, film, rods, tubes, and as a liquid-coating material.

Ethyl Cellulose is the best of the cellulosics for resist-

236

ance to intense cold. Resistant to alkalies and weak acids, it should be kept away from solvents and oils. In its raw form it is supplied as granules, flake, sheet, rod, tube, film, or foil and can be molded by injection or compression and can be extruded, drawn, or machined.

The *Alkyds* are thermosetting plastics whose greatest application is in paints and lacquers for automobiles, refrigerators, and stoves. (See *Paints and Varnishes*) As molding materials they are found in electrical equipment such as connectors, light switches, motor insulator and mounting cases, television tuning devices, and tube supports. Alkyd materials are heat resistant and impervious to acids, alcohol, oils, and moisture. Supplied to fabricators as molding powder or liquid resin, alkyds are used to

Plastics are made from many chemical formulations and raw materials, but one of the most curious is *Casein,* which is produced by treating the protein of skim milk with formaldehyde. The result is a strong, rigid, thermosetting material which is resistant to a wide variety of chemicals. It is affected by moisture and humidity changes and therefore is not suitable for outdoor use. Some of its applications include buttons, beads, adhesives, toys, and knitting needles. Generally it is machine formed from sheets, rods, or tubes. It can also be obtained as a powder or liquid.

There are three types of *Cold Molded* plastics, known as *Bitumin, Phenolic* and *Cement Asbestos*. Heat and arc resistant, they make good electrical insulators and are

Highly purified cellulose, basic raw material of many plastics, now in sheet form, is dried in hot air dryers and wound onto jumbo rolls. It will be cut into various sizes for shipment.

produce a great variety of electrical parts by compression molding.

Another group of thermosetting materials are the *Allylics,* which are also used widely in electrical equipment. They can stand up to extreme heat and can be used for long periods in temperatures as high as 350° F. Finished products are made from monomers, prepolymers, and molding powders by compression molding, lamination, and impregnation.

Colorful, tough plastic tableware is usually made of *Melamine*. This thermosetting "amino" plastic has such excellent properties of strength, chemical resistance, heat and weather resistance that it is used for tabletops, baking enamel finishes, plywood adhesives, and for a great variety of handles, knobs, and buttons.

Urea, another amino plastic, has properties similar to melamine.

molded by heavy pressure and subsequent curing into electrical plugs, handles, knobs, small gears, game markers, and toy building blocks.

Epoxy resins are used to bond metals, glass, and ceramics as well as other plastics. Having good electrical properties, they are employed for printed circuits and other electronic parts. Because of their durability under all sorts of weather conditions, they make excellent surface coatings and sealing compounds. They are available as resins and in the form of foamed blocks, liquids, and adhesives.

Providing stability over a wide range of temperatures, low coefficient of friction, and high resistance to corrosion, *Fluorocarbons* are important in the making of gaskets, pump diaphragms, and high voltage insulation. Under this classification are *Vinylidene, Fluoride, Fluorinated Ethylene Propylene, Tetrafluoroethylene* and the granddaddy

237

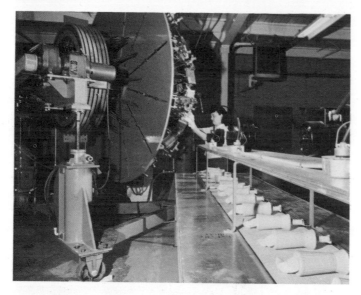

Blow molding by machinery 'is used in the manufacture of plastic bottles and containers. Molten plastic is forced into a mold, then air inflates it like a balloon, forcing it against the sides of the mold.

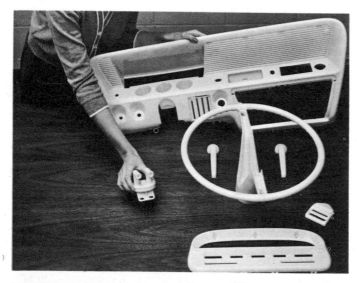

A few typical moldings of Celcon plastic for automobile construction. Parts include dashboard panels, water pump, seat buckle, steering wheel and door handles. Celcon is an acetal copolymer plastic.

of long-named plastics, with 26 letters, *Polychlorotrifluoroethylene!* All are thermoplastic materials which are molded, extruded, and machined.

A much more familiar material which has won the undying acclaim of women everywhere, is *Nylon*. This versatile thermoplastic material embraces a number of related polyamide resins which are used to make thread for hosiery and other woven fabrics, brush bristles, fishing lines, faucet washers, gears, tumblers, and dozens of other familiar products. Nylon, noted for its high tensile strength and its resiliency, is impervious to most household chemicals, greases, and solvents but is susceptible to food stains. Molding powder, sheets, rods, tubes, and filaments are available to manufacturers for injection, compression, and blow molding, as well as for extrusion.

Several types of *Phenolics* are manufactured for a host of products which range from radio and television cabinets to jewelry; from brake linings to jukebox housing parts. Thermosetting phenolics are hard and tough and can take

temperatures up to 400° F. Being poor conductors of heat, they make excellent handles for cooking utensils. Included in this category are *Phenol-Furfural, Phenol-Formaldehyde, Cast Phenolic* and *Resorcinol.*

One of the newest plastics is *Polycarbonate Resin* which was first introduced in 1957. Extremely hard for a thermoplastic, it can absorb hammer blows without shattering. It is being used for electronic connections, aircraft and automobile parts. Primarily a molding resin, it is also supplied as film, extrusions, fibers, elastomers, and coatings.

For molding large objects such as automobile bodies, airplane parts, translucent roofs, and many other products both large and small, the *Polyesters* are invaluable. One of their important attributes is their ability to be formed under very low pressure and at ordinary room temperatures. Yet they are tough, chemical proof and weather resistant. Produced in the raw state as liquids, dry powder, premix molding compounds, and as sheets, rods, and tubes, they can then be formed by reinforcing, casting, molding, impregnating, and premixing.

Of the three plastics boasting the highest volume of production in recent years, *Polyethylene* exceeded one billion, three hundred fifty million pounds in 1960. This popular thermoplastic is everywhere in evidence as squeezable bottles, flexible ice cube trays, tumblers, transparent or translucent bags, toys, rainwear and various types of tubing. It is strong and can be made flexible or rigid. It remains pliable in extreme cold, even as low as minus 100° F. Although certain formulations can withstand boiling water, polyethylene should be kept away from open flames. Pellets, powder, sheet, film, filament, rod, tube and foamed raw forms are finished by injection, extrusion, compression, blow molding, calendering, coating, casting, and vacuum forming. It is made in a wide range of colors, clear transparent, translucent, or opaque.

Almost as widely used, *Polystyrene* or *Styrene* production has passed a billion pounds per year. It is found in kitchen utensils and containers, wall tile, instrument panels, radio housings, and hundreds of toys. Tasteless and odorless, as is polyethylene, it is excellent for food containers, although it should not come in contact with rind oil of citrus fruit, cleaning fluids, gasoline, turpentine, nail polish, or nail polish remover. Fabricators can obtain polystyrene molding powder, sheets, rods, foamed blocks, liquids, adhesives and coatings. A thermoplastic, it can be injection or compression molded; extruded, laminated, or machined.

In the electrical industry, another important family of plastic materials is the *Silicones*. Many switch parts, equipment for induction heating, and a variety of insulations are made with silicones, silicone-glass laminates and silicone rubber. Parts formed of this material may be machined, molded, or cast.

Urethanes offer a completely different range of materials from the general run of plastics since they have some remarkable qualities of elasticity and adhesion. Urethane foam is familiar in cushions, automobile seats, mattresses, various types of padding, artificial sponges, and rug underlays. In addition, urethane formulations can be employed to bond some strangely unrelated substances such as rubber to metal, synthetic fibers to synthetic rubber, rubber to ceramics, and leather to leather. As a coating, urethane provides decorative protection to wood, metals, rubber, textiles, concrete, paper, and leather, to list only a few possible applications.

Among the plastics in most demand are the *Vinyls,* annual production of which amounts to some billion and a quarter pounds. Found in toys, shower curtains, rainwear, garden hose, phonograph records, electric plugs, upholstering materials, floor tiles, and wall coverings, these thermoplastic compounds are amazingly versatile. They are strong, heat and cold resistant, though they should be kept away from open flame or direct heat. For decorative purposes they have a great range of uses, as they may be printed or embossed, and may be made in an almost unlimited number of colors and textures. The various types may be molded, extruded, cast, and calendered; they are available as powders, resins, coatings, sheets, rods, tubes, adhesives, film, organosols, and plastisols.

MOLDING AND FABRICATING PROCESSES

One of the great advantages of plastics is their adaptability to all sorts of manufacturing processes and requirements. They can be cut, molded, formed, stamped, rolled, and cast. Some plastics can be processed by all or any of these methods. Several molding methods are commonly used.

By compression molding, most thermosetting plastics are squeezed into shapes under heat and pressure. Usually a molding powder is mixed with other materials, such as wood flour, cellulose, or asbestos. It is put into a heated mold which, when closed, presses the mixture into the desired shape. Heat causes the thermosetting plastic to undergo chemical change, permanently hardening it into the formed product. Another kind of compression molding, known as the transfer method, consists of forcing a heat-softened mixture into the mold by means of a hydraulic plunger. It is most used where intricate shapes are desired, since the liquid plastic flows more easily into minute crevices or holes.

For thermoplastic materials, injection molding is the most common process. From a large hopper, the raw material passes into an oven where it is melted into a liquid. High pressure then forces the fluid through a small opening into a closed mold where it cools and solidifies. Finally the mold is opened and the finished plastic product is ejected. Automatic equipment carries out these operations in large plastics manufacturing plants. Because thermosetting materials liquify, then quickly harden permanently when subjected to heat, special equipment is used for their injection. Known as jet molding and offset molding, the machines heat the thermosetting material to its liquid state at the moment it reaches the nozzle and passes into the mold. Thus it does not have time to harden before it can be formed.

Another method of forming thermoplastic compounds is blow molding. As in the making of many glass products, such as light bulbs (See *Glass*), a required amount of molten plastic is inserted into a mold, then air inflates it like a balloon, forcing the material against the sides of the mold. This process is generally used to manufacture plastic bottles and other containers.

For making products which consist of thin layers of material in specified shapes, such as bathing caps or inflatable toys, solvent molding does the job. This consists of dipping molds into plastic solutions and withdrawing the molds after a certain amount of plastic has adhered to them. In some instances solvent molding is used as a method of coating, and the "mold" thus becomes a permanent part of the finished product. Casting is actually a form of molding, the difference being that no pressure is exerted. Liquid plastic is poured into the cast and allowed to harden.

Various methods have been devised for coating metal, paper, wood, glass, ceramics, or other materials with plastics. Both thermosetting and thermoplastic substances can be used as coatings. Some are sprayed, rolled, dipped, brushed, or knife coated. Spread or knife coating consists of having the plastic flowed onto the other material as it moves over rollers. A coating "knife" smooths and spreads the plastic and controls the thickness of the coating layer. Fluid plastic can also be transferred from a revolving roller, which picks up the coating and deposits a layer onto a web of supporting material passing under it.

In the Houston, Texas, plant of Celanese Polymer Company, spaghetti-like strands of Fortiflex travel through a water bath prior to being chopped into pellets, the form used by extruders and blow molders.

To produce tubes, rods, sheeting, and filaments, extrusion molding is employed. An extrusion mold is fed dry plastic raw material, such as powder or pellets, into an elongated heating chamber. In this chamber, a screw mechanism revolves continuously, forcing molten plastic through an opening or openings at one end of the heating chamber. The shape of the aperture determines the form of the extruded plastic. Rods, tubes, and filaments are generally made by extrusion, and wires or cables may be coated by having a length of wire pass through the extruder die along with the plastic. Conveyors carry the lengths of extruded material through water or cool air blowers to hasten the hardening process.

Some thermoplastics are converted to a thin film or sheeting by calendering, or forcing the material through a series of heated rollers. These rollers may impart a textured surface to the plastic, or may be smooth. Calendering is also used for laminating plastic to various other materials, such as fabrics and paper. To bond thermosetting plastics to other materials, "high-pressure" laminating is usually employed. Sheets of wood, paper, glass fibers, or cloth are impregnated with plastics, then the sheets are piled, several layers deep, and placed between two highly polished steel plates. Tremendous hydraulic pressure of about 1,100 lb. per square inch is exerted to squeeze the sheets while heated platens cure the thermosetting material. The several layers are thus formed into a single laminated sheet.

For many plastic products, fabricating is accomplished by machining similar to the operations used with wood and metal. Plastic sheets, rods, and tubes may be drilled, die-cut, sawed, milled, turned on a lathe, ground, or polished. Other fabricating methods include sewing, cutting, and sealing of various plastic films in the making of raincoats, upholstery, luggage, bags, and inflatable toys. These operations are comparable to those used in working with textiles. Pattern cutters shape the material, then the sections or pieces are joined by sewing or heat sealing. Decorative finishing is carried out by various printing processes (See *Printing*), etching, embossing, spraying, dusting, painting, and air blasting.

SCOPE OF THE INDUSTRY

In the early 1960's this precocious infant of the industrial world comprised about 6,000 companies in the United States. These included manufacturers of the raw compounds and plastic resins, processors and fabricators. The majority of the 200-odd material manufacturers are chemical firms (See *Chemicals*) although some companies specialize in formulating plastic resins from basic raw chemicals. There are about 2,000 molding firms specializing in the manufacture of plastic toys, handles, instrument and machine parts, and hundreds of other molded products. Another 350 companies are engaged in extruding filaments, sheets, film, rods, tubing, and pipes. Fabricators comprise some 3,000 firms which convert plastic materials to such products as shower curtains, raincoats, luggage, and furniture.

This vast complex of industries, located in all parts of the United States and Canada, is producing nearly seven

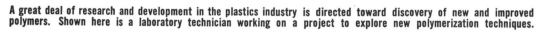

A great deal of research and development in the plastics industry is directed toward discovery of new and improved polymers. Shown here is a laboratory technician working on a project to explore new polymerization techniques.

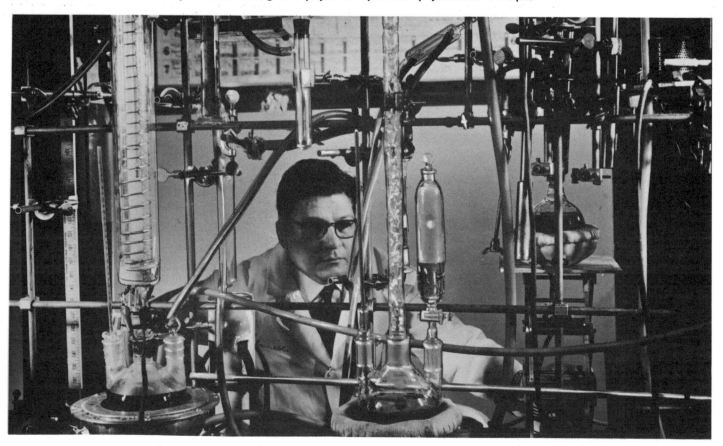

Plastic threads and cord have become important materials in the textile industry (which see). Here, tire cord of nylon is threaded through porcelain eyelets to prevent overlapping. It will then be dipped in liquid latex.

billion pounds of plastic materials annually and is growing steadily. In the 10 years between 1945 and 1955, the plastics industry increased 300%.

One of the remarkable things about the industry as a whole is that small companies as well as industrial giants are successfully engaged in plastics manufacturing and fabricating. There are many opportunities for individual and local enterprise. At the same time, the greatest American corporations are involved, including such names as Du Pont, Eastman Chemical Products (division of Eastman Kodak), Minnesota Mining and Manufacturing, Monsanto, Dow Chemical, Union Carbide, and many others.

Within the general categories of plastics outlined earlier in this chapter are many familiar brand names created by individual companies. To list a few: Cellophane (Du Pont); Scotch tape (Minnesota Mining); Tenite plastics (Eastman); Bakelite (Union Carbide); Velon (Firestone); Polyfilm (Dow Chemical); Styrofoam (Dow Chemical); Fiberglas (Owens-Corning Fiberglas); Chromspun (Eastman); Dacron (Du Pont); Mylar (Du Pont); Lucite (Du Pont); Celcon (Celanese); Fortiflex (Celanese).

OPPORTUNITIES GALORE

As in any of the chemically based industries, plastics have a promising future. With comparatively small capital outlay a modest plastic fabricating or processing operation can be established. This should not be attempted, however, without thorough and basic knowledge of the selected field, for plastics possess no magic for creating success without adequate training or preparation. Another field for the small businessman is the wholesaling or retailing of plastic materials in sheet, film, rod, tube, and pipe form.

Among the large chemical firms and plastics manufacturers, there is, of course, a great need for research chemists, chemical engineers, machine operators, die and mold makers, business administrators, sales personnel, and many other classifications of skilled and unskilled workers. Largest area for employment is among the processors who need molding machine operators, finishers, mold and product designers, chemical and mechanical engineers, as well as management, sales and office personnel. Fabricators employ jig makers, machinists, assemblers, and finishers.

Because of the explosive growth of this industry, a great many schools and colleges have added instruction and courses of study in plastics to their curricula. Some of these programs are included as part of the courses in chemistry or other related subjects; others are courses devoted exclusively to the plastics field.

Unquestionably, this is one of the most exciting of modern American industries. It has come a long way in a short span of years and its future appears limitless.

42 Toys and Games

Who can resist a toy shop window? This tempting display is one of the outstanding windows at the New York store of F. A. O. Schwarz, a leading U.S. toy merchant.

Without toys, the world would be a dreary place. Toys provide for children a realm of fun and fantasy, at the same time offering pleasant means of learning about adult activities. One of the largest segments of the industry is the manufacture of educational toys and games. Nevertheless, the fascination of toys lies largely in their ability to transport their owners into a land of imagination and dreams, and literature abounds in stories and poems about that wonderful province of childhood—Toyland.

Yet the gates of Toyland are by no means closed to adults. Today, with the great upsurge of hobby shops, sale of elaborate scale-model toys to adult customers is big business. Some of the world's leading personalities are ardent collectors of toy soldiers or are model railroad enthusiasts.

Among the first toys were dolls and toy animals, examples of which have been found in many excavations of ancient civilizations. Terra-cotta animals were made in Rhodes at least 2000 B.C., while human dolls, made of wood, clay, and fabrics from Greece and ancient Egypt, dating back to 500 B.C., may be seen in museums today.

In the Middle Ages, crude wood carvings were the most prevalent toys, though even as early as A.D. 1000, clockwork mechanical toys were made by skilled clockmakers. It was not until the eighteenth century, however, that mechanical toys were available to any but the wealthiest families.

During the Industrial Revolution, as toy making developed into a major industry, Germany dominated the world market. From 1850 to the outbreak of World War I, whole villages in Germany and Switzerland were occupied in the making of all sorts of ingenious toys, many of which were carved and put together by craftsmen working in their homes. During this period there were no more than 75 American toy manufacturers. Their chief products were dolls, sleds, rocking horses, trains, and various games.

World War I closed off the German toy imports, and when U. S. toy makers began to produce more dolls with American-style clothes and other toys with strictly American characteristics, they found an eager market. Children in the United States and Canada preferred toys with domestic styling, particularly cars, boats, planes, and miniature housekeeping appliances, such as stoves, ironing boards, doll carriages, sweepers, and dustpans. The extent of the American industry's growth after the war is shown by the fact that in 1909, U.S. toy production was valued at only seventeen million dollars. By 1947, the volume was about three hundred forty million dollars; there were one thousand three hundred thirty-four manufacturers employing over fifty thousand workers. Now the industry is producing an annual volume worth nearly a billion dollars. At the same time, American toy exports have exceeded imports in recent years.

It would be natural to assume that the toy industry is one of the most enjoyable of business activities, and undoubtedly those who are engaged in designing toys and working out new games thoroughly enjoy their work. But as a manufacturing industry, toy making is one of the most highly competitive in America. Representatives of toy companies, who attend the annual toy fair held in New York every spring, take their business with deadly seriousness. The battle for markets and for the sale of new toys and novelty items to the large chains and department stores is often a cutthroat game played for high monetary stakes.

KINDS OF TOYS

Toys are made of virtually every material under the sun. However, the majority fall under certain general classifications, and many are produced by specialized firms which limit production to given categories. For preschool children, wooden toys are still popular. From the simplest wooden blocks to a variety of action pull toys, they are comparatively inexpensive, hard to break, and will not cut or scratch small children. Among the leaders in this field are Sifo Co., and Playskool Mfg. Co.

During the latter part of the nineteenth century and prior to World War II, metal toys were made in tremendous quantities by U.S. manufacturers. Sheet tin was used for dollhouses, doll furniture, wagons, trucks, trains, and even for toy animals, clowns and so forth. While such toys are still popular, the volume has greatly decreased as the use of plastics has come to dominate the field.

Without question, the development of plastics has been the greatest boon to the toy industry in all its long history. (See *Plastics*) Plastics can be injection molded, extruded, or cast into virtually any shape; they can be soft, rigid, clear as glass or made in a variety of brilliant colors. For dolls, plastic materials can simulate the feel and texture of human flesh in faces, hands, and feet. The most intricate toy cars, trucks, and model railroad accessories are molded in various kinds of plastics. Although these materials are inexpensive and toys made of them can be reproduced in great volume at low cost, the original molds represent substantial investments for toy manufacturers, and a single mold may cost from $500 to $25,000. Today, at least 50% of all toys produced in the United States are made entirely or partly of plastics.

Clockwork, or "windup" toys powered by spring mechanisms, while not as popular as they were before the advent of electricity, are still produced in large numbers. Al-

These tin horses are examples of some of the earliest mass-produced toys to be made in America. They delighted boys and girls in the 1850's.

Wooden toys have always been popular for young children. This lithographed wooden fire engine and fire house were made in the U.S. between 1890 and 1910.

(Upper) A 1907 model steam engine featured the first working headlight. (Lower) First enclosed model built by Lionel was this Baltimore and Ohio car made in 1900. Tracks were strips of steel set in wooden blocks.

243

though most are being imported from Japan and West Germany, such American firms as Louis Marx & Co. and Mattel Inc. are active in this field.

Some of the most marvelous playthings ever made are the electrical and scientific toys which have been developed by American manufacturers. For many years, the American electric train has been one of the supreme achievements of the toy maker's art. In recent years particularly, with the increasing demand by youngsters and hobbyists alike, HO gauge trains have reached a state of near perfection. Tiny locomotives, freight and passenger cars are reproduced in exact scale and with attention to the most minute detail. Steam-type locomotives puff smoke and sound realistic whistles. In addition, accessories provide the model builder with everything needed to construct a complete miniature village or rural landscape. (See *Railroading*) Two of the largest manufacturers of electric trains and accessories are A. C. Gilbert Co. and The Lionel Corp.

In this age of electronics, space exploration, and chemical research, American boys and girls can find a vast array of rocket and space toys, chemical sets, and kits for the construction of a variety of electronic devices, many of which are on an advanced level. Some of the so-called "toy" radio kits, for example, can be used to set up actual operating shortwave transmitters and receivers. American and Canadian toys, made on the assembly-line principle, surpass those from any other part of the world, particularly in the field of elaborate, mechanical playthings.

Games are generally produced by specialized companies, sometimes called game "publishers." Various new board and card games are constantly being created by staffs of these companies, led by such firms as Milton Bradley Co., Selchow & Righter Co., and Parker Bros., Inc. Occasionally when a new game is produced by someone privately, it achieves considerable popularity and then is bought out by one of the large game manufacturers. Such was the case with *Scrabble,* which became a national rage in the 1950's. One of the mysteries of the game business is why certain games suddenly become popular. Often they die out as quickly as they gain national attention. Meanwhile, many standard games hold a large and steady market year after year.

THE U. S. TOY INDUSTRY

Most American toy and game manufacturing is located in New England, the Middle Atlantic, and the North Central States. About 1,000 firms are distributed throughout Massachusetts, Connecticut, New York, Pennsylvania, New Jersey, Ohio, Illinois, and Michigan. Spurred by high shipping costs from the East to the West Coast, a number of California toy companies have been gaining importance in recent years.

Although Christmas remains the major toy-buying season of the year, the seasonal character of this industry has been leveling off as year-round purchasing of toys has been on the increase. Due to the fiercely competitive nature of the industry, the prices of U.S. toys have remained remarkably constant over long periods. At the same time, many toy firms report difficulty making profits. Nevertheless, it seems likely that the production of toys and games will continue to increase. This is an industry where original ideas and designs are constantly creating exciting possibilities for new business, and where small manufacturers can compete with large ones by having sufficiently attractive and novel products.

Duplicating in minute detail the features of a modern metropolis, this exhibit of electric trains and mechanical toys contains 350 feet of track, lights, trees, automobiles, planes, helicopters, buildings, farms, waterfalls, rivers, and freeways.

43 Fabrics and Textiles

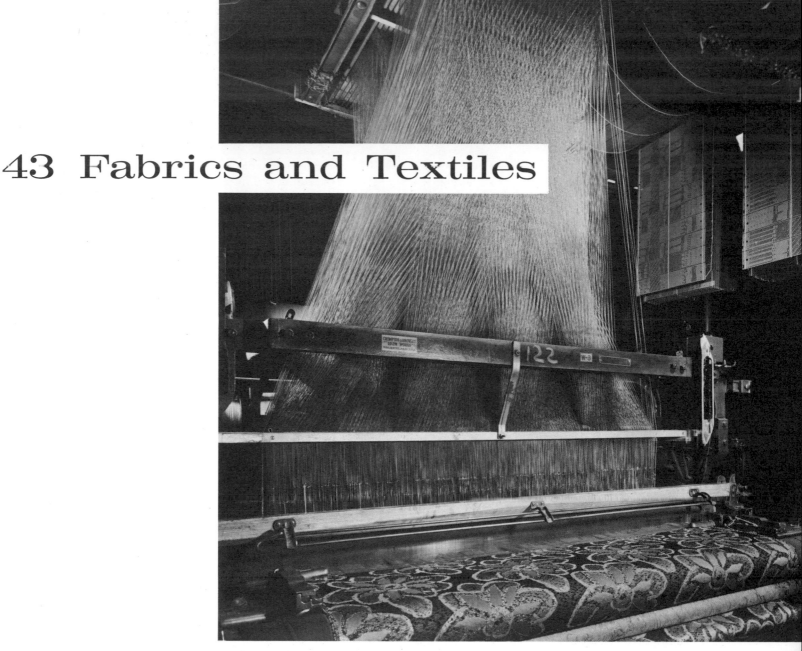

A double Jacquard power loom is shown weaving upholstery fabric (brocatel) at Craftex Mills in Philadelphia. At the right are two sets of punched cards which guide the selective weaving of the complex pattern.

The art of weaving goes back into the antiquity of the New Stone Age, and archaeologists have found garments made of woven materials and fabrics among the remains of nearly every prehistoric settlement. Some of the best preserved fabrics of ancient times have been found in cave dwellings in America. Richly embroidered cloth was left in the Egyptian tombs, indicating a highly developed craft of weaving linen and cotton. Magnificent silks, damasks, and brocades were made in ancient China, while the peoples of Siberia and the Crimea had developed woolen materials.

Along with methods of spinning thread and weaving it into fabrics, most of the ancient peoples developed techniques for dyeing and printing cloth, using earth colors and stains from other natural sources.

Until the Industrial Revolution, crude spinning wheels and looms operated by the hands and feet of the weavers were the only machines available for this essential industry. Then, with the introduction of steam power, the manufacture of textiles began to be mechanized. Before the American Revolution, British textile mills were producing machine-made cotton fabrics from raw material supplied by colonial cotton plantations. Introduced in 1770, the Hargreaves spinning jenny which could spin several strands of yarn at one time, and the Arkwright water frame for making a strong warp yarn, were among the early machines that contributed to the explosive growth of a modern textile industry in England. America's war for independence was partly motivated by the desire of colonists to establish their own home textile industries, an enterprise frowned upon by the British factory owners.

RAW MATERIALS

In order to produce the thread and yarn for weaving, felting, braiding, knotting or knitting fabrics it is necessary to find suitable fibers. Today, the textile industry makes use of four main classifications of fibers. They are the animal fibers, including wool, hair, and silk; vegetable fibers, comprising cotton, linen, jute, Asian ramie, hemp (an Asiatic herb), and tropical kapok; mineral fibers, such as metallic threads made by winding fine strips of gold, silver, or aluminum around another fiber, and asbestos

Beam attachments, or giant spools, for a Jacquard loom carry between 5,000 to 9,600 warp threads.

which is a magnesium silicate (See *Mining*); and finally the chemical fibers which include the new synthetics, nylon, orlon, dacron, and so forth.

Certain man-made or synthetic fibers fall into the mineral or vegetable classifications. Rayon, for example, is made from cellulose, a vegetable product. Fiber glass, a mineral derivative, is composed of fine strands of glass.

Each type of fiber has certain individual qualities. Silk, which has the longest fibers, possesses a high luster and is very strong. Cotton fibers are very short; they produce cloth with good heat conductivity, excellent for cool, summer wear. Most elastic of natural fibers, wool is also a poor conductor of heat. For this reason it retains body temperature and is one of the warmest of materials for cold weather clothing or for blankets.

WOOL, which comes largely from sheep, varies in quality and texture with different species. The longest-fibered wool is produced by the native English sheep. The merino, a Spanish breed noted for a fine-textured white wool, is now raised in many parts of the world. Most American wool comes from the sheep ranches in the midwestern states, though there are also large herds in Texas, New Mexico, Arizona, and the Rocky Mountain states. (See *Farming*) Spinning of wool produces one of two types of yarn: *worsted* or *woolen*. Worsted yarn is made by a process of washing, scouring, carding, and combing the fibers, then twisting them tightly by spinning. This results in a smooth, hard-surfaced yarn. By contrast, uncombed woolen yarns are soft and fuzzy. Special wools are made from a variety of long-haired animals: mohair, from a Turkish angora goat; cashmere, from the fine, silky hair of a Himalayan goat; camel hair, from the bactrian or the dromedary camel; vicuna, from a rare, wild South American animal bearing wool of the softest quality; llama and alpaca, from the two South American wool-bearing animals of those names.

Although SILK is strictly an Oriental product, the United States leads the world in the manufacture of silk fabrics. In China, Formosa, and Japan, cultivated silkworms are fed mulberry leaves. About 30 days after hatching they begin to spin their cocoons, which are composed of long silken threads created by a process known only to the worms! To obtain the fibers, the cocoons are unwound, their thin, yellowish filaments being drawn onto reels. Ends that are too short for reeling may be converted to spun silk, a material with less elasticity and tensile strength than the fine reeled silk.

COTTON, which is still a major agricultural product of the Southern states (See *Farming*), comes from the seed-pods of cotton plants. There are several varieties of these plants, each producing different types and qualities of fibers. American pima cotton is among the world's finest. After seeds have been combed out by ginning, the raw cotton is baled and sent to mills where carding removes foreign matter, and further combing pulls out the shortest fibers. Spinning then twists the fibers into yarn, and by twisting two or more single strands of yarn together, two-ply, three-ply, and heavier cotton yarns are produced. The first manufacturer of cotton thread was Clark Brothers who still produce sewing spools with the familiar "O.N.T." label (Our New Thread).

Possibly the first source of textile fiber used by man was the FLAX plant from which LINEN is made. Although flax cultivation and linen weaving are important industries in Europe, comparatively small amounts of linen are produced in the United States. Flax fibers are obtained by crushing dried stems of the plant. Short fibers used for cheap toweling are known as *tow;* the best long fibers, or *line,* are the ones used in the manufacture of fine linen tablecloths, handkerchiefs, and sheets.

In the early 1880's, a Frenchman by the name of Hilaire de Chardonnet found a way to create a synthetic fiber from cellulose. However, it was highly inflammable, and others sought to improve the process. As various types of cellulosic threads were developed, they came to be known by the general name of RAYON.

Shortly after World War I, cellulose was combined with acetic acid to produce an acetate rayon thread which is the type in general use today. U.S. production of rayon leads all other nations, although nearly every country in the world has a rayon industry. A leader in this field is Celanese Corp. of America, the world's largest producer of acetate yarn.

One of the most important of synthetic fibers is nylon, a creation which the Du Pont Corp. introduced in 1938. For its raw materials nylon production requires coal, air, and water from which tar, oxygen, and hydrogen are extracted. (See *Chemicals, Plastics*) Nylon is comparable to natural silk, in that it is strong, elastic, and washable. It is a poor conductor of heat.

As chemical research continued to create synthetic materials, one new fiber after another came onto the market. In 1920, man-made fibers and yarns were laboratory curiosities. Today, there are more than twenty synthetic fibers being commercially produced by a two-billion-dollar-a-year segment of the textile industry.

SPINNING AND WEAVING OPERATIONS

The conversion of natural fibers to yarn was first done by pulling them into a strand, then twisting them by rolling the strand between the palms of the hands. Then the spindle was devised. This was merely a slim wooden shaft on which the yarn was wound as it was twisted. In the sixth century, Europeans began using the spinning wheel which had originated in India.

Meanwhile, the European handloom brought weaving to as high a state of mechanical development as was possible before the application of power. Modern power looms evolved from this device which performed the three fundamental steps in the weaving process: shedding, picking, and beating up.

Shedding consists of lifting up alternate threads of the lengthwise "warp," to permit the passage of the crosswise threads called the "filler" or "weft." In the European handloom it was done by means of parallel wires stretched on a frame known as a heddle frame. Alternate warp threads are passed through eyelets fastened at the center of each wire on the heddle frame. For simple weaving, two heddle frames are used, one to lift the even-numbered threads, the other to depress odd-numbered threads, but for more complicated weaving patterns, as many as a dozen frames may be employed.

Picking involves the insertion of the filler yarn, and it is accomplished by shooting a shuttle across the loom and through the raised threads of the warp. The torpedo-shaped shuttle carries a bobbin of yarn which permits the yarn to unwind through a small hole in the shuttle's side. Throwing the shuttle by hand continued until the invention of a spring mechanism to propel the "flying shuttle" in 1733.

Finally, "beating up," or pushing the weft threads firmly in place, was performed on the handloom by means of a comb-like reed frame, which the operator pulled toward himself from the top of the loom, pressing the teeth of the reed between the warp threads and against the last filler thread.

This basic process of hand weaving is still used in

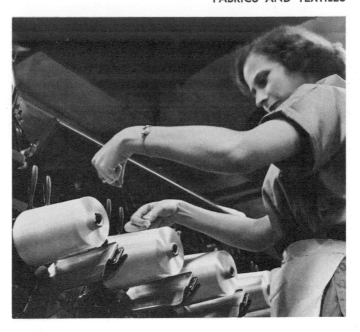

Coning rayon yarn at a plant at Rock Hill, S.C.

Prior to beaming or winding on giant spools, yarn is drawn and unwound from a series of small spools. This operation is called "creeling."

many parts of the world. But it was the development of power looms that signaled the start of the entire Industrial Revolution.

Today's manufacture of textiles follows all the steps of primitive weaving but on a gigantic scale and with automatic machinery. Spinning machines consist of two principal types, known as the frame and the mule. Frame spinning is the method most used in the wool and cotton industries. On each side of a stationary frame are about 100 revolving spindles which are fed the yarn through a series of rollers. A strand of yarn is first passed through three pairs of rollers, each succeeding pair revolving at a faster speed. This causes a pull that draws, or elongates the thread. Next, the strand is twisted as it moves through a ring called the "traveler," due to the fact that it moves freely around a circular track with the spindle in the center. So rapidly does the spindle revolve as it winds the strand that a slight tension is exerted on the yarn as it passes through the traveler ring. The combined whirling action and slight drag of the ring serves to twist the fibers.

Mule spinning derived its name from the fact that the machine is a hybrid of two earlier devices. While the yarn is drawn through rotating rollers as in frame spinning, it is wound on a spindle mounted on a moving carriage. As the carriage moves away from the drawing rollers on a track eight- to ten-feet long, the yarn is twisted and drawn at the same time. The carriage then returns to its original position winding the drawn strand as it goes, and the cycle is repeated. Mule spinning is a slower operation which produces a fluffier yarn than does the frame method.

Since silk and synthetic filaments are available in 300- to 700-yard lengths, the drawing phase of the spinning operation is unnecessary for these materials. Fine filaments are merely twisted in various numbers of plies to provide yarns of different thicknesses and strength.

Preparatory to weaving, yarns are "warped," or wound from spools and cones to a giant spool known as a beam.

They are then put through slashers which coat the strands with starch, or sizing, to provide a smooth surface and increase the strength of the yarn.

WEAVING

A beam of finished yarn, which may weigh 700 to 800 lb., is now "harnessed" to the loom, meaning that the warp threads have been drawn by workers through heddle wires in whatever sequence is required for a particular style of weave. Finally the loom is set in motion and weaving begins. Power loom speeds are measured by the number of picks per minute, which is the number of times the shuttle travels across the warp each minute. When yarn from a bobbin has been depleted, an automatic device ejects the empty bobbin and replaces a fresh one in the shuttle within the brief fraction of a second while the shuttle is between trips across the warp. The Northrup "battery" loom, developed in 1895, acquired its name from the fact that a circular battery of filled bobbins rotated to move a fresh bobbin into position with each replacement.

For many years, the textile mill's greatest problem was the breaking of threads during weaving operations. Operators were constantly on the alert to shut off power the moment a break occurred. About 1900, however, automatic stop devices eliminated the necessity of this supervision. Today, a single weaver may tend as many as 100 looms operating simultaneously. Along with increased speeds, power looms have been improved with multiple shuttles carrying yarns of several different colors. These can be arranged to follow automatic sequences in the weaving of patterns.

When widths of fabric leave looms, the material still requires finishing operations. Cotton generally emerges as "gray goods" which must then be bleached, dyed, printed, and sometimes sized before it is ready for market. Usually finishing operations are carried on in separate mills, although there are weavers who carry out these processes themselves.

SEGMENTS OF THE INDUSTRY

Textile industries are divided into a number of specialized categories which include mills for the manufacture of yarns by spinning natural fibers or by extruding various synthetic filaments; weaving or knitting mills; and finishing mills where woven fabrics are dyed, bleached, sized, and printed. (See *Printing*) The goods thus manufactured may be finished products such as bed sheets, blankets, or hosiery; or yard goods which are bought by clothing firms and other types of manufacturers for the making of wearing apparel; or a variety of cloth goods requiring cutting and sewing. Those processes take the materials into another group of industries, the garment or needle trades. (See *Wearing Apparel*)

Because there are so many raw materials and woven products and so many steps in the processing of textiles, the industry is marked by considerable specialization. Spinning mills generally limit their operations to a single fiber, such as cotton, silk, wool, or a certain type of synthetic yarn. Even further specialization is seen within these categories. For example, a factory may make only one of several types of wool yarn.

As a supply industry to the garment trades, textile manufacturing is greatly affected by changes of fashion. (See *Fashions*) A sudden style shift may create unexpected demand for a certain fabric, or may decrease the popularity of another. Fashion changes are by no means limited to clothing, but are felt by the manufacturers of draperies, upholstery, and even such items as towels, blankets, and bed sheets. This influence upon the market is an unstable factor which gives the textile manufacturer a serious problem, one over which he has little or no control. Some of the larger and more progressive firms have attempted to stabilize their market and to gain a larger share of consumers' dollars by establishing active public relations departments. Through promotion and public relations, a rayon firm may, for example, be able to popularize new and effective uses of rayon which will be reflected in current styles and fashions. But the problem remains a serious one for this diversified, highly complex industry.

Prices of fibers and fabrics fluctuate greatly as a result of market instability. This is further complicated by the fact that, when prices are beginning to rise, distributors and fabricators rush to buy, building up inventories far beyond immediate needs. This buildup is invariably followed by a lean period for the textile mills.

Although textile manufacturing is highly mechanized, most plants are small in comparison with those of other primary industries such as steel, chemicals, petroleum, and rubber. Even large textile firms tend to operate a number of medium-sized mills, rather than one large one. The reason lies in the diversity and specialization mentioned earlier, as well as in the fact that most of the operations involved do not require large-scale equipment or production. Generally speaking, small mills can be operated as efficiently and as profitably as large ones.

A large percentage of workers in textile mills are women (in the United States about 42%) due to the fact that many of the mechanized operations involve light work, and that women are paid generally lower wages. The effort to keep labor costs low has also resulted in major geographical shifts of textile mills. Many factories have been moved from New England and the Northeast to the South.

THE FUTURE

While it is difficult to predict what changes may occur in the textile industry, it remains an essential activity. Taking the industry as a whole, demand for its products is steady, and with population increase, consumption of textiles may be expected to rise accordingly. At the same time, technology in this field has been at a high level for many years. Only in the realm of synthetic fibers, which may actually be considered a segment of the chemical and plastics industries, has there been significant or fundamental change. It is probable that chemical research will continue to bring new and better fabrics into being, and that most of the industry's future developments will be in that direction.

44 Tobacco

Tobacco ranks fourth among American farmers' cash crops and is grown on more than half a million U.S. farms.

When a shipload of 90 English girls arrived in Jamestown, Va. in 1619, bachelors who had been awaiting them happily paid marriage fees of 120 lb. of tobacco to gain their brides. Although Columbus had failed to realize the value of this "Indian weed" when friendly Indians gave him some leaves as a welcoming gift, it did not take Europeans long to learn the pleasure they could derive from "that bewitching vegetable."

Tobacco growing and the manufacture of tobacco products make up an industry exclusively American in origin. American Indians in the Caribbean Islands and in North and South America smoked tobacco in pipes, or rolled it in cornhusks. They chewed it and snuffed its fragrant smoke through Y-shaped *tobagos*. One of the sailors who sailed with Columbus, Roderigo de Jerez, took some tobacco back to Spain. Presumably he was the first person to smoke a pipe in Europe, and according to the story, his performance so frightened the townspeople that they summoned police, thinking he was breathing fire.

In Colonial America huge barrels, or hogsheads, of tobacco were transported by rolling them long distances. After poles were attached to a hogshead's axis, the poles were run through a horse's harness. Thus the hogshead was pulled along the road like a bulky wheel.

At first, colonists and Europeans smoked tobacco in pipes, adopting the popular Indian custom, but in the Revolutionary period, snuff was widely used. One of the early makers of snuff, Pierre Lorillard, described his rather involved recipe: Take a good strong virgin tobacco without stems. Cut this in pieces and make it wet in a barrel. Set it in sweet (sweat) room at 100 degrees for 12 days. Make into powder, let stand three to four months, adding 1½ lbs. salmoniac, 2 lbs. tamarind, 2 oz. vanilla bean, 1 oz. tonka bean, 1 oz. camomile flowers.

Cigars became popular after the Mexican war, for cigar smoking was prevalent in Mexico at that time. Soon drivers plying the frontier roads were seen puffing foot-long "stogies," a name derived from their Conestoga wagons. Meanwhile, cigarettes were being introduced to British soldiers by the Egyptians and Turks. The story is told of an Egyptian gunner whose pipe was shattered during a battle between Egyptians and Turks in 1832. He made use of handy paper spills to roll his tobacco. The idea caught on rapidly, and soldiers everywhere began to "roll their own." American tobacconists soon offered the makings for hand-rolled cigarettes. Not until the 1880's did machines, capable of producing 50,000 cigarettes a day, change the world's smoking habits by making ready-made cigarettes both inexpensive and plentiful.

GROWING THE BEWITCHING VEGETABLE

Although tobacco ranks fourth among American farmers' cash crops and is grown on more than half a million U. S. farms, it is by no means an easy plant to cultivate. Soil, rainfall, and temperature must be just right to produce good tobaccos. *Nicotiana tabacum* acquired its botanical name from the Frenchman, Jean Nicot, who is credited with introducing it to France, and from the Carib word for inhaling, *tabaco*. There are several varieties which may be combined to make blends. Some grow best in the South; others do well in the cooler regions of Ontario, Connecticut, and Michigan.

Broadleaf or *seedleaf* is found in the Connecticut Valley, Florida, and Georgia. It is used for the binders and wrappers of cigars. *Havana seed,* also grown extensively in the Connecticut Valley, provides cigar binder and filler (broken bits of tobacco in the cigar's center). A great deal of filler tobacco is grown in the Lancaster region of Pennsylvania, and in the Miami Valley of Ohio.

For the processing of tobacco, different types are cured in special ways. In long, curing sheds the leaves are dried, either by fire-curing or flue-curing. Fire-curing is accom-

Choice leaves are gathered and strung on poles to be hung in curing sheds where they will be dried either by fire-curing or flue-curing.

Inside the curing barn, tobacco men inspect the leaves. Varieties of tobacco are cured in different ways to impart distinctive flavor and aroma.

A tobacco auction is a colorful activity; buyers must be expert judges of tobacco. Tobacco companies say it requires five years to train buyers.

plished by lighting slow fires on the floor of a log barn. The tobacco leaves are subjected to a temperature of 90° F. until they become yellow. Then the heat is increased to 130°. The process takes from three to five days. In flue-curing, the leaves are dried by heat, but without their being exposed to the smoke of fires. For this method, sheds are constructed with large pipes, or flues, to carry off smoke and gases as the temperature inside the barn is raised to 170° F. Oil and gas burners are generally used for flue-curing. The most common curing method, especially for cigar tobaccos, is air-curing. If weather is favorable, the leaves are dried without artificial heat, either outdoors or inside latticed sheds.

Each of the curing methods imparts distinctive aroma and flavor to the tobacco. Flue-cured or Bright Tobacco is grown mostly in Virginia, North Carolina, and Florida. Darker in color, fire-cured types are found in western Kentucky, Tennessee, and Virginia, while the air-cured tobaccos grow well in the limestone soils of Kentucky, East Tennessee, and Ohio.

After tobacco has been cured, it is piled in baskets and put in warehouses to be auctioned. This is an exacting phase of the tobacco industry, for buyers must be expert judges of good tobacco. Large tobacco companies say it requires five years to train their buyers. Moving along between the rows of baskets, buyers examine the leaves, which are graded by quality. Meanwhile, the auctioneer chants bids in a strange jargon incomprehensible to all but the initiated. By almost imperceptible signs, buyers make their bids. The entire procedure is handled rapidly and with dispatch. No time is wasted in arguments or in haggling over price or quality. If a farmer finds a bid unacceptable, he indicates refusal by "turning his sales ticket." His tobacco will be offered at a later auction, sometimes in another warehouse.

CIGAR AND CIGARETTE MANUFACTURING

Before it can be used, tobacco must be fermented. The leaves are piled in heaps, heated, and then repiled. In corrugated metal or brick warehouses, the tobacco is aged for two years or more in 1000-lb. hogsheads. Leaf storage represents two-thirds of manufacturers' assets.

Modern machinery has been devised to make up to 1,200 cigarettes per minute. Blends from a number of different tobaccos, such as Virginia, Maryland, Turkish and Burley, are automatically pulverized, mixed, and rolled in special paper made of flax straw. Other machines pack the cigarettes, wrap the packages in cellophane and add the strip of cellophane tape for opening the pack.

Cigars are made at a considerably slower speed on machines that wrap broadleaf around filler and binder at a rate of 780 to 900 an hour. Until 1918, when the first successful cigar-making machine was developed, all cigars were wrapped by hand.

Today, some three million people are employed in U.S. cigar and cigarette factories and in related industries which include the making of special papers, packaging, shipping, advertising, and marketing. More than a million and a half retail stores sell tobacco products which annually amount to some six and one-half billion cigars, seventy-

250

Tobacco, prepared for stemming, is stored in a large warehouse. Before it can be used, tobacco must be fermented.

Hogsheads of aging tobacco are stored in one of the mammoth warehouses of a tobacco company. Each hogshead contains about 1000 pounds.

four million pounds of pipe-smoking tobacco, sixty-eight million pounds of chewing tobacco, thirty-five million pounds of snuff and between four hundred and five hundred *billion* cigarettes. The total retail value of tobacco products sold amounts to about seven billion dollars a year, with two and one-half to three billion dollars paid in federal, state, and municipal taxes.

TOBACCO RESEARCH

The large tobacco firms, such as P. Lorillard Co., American Tobacco Co., Brown & Williamson Tobacco Corp., and Liggett & Myers Tobacco Co., conduct extensive research in their well-equipped laboratories. Their purpose is to improve blends, and impart better flavor and aroma to their tobacco products. Burning qualities of papers and tobacco are also tested and improved.

In recent years various types of filters have been devised to remove harmful tars and other agents from the smoke of cigarettes. Some of the most significant research now being done is in the realm of medicine. Tobacco technicians are attempting to find causes of cancer, particularly lung cancer, which has been attributed in some cases to heavy smoking. Proof has not yet been established that cigarette smoking can contribute to the incidence of lung cancer, but if it should ever be demonstrated conclusively, tobacco researchers hope to find ways of rendering cigarettes harmless. The industry is making every effort to learn the truth and to give people safe smoking pleasure.

Tobacco laboratories are well equipped for research in organic chemistry. In a Liggett & Myers tracer laboratory, for example, is the most up-to-date equipment for low-level radioactive tracer investigations. Instrumentation laboratories contain facilities for ultraviolet, infrared, fluorescent, and visible spectrophotometry. Pilot plants with special temperature and humidity controls are used to study every phase of cigarette manufacture, including leaf handling, steaming, casing, drying, tobacco cutting, cigarette making, and packaging.

The tobacco industry, one of America's largest, has been threatened time and again by antagonists who seek to prove the harmful effects of smoking. Yet through chemical and medical research, there is every reason to believe that tobacco will continue to give mankind pleasure and relaxation as it has for centuries past.

Packaging machinery delivers thousands of packs of cigarettes and automatically boxes them, ten packs to a carton.

Workers on a cigarette production line at an American Tobacco Company plant use scales at a weight control point.

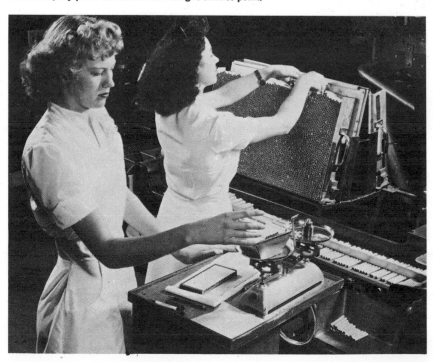

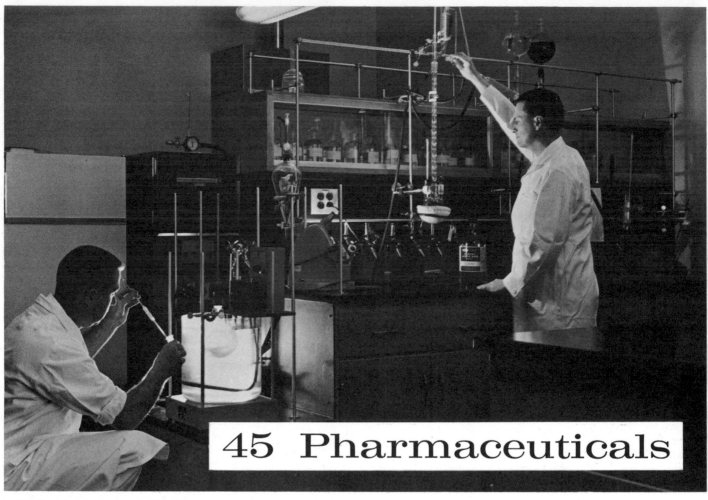

45 Pharmaceuticals

Technicians at a laboratory of CIBA Pharmaceutical Company's Developmental Research Center investigate a potential chemical process. Ultramodern equipment provides American pharmaceutical chemists with the ultimate in technological facilities.

In this atomic and chemical age, the witch doctors and medicine men are laboratory scientists and chemists, and their magic is far more potent than anything the superstitions of primitive peoples could devise. Within a period of 25 years, the development of "wonder drugs" has drastically changed the concepts of medicine and has perfected cures for diseases considered incurable for centuries. Yet the use of drugs is by no means a modern idea. The ancient Egyptians, Greeks, and Chinese all prescribed medicines for various ills, and the American Indians were familiar with many beneficial herbs.

Some of the medicines used in ancient times were based upon pure superstition and were connected with curious rituals. For example, the Chinese gave beans to patients with kidney ailments, purely because the kidney is bean shaped. In cases of yellow jaundice, they prescribed yellow saffron. We find records of the ancients feeding tigers' livers to soldiers in the belief that such a diet would give them the strength and courage of tigers! On the other hand, effective pain-killing drugs were in use in very early times. Greek physicians used small doses of hemlock or mandrake root, mixed into wine to prepare their patients for operations. Opium, made from poppy juice, and marihuana were known as pain-killers in the Orient many centuries ago, but their habit-forming properties made them

dangerous and difficult to control. Without sufficient knowledge to standardize dosage, the physicians frequently made tragic errors; many became fearful of using drugs at all.

Until comparatively recent times, medicines were used to attack symptoms, rather than the diseases themselves. This was due to the fact that, without modern microscopes, men had no idea of the real sources of illness. Able to observe only the superficial results of disease, they might attack several symptoms with different medicines, where one drug could have destroyed the single microorganism that was doing the damage.

ORIGINS OF THE PHARMACEUTICAL INDUSTRY

Modern chemical drugs began to emerge from widely scattered research efforts and from a number of exciting discoveries. In 1846, William Thomas Green Morton demonstrated to skeptical colleagues that ethyl ether could be safely used to anesthetize a patient during surgery. Sodium salicylate (aspirin) was employed as a pain reliever as early as 1875. (See *Chemicals*) In 1867 an English surgeon, Joseph Lister, made use of deadly carbolic acid to disinfect wounds, without harming the patients. Iodine, camphor, potassium bromide and other chemical compounds came into wide use and were soon in such demand during the late nineteenth century that firms began to manufacture them in quantity. Most of these old-fashioned remedies have since been replaced by more effective compounds.

As doctors began to prescribe more and more medicines, American pharmacies and "drug" stores ordered quantities of the necessary ingredients from chemical firms. It was not long before the manufacture of chemical drug compounds became a specialty, and a number of large drug-making companies grew up with the new frontier of medicine. Today, these corporations are engaged in a multibillion-dollar American drug industry which is a wonder of the world. These are leading firms in this field: Eli Lilly & Co.; Upjohn Co.; Parke, Davis & Co.; Smith Kline & French Laboratories; Lederle Laboratories (div. of American Cyanamid); Merck Sharp & Dohme (div. of Merck & Co.); Wyeth Laboratories (div. of American Home Products); E. R. Squibb (div. of Olin Mathieson); Abbott Laboratories; and Charles Pfizer & Sons. Without question, American medical and pharmaceutical science leads all other nations, while people in every corner of the globe look to the United States as their hope for stamping out sickness and disease. If the United States offered oppressed peoples no other freedom, the promise of freedom from disease could be our rallying cry for world leadership.

HOW NEW DRUGS ARE CREATED

After the French scientist Louis Pasteur proved to the world that microscopic bacteria caused many human diseases, the search for medicines to kill these harmful organisms, the science of chemotherapy, became a major concern of the medical world. As researchers in hospitals and in chemical laboratories began to work out a few of the complex answers to disease, the pharmaceutical companies undertook to manufacture the proven medicines in quantity. Yet until 1910 when quinine was developed for the treatment of malaria, no "specific" had been made for attacking an isolated type of bacteria. Nowadays, due to a number of recent breakthroughs, large and steadily increasing numbers of specific drugs are being manufactured.

Let us visit a modern pharmaceutical laboratory where scientists are studying the functions of a small human gland. This gland is a pad of wrinkled tissue attached to the upper part of the kidney. It is known as the adrenal gland. This amazing organ is a chemical factory which produces some of the most subtle and elusive secrets of life. Through years of study, scientists have learned that the adrenal gland contains two separate and independent chemical plants. One is the cortex, or covering; the other, a brownish inner core called the medulla, produces epinephrine (adrenalin), a hormone responsible for the normal functioning of our nervous systems, blood pressure, and heart rate. This hormone has been isolated in crystalline form.

But this comparatively simple chemical represents only one of the many complex secrets which chemists are trying to wrest from a study of the adrenal gland. By analyzing its secretions they are hopeful of discovering means of curing mental illness, heart disease, cancer, and of arresting the aging process.

253

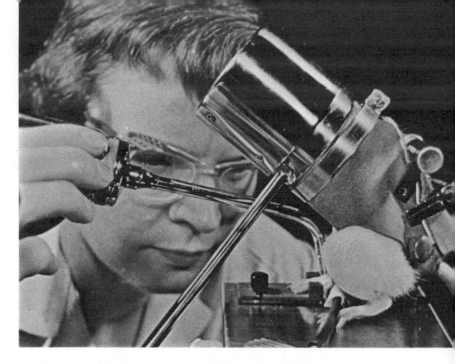

To screen certain new compounds, scientists produce high blood pressure in rats by surgery. Then, after injecting a new compound into the animals, they check the effect with this photoelectric tensometer.

Meanwhile, laboratory technicians are examining viruses, bacteria, protozoa, and algae. In these organisms they have uncovered and cataloged certain chemicals called "nucleic acids." Known as DNA (deoxyribonucleic acid) and RNA (ribonucleic acid) they may hold the chemical secret of heredity and of life itself, for they are found in flowering plants and in higher animals as well as in the various microorganisms.

Work within the laboratories of pharmaceutical firms is slow and painstaking by the standards of many of our fast-paced, machine-driven industries. Thousands upon thousands of test slides and cultures are made and watched, and careful records are kept of step-by-step chemical actions and reactions before a single important result may be observed. Small animals, such as white rats, are given injections of various hormones, chemicals, or drugs. Their reactions or symptoms are studied and recorded through entire life cycles, sometimes through several generations.

From their study of adrenal chemistry, researchers developed a series of drugs called "corticosteroids," the best known of which is cortisone. Having established that adrenal cortex hormones are centered on a system of car-

Embryonated eggs are infected with virus and then treated with new compounds. The use of an egg candling machine permits periodic examination to determine the effect on the embryo.

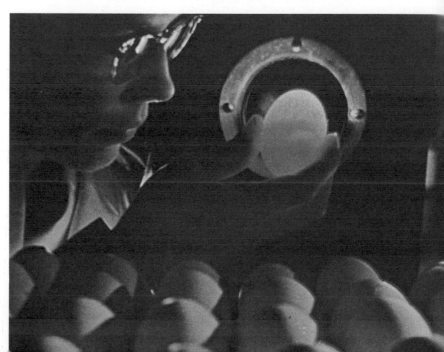

A chemical engineer checks out a continuous high vacuum still. The still is used for purification of high molecular weight materials at a pharmaceutical laboratory.

bon, hydrogen, and oxygen atoms, called the steroid nucleus, scientists experimented with changes in the basic structure, adding or subtracting atoms to see what effects such alterations would have on actions of the steroid compounds in the body.

Using tons of animal adrenals, laboratory workers spent fruitless years trying to analyze miniscule amounts of extracts from the adrenal cortex. In the 1930's Edward C. Kendall of the Mayo Clinic, Tadeus Reichstein in Switzerland, William W. Swingle at Princeton University, Oskar Wintersteiner and J. J. Pfiffner of Columbia University all were working to isolate pure cortical substances. Out of 21 isolated compounds, one showed an exceptional arrangement of oxygen atoms. This was *deoxycorticosterone*. It proved to be a partially effective treatment for Addison's disease. However, the yield of various adrenal compounds from animal glands was so small, that researchers knew they must find a more plentiful source of cortical steroids or must develop more effective methods of creating complex molecules from simple atomic structures.

By this time millions of dollars had been poured into adrenocortical research by pharmaceutical firms. From 1944 to 1948 Merck & Co. scientists worked with two adrenal compounds known as Compound A and Compound E. The big breakthrough came in 1949 when Dr. Philip Hench gave doses of Compound E to rheumatoid arthritis patients at the Mayo Clinic. Results were sensational. Hopelessly crippled arthritics were given quick release from pain and were restored to activity almost overnight. But more of this amazing cortisone was needed. Merck & Co. and Schering Corp. began to manufacture and market it. This required intricate equipment, quan-

tities of raw materials, utmost care in quality control and expert technical supervision. At last, after nearly a century of research and study of adrenal steroids, cortisone was in production and was found to be a miraculous drug for treating many human ills, including severe allergies, skin conditions, eye and intestinal inflammations.

Such is the story, much too briefly told, of a wonder drug. The problems and frustrations, the millions of dollars expended, the hundreds of experiments which lead nowhere, can only be briefly indicated. The greatest difficulty is often that of finding a way to produce a serum or drug in sufficient quantity to be useful to humanity. Such was the case with cortisone. Merck's introductory price of cortisone was $200 per gram. By 1950, this had dropped to $22.40 per gram and when Upjohn Co. perfected a low-cost process of production, the price dipped to $4.00. Meanwhile, Merck discovered a way to synthesize hydrocortisone, a natural hormone of the adrenal cortex. This competition caused Schering Corp. to employ a microbiologist who would devote most of his time to corticosteroid work.

One of the methods used for creating new compounds involves fermentation. The microbiologist employs certain microbes which cause oxidation and thus bring about chemical changes in the materials exposed to them. In 1953, in the Schering laboratories, some of these microbes caused a change in cortisone molecules. Having dislodged two hydrogen atoms from the cortisone molecule, they had brought into being a new molecule. The value of this transformation remained to be seen, but early tests indicated that the new compound would be three to five times more powerful than the original cortisone. In addition, it had reduced salt retention which made the earlier compound objectionable in the treatment of some patients.

After some cautious testing Schering decided to produce the new prednisone and prednisolone. In a 150-gallon tank containing cortisone, microbes, and certain nutrients on which the microbes could feed, the first production batch of the drug was made successfully. Hydrocortisone was given the same treatment. The microbes turned cortisone to prednisone and hydrocortisone to prednisolone. Next, the firm invested close to three million dollars in a huge cortisone inventory, began production in a 1,000-gallon fermenter, then quickly increased the volume in a 22,000-gallon tank. So critical are the factors in production of a chemical compound of this kind that the slightest deviation in procedure may ruin thousands of dollars' worth of raw materials. The fermentation process in making prednisone, for example, must be arrested at precisely the right time, for if microbes are allowed to work on the cortisone too long, the drug becomes worthless.

In 1957, Upjohn followed Schering's breakthrough with the production of another steroid compound, methylprednisolone. Squibb and Lederle simultaneously announced triamcinolone in 1958. Merck's contribution was another breakthrough. Their dexamethasone has an average antirheumatic potency about 35 times that of cortisone and shows a substantial reduction in troublesome side effects.

Two principal processes are employed in the production of fermentation compounds: *growth,* and then *extraction* of a purified material for medical use. In the first phase, a small test tube containing a colony of microorganisms is used to inoculate a series of "shaker flasks." Thus the colony grows and multiplies sufficiently to take care of large-scale production. The cultures are kept in a room where constant temperature is precisely controlled, and where the flasks are continuously shaken automatically in order to keep life-giving oxygen moving through the microbe colony. Next, the microorganisms are placed in a small tank. If, at this stage, the most minute amount of undesirable bacteria has contaminated the batch, it must be destroyed. Step by step, approved batches are transferred to larger fermentation tanks until a small test tube of microorganisms has grown to several thousand gallons of useful bacteria.

To keep the culture alive in the large tanks, thousands of cubic feet of sterilized air are circulated through the fermenters while agitators keep the mixture in constant motion. Heat, generated by the growing process, is kept down by a water-cooling system.

The second phase begins when the "beer" is ready to be harvested. The useful compound must be extracted by one of several methods. These include filtering, extracting with a solvent, distillation, or crystallization.

All of these stages in the processing of antibiotics and other fermentation products are complex, critical operations requiring the most careful supervision. For the obvious reason that microorganisms keep growing right through weekends and holidays, the fermentation must be watched around the clock, seven days a week. Microbes have no unions and recognize no legal holidays. Absolute purity and sterilization of tanks and other equipment must be maintained at all times. There is no more exacting work in all industry, for the stakes are high, literally a matter of life and death.

SULFA AND PENICILLIN

The developments in cortisone drugs follow a general pattern that illustrates the nature of this highly complex pharmaceutical industry. Earlier, the much publicized sulfa drugs had evolved through similar painstaking research. Dr. Gerhard Domagk, a German, discovered that a white powder derived from coal tar attacked streptococci germs. Within two or three years, sulfa, as the drug became known, was being tested in France, England, and the United States. Sulfanilamide, sulfapyridine, and hundreds of other variants were made and tested for a number of diseases. In World War II, sulfa drugs performed miracles on infections.

Penicillin was discovered accidentally in 1928 when a Scottish bacteriologist, Dr. Alexander Fleming, noticed that one of his glass containers, in which he had been growing bacteria, had become contaminated with a moldy substance. He nearly threw the contents away when he observed that the staphylococci germs were being destroyed by the mold, which he called *penicillium.* However, it was Dr. Rene Dubos of the Rockefeller Institute who gave antibiotic research its greatest stimulus in 1939, when he demonstrated that "good" bacteria could be used

In the pharmaceutical industry absolute cleanliness is a must. An employee at Smith Kline & French Laboratories in Philadelphia places equipment in a giant autoclave for sterilizing.

A researcher for Smith Kline & French Laboratories extracts alkaloids from natural products which may include plants from the far corners of the world.

to fight diseases caused by "bad" bacteria. In 1940 Dubos was furnished with quantities of a bacterial toxin known as tyrothricin by Merck & Co., and he began experimental work with penicillium cultures. By 1941, Merck's fermentation methods were showing results.

The resulting drug, penicillin, was first used on a human patient that year, but not until 1943 was any important production accomplished, most of it in plants within the United States.

Streptomycin, another important antibiotic, was found through long laboratory exploration by Dr. Selman A. Waksman, a Russian-born scientist, at Rutgers University. His breakthrough came in 1944, and the drug's greatest use has been in the treatment of tuberculosis. In 1946, U.S. production of streptomycin was 20,000 grams per month. This increased so rapidly that, by 1951, the December output alone had reached eighteen million grams.

Other well-known wonder drugs include aureomycin,

chloromycetin, and terramycin. Dozens of others, as well as many variations on the original formulas, have been developed during the past 10 years. Thus the search for new and better medicines continues in hundreds of laboratories.

MARKETING DRUGS

The pharmaceutical industry is unique in many ways. In the marketing of its products it spends millions of dollars for a special type of educational advertising. Unlike most commercial campaigns, pharmaceutical advertising is seldom addressed to the general public but goes to physicians and pharmacists in the form of clinical reports and technical booklets describing new drugs, their applications, dosage, with only the most conservative, factual claims for their effectiveness.

Sample tablets, capsules, or small bottles of liquid are distributed to doctors as one of the first steps in the introduction of new drugs. Sometimes samples are sent to every pharmacy in the United States, at tremendous cost to the manufacturer, so that prescriptions can be filled wherever there may be a call for the compound. Charges that the prices of drugs are exorbitant have resulted in

After government approval a new drug goes into production in huge tanks and kettles which perform the same functions as are carried out in the laboratories, but on a scale thousands of times larger.

From chemical manufacturing the new product goes to pharmaceutical manufacturing. Solutions made here are transported to the filling rooms.

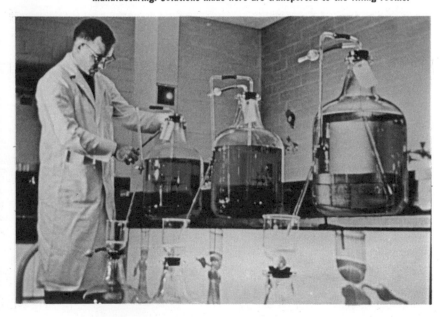

Congressional investigation of the industry's practices; yet a glimpse of the gigantic research programs and the risks involved in attempts to mass-produce a newly created compound, leads one to wonder how the prices can be held low.

When a new drug or biological product (such as Dr. Jonas Salk's polio vaccine) has been perfected and successfully used in clinical trials, it may be manufactured exclusively by the single pharmaceutical firm which developed it. On the other hand, often when an important breakthrough occurs, the essential information concerning the new development becomes generally known. In the absence of strong patent protection, the advance may be shared by a number of firms, each of which develops its own production methods or variants of the product. Frequently, the competition among major pharmaceutical companies is in the realm of alternative modifications or more efficient means of manufacturing given compounds. Even when a valuable drug is fully protected by patents, its manufacture may well be licensed to other competing companies.

PATENTS AND LICENSES

The possibility of obtaining patents on the formulas or special processes for making medicinal compounds acts as an incentive to private firms to create new drugs. Nevertheless, in most cases, the managements of major pharmaceutical companies have a high sense of responsibility, recognizing that their products are often too desperately needed to be held exclusively when their own production facilities are inadequate to fill demand. In a typical case, the executives of one well-known company debated whether to retain exclusive rights to an important new compound, which they had created in their laboratory and on which they had applied for a patent, or to license others to manufacture it. Their decision was to license competitors the world over, particularly those who themselves had done research in the field and who, in many cases, had also made scientific contributions. Another factor influencing their decision was the urgent need for large quantities of the product to meet a heavy demand. While it was vital to the firm's success that they receive royalties in return for the huge investment they had put into research and development, of even greater importance was the need to give relief to thousands of suffering persons. As a result, several large firms and all mankind have benefited, while the originating company is receiving income from royalties as well as from its own distribution of the drug, which it is able to market as fast as its facilities can produce, even with the competition of licensees.

FORECAST

This is an industry of the most highly skilled of skilled technicians. Its future belongs to the chemists, the microbiologists, the bacteriologists, the laboratory men and women who see the world through microscopes. That future is unlimited. For those who are excited by the challenge of learning the innermost secrets of life itself, the pharmaceutical industry offers countless, stimulating, and well-paid positions.

46 Soaps and Detergents

Soapmaking is no longer a simple process of boiling fats and oils. Production of soap and synthetic detergents today requires modern laboratories, machine shops, and intricate equipment as in this Procter & Gamble pilot plant.

So commonplace a commodity is soap, and so undramatic and mundane are its uses that few people realize how vital it is to the modern world. Without soaps and detergents, dirt and disease would be rampant, and many industries would be unable to operate.

A story is told that in ancient Rome there was a riverbank along the Tiber where a clay softened the water and provided an excellent place for washing clothes. According to this story, the clay had been formed by a mixture of tallow and wood ashes which had come from burning sacrificial fires and tallow candles on a nearby hill. Whether or not this story is true, it is probable that soap resulted from some accidental discovery. In any case, soap was used in France as early as the year 200. Around the eighth century, Spanish soap makers developed castile soap, made from olive oil and soda. But until the 1800's, soap was an expensive luxury. In Colonial America, housewives made their own crude yellow soap by boiling tallow or lard mixed with lye or potash, a product of leached wood ashes.

HOW DOES SOAP CLEAN?

The chemical properties of soap result from the reaction of a caustic alkali with a fat or fatty acid. Due to its surface tension, water will not penetrate a greasy surface, but the surface tension of soapy water becomes greatly reduced, so that it can soak into greasy dirt, loosen it, and form an emulsion of water and grease. This can then be rinsed away. Soaps and detergents are sometimes classed under the general heading of "surface-active materials." In such materials are two major groups of molecules: one

group contains a hydrocarbon nucleus which is fat-soluble and water-insoluble; the other is attached to the hydrocarbon nucleus and is water-soluble and fat-insoluble. Most detergents have one or more hydrophobic (water-insoluble) and lipophilic (fat-soluble) groups within each molecule.

SOAP MANUFACTURE

In the modern soap factory, most of the basic steps of old-time soapmaking are carried out, but on a much larger scale and with certain refinements. Fresh fats and oils, comprising the soap stock, and an alkali (usually a soda solution) are poured gradually into huge steam-heated boiling kettles. The batch is continuously boiled for about 48 hours. An experienced soap boiler must watch an open kettle constantly to guard against frothing of the boiling liquid, but modern plants have mechanical temperature and pressure controls to prevent boiling over.

The next step, called "graining out," separates glycerin and lye liquor from the soap curd by the addition of several tons of salt to the giant kettle. The brine carries impurities and glycerin to the bottom of the kettle and is drained off, while the curds, which are insoluble in brine, remain in the tank. When saponified soap, which is free of fat, is boiled in a brine solution, the batch is separated into an upper, crystalline layer known as neat soap, and a lower residue layer that is later treated to recover glycerin, an important by-product. While the neat soap is still warm, it is pumped from the kettle through a mixer called the crutcher. There the soap is beaten into a fluffy consistency while color, perfume, preservatives, and other special finishing substances may be added. Finally the mixture is poured into large frames, allowed to cool and harden, and the hardened slabs, weighing 1,000 to 1,500 lb. are divided into small cakes by cutting machines. Brand names and designs are stamped into the cakes at a production rate of one hundred thousand or more per day.

By a similar method, cold process soap is made, but the mixture is not grained with brine. As a result, glycerin remains in the batch, producing soft soaps, various types of liquid soaps, and shampoos.

In 1935, the Clayton process came into use. By this method, the fat and caustic soda mixture is pumped through a series of coils, heated to bring about saponification at temperatures of about 250° to 300° F. Next the charge is preheated under pressure to 500° to 600° F. and flashed into a vacuum chamber where glycerin and water are removed by distillation.

SPECIAL SOAPS

To produce milled soaps, flakes are formed on a chilled roller as the molten soap flows from the kettle. After perfume is added in a mixer, the flakes are passed between granite rollers, forced through a compressor and formed into a solid bar. Prior to the milling operation, soap may be scraped off the cooling roller and packaged as flakes or chips. If the molten soap mixture is sprayed into a drying tank, tiny beads of soap are formed. This finely granulated soap is used for dishwashing and other household uses, as it dissolves quickly and forms a heavy lather.

There are also medicated soaps, grit soaps containing abrasive substances for removing heavy layers of grease, and insoluble soaps. The latter are used in making heavy lubricating oils and greases, oil paints and water-repellent coatings.

DETERGENTS

The first synthetic detergent, produced in 1834, was actually a soap modified with sulfated olive oil. Various other sulfated oils made their appearance during the next 50 years. These included sulfated castor oil, popularly

Twelve huge soap kettles, each with 180,000-pound liquid capacity that can produce 629,504 bars of unfinished soap, are tended by veteran soapmakers who boil the soap before processing.

known as Turkey red oil, which was used for dyeing calico; they provided the basic ingredients for. a number of detergents. Then in the 1880's, alkali salts of naphthenic acids were discovered to be good washing agents, and since the turn of the century more than 500 synthetic detergent formulas have been developed in the United States. U.S. industries consume some fifty million pounds of sulfated oils each year.

Among the major groups of chemical detergents are the following: sulfated castor oil, peanut oil, cottonseed oil, soybean oil, neatsfoot oil; sulfated cod, sperm, other fish oils; sulfated tallow; sulfonated naphthenic acids made from fractionated petroleum (See *Petroleum*) and producing mahogany soaps and detergents used extensively in the textile industry (See *Fabrics and Textiles*); sulfonated hydrocarbons, products of paraffin hydrocarbons, which have excellent detergent action on wools (rugs), silks, and other fabrics, though they are not good for cotton; fatty-alcohol sulfates made by mixing lauryl, cetyl, and oleyl alcohols with sulfuric acid; and fatty-acid condensation products manufactured by heating fat with glycol or glycerol.

SCOPE OF THE INDUSTRY

This vitally important U.S. industry annually produces close to five billion pounds of soap and detergents with a retail value of about one and one-half billion dollars. Consumption is steadily increasing. Firms in this field are widely distributed, and· they vary greatly in size. Many specialize; some produce synthetic detergents, others, perfumed toilet soaps. The chemical companies furnish the basic ingredients for detergents (See *Chemicals*), while soap companies draw heavily on the tallow and lard by-products of the meat-packing industry. (See *Food Products*) In some cases, chemical firms are themselves the manufacturers of special detergents used in industrial processing, dry-cleaning and laundry plants, homes, hospitals, and hotels. Among the major soap manufacturers are the Procter and Gamble Co., Lever Brothers Co., Colgate-Palmolive Co., and Samuel Fels and Co.

One of the most interesting stories in the development of American industries and their products is that of Procter and Gamble's discovery of the floating soap which they called "ivory soap." In 1878, when David Gamble was working on a formula for making a hard, white soap without using expensive olive oil, a workman forgot to shut off the steam power in the beaters during lunch time. This whipped more air into the molten soap, and as a result the finished soap bars floated on the surface of water. Excited by the discovery, Harley Procter launched an advertising campaign that made commercial history. The phrases "99 44/100% Pure" and "It Floats" became national catchwords. (See *Advertising*)

Soap and detergent production comprise a great industry that promises to grow along with the increase of population and the rapid development of new industrial processes. The greatest increases appear to be occurring in the field of chemical detergents. Here is another of the many vital industries dependent upon and stimulated by chemical research.

47 Jewelry

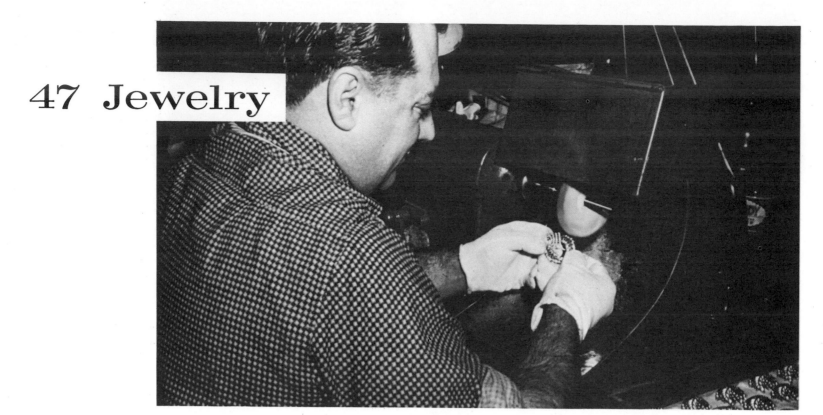

After soldering and assembly operations have been completed, each piece of costume jewelry is polished to a high luster in a modern jewelry factory. Intricate care and craftsmanship is required even for "mass-produced" jewelry.

Never satisfied with things as they are, humans have labored ceaselessly to ornament their homes, their furniture, their garden plots, books and records, and even their own persons. The desire for handsome rings, bracelets, pins, and necklaces is common to all peoples in all lands and ages.

Probably the oldest form of jewelry was the bead or, in its original form, colored pebble. Some ancient peoples traded beads as a kind of money, and as rare gemstones were discovered, scarcity and beauty became measures of value. Soon the craftsmen of antiquity began to carve, to fashion intricate designs by bending strips of metal, and finally to use precious metals, gold and silver, forming exquisite settings for highly polished gems.

Many of these ancient ornaments still survive. Their art has never been surpassed. In excavations of royal tombs at Ur in Mesopotamia, archaeologists have found gold and lapis lazuli jewelry dating about 3500 B.C. Magnificent necklaces and girdles of gold with inlays of semiprecious stones were made during the reign of Ptolemy III in Egypt 247 to 222 B.C. Many ancient beliefs and customs are represented in these relics, giving us glimpses of superstition and mysticism. Magic talismans which were supposed to ward off evil forces often took the form of superbly designed pins, rings, and amulets.

MODERN JEWELRY MAKING

The design and creation of jewelry for both men and women has constituted an important craft over the centuries, and while styles and fashions have changed many times, jewelry making is still an active industry. In the United States, it is an industry that runs the gamut from the individual, private-shop jeweler who hand-fashions custom-made jewelry at high prices, to the mass producers of inexpensive costume jewelry, and quality firms which

offer deluxe creations at a wide range of prices. All really fine jewelry is made by hand.

Today's trend, as in other modern design, has been toward simplicity and austerity, particularly in respect to men's costume jewelry, such as cuff links, tie and collar clasps, and rings. Designers strive to make the most of the natural beauty of their materials.

The basis of the majority of jewelry is a precious metal and, of course, gold is the substance most widely used. (See *Mining*) Of all the materials available, gold has the most ideal properties. It never tarnishes or deteriorates but retains a brilliant luster under virtually any conditions. Furthermore, of 72 known element metals, gold and copper are the only ones possessing color. All others are colorless, or white. Since pure gold is soft, it must be alloyed with copper or silver, or a combination of the two. White gold results from alloying pure gold with nickel. These alloys are termed karat golds; a karat being equal to 1/24 part by weight. Thus, pure gold would be 24-karat gold; 14-karat gold contains 14 parts pure gold and 10 parts alloy metal. Frequently the alloy will be five parts silver and five parts copper, providing a gold with the hardness of mild steel but which can be carved, bent, hammered, or engraved in the most delicate of designs.

Less expensive golds are produced by various processes. For cheap costume jewelry, brass or pewter strips are given a "flash" finish of gold by electroplating. This, of course, wears off quickly. A superior type of plating is rolled gold plate. This is produced by welding a bar of 14-karat gold to foundation metal. As the laminated bar is rolled to a desired thickness, the gold becomes harder, forming a heavy, durable layer which will wear for years.

Whereas a great deal of jewelry is made entirely of gold or silver, it may also be set with glass, semiprecious or precious stones. Foremost of the precious gemstones are the diamond, the ruby, the emerald, and the sapphire. After these are dozens of semiprecious gems, including tourmalines, topazes, zircons, opals, garnets, aquamarines, amethysts; and rhinestones made of glass.

GEM CUTTING

An important factor in determining a gem's value is its cutting, and this involves a specialized and highly skilled craft. To become an expert cutter requires years of practice. There are a variety of standard cuts used by lapidaries and transparent stones are generally cut in planes. Some of the most common forms are the following: the rose cut (a circular, pyramidal form); the emerald cut (a squared treatment); brilliant cut (another circular form, cone shaped on the under side); and step or trap cut (a rectangular cutting similar to the emerald cut). These cuts provide many facets which serve to reflect light and give the gem its sparkle. Translucent or opaque stones, on the other hand, are usually rounded and smoothly polished.

The lapidary works with small revolving disks, emery,

Contemporary custom-made jewelry in the style of early Renaissance ornaments is wrought by hand by only a few American craftsmen. These unusual pieces were made by Ted Lowy of South Orange, N. J.

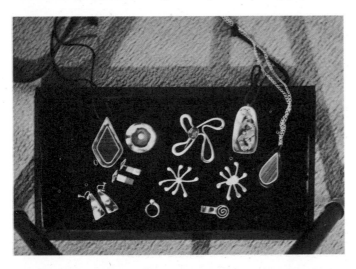

Here the jewelry craftsman, Ted Lowy, is at work on a handsomely designed pin, hammering the precious metal into shape on a miniature anvil.

Small rhinestones are set in the stone cavities which have previously been drilled for a piece of costume jewelry. The stones shown are very small, requiring an operator with great skill and good vision.

and fine, diamond-tipped or corundum drills. Diamonds can be split along cleavage planes in four directions. Certain other stones can be divided in only one direction. The objective is to keep a stone as large as possible, at the same time achieving symmetry and brilliance through its multiple facets.

Weights of gems are measured in carats, a carat equaling 200 milligrams or one-fifth of a gram.

The story of gems is filled with legend and mystery, and some of the world's famous stones have been the centers of violent, sometimes bloody histories. For some 5,000 years, the fabulous Kohinoor diamond has been changing hands; the Hope blue diamond is supposed to bring evil to its owner; and a few years ago, the giant Cullinan diamond, which weighed nearly a pound and one-half, was divided into smaller gems for the British royal collection. Another great diamond, unearthed at the Golconda mines in India and known as the Great Mogul, has disappeared, no one knows where.

Although the business of jewelry making in America is by no means one of the industrial giants, it is nonetheless a fascinating field in which designers and hand craftsmen play an important role. Good jewelry requires engineering in miniature, for many modern pieces are functional as well as decorative. Such items as tie holders, belt buckles, pins and various types of clasps for women's garments must be made with tiny bearings, pivots, locks, and springs. Necklaces, bracelets, and brooches, while primarily ornamental, also require functional clasps.

Like the wearing apparel industries (which see), jewelry production is subject to fashion trends. As a result, leading jewelry firms employ fashion experts in their design departments.

This small, highly specialized industry has been gaining importance in America as tasteful design has put it in a competitive position with foreign importations. While the greatest volume is still in cheap, mass-produced costume jewelry with glass imitation gems (called "paste"), quartz, or other low-value stones, the genuine quality jewelry made by leading U.S. firms compares with the world's finest.

48 Marketing

One of the major changes in modern marketing has come with the development of shopping centers. This architect's model of the Mission Valley Shopping Center shows tree-shaded parking area for 5,000 cars, a Montgomery Ward store, a May Company store, and accommodations for 50 specialty shops.

While all industry begins with finance and must draw initial sustenance from capital accumulation, it could not long prosper without getting its products into the hands of consumers. As finance is industry's lifeblood, good merchandising is the air it breathes. All the marvels of American industry would be as vacuous as daydreams without the marketplace and without fast, efficient methods of keeping goods flowing from factories to the retail stores.

Trading, which was one of mankind's earliest activities, was first carried on professionally by itinerant peddlers, and there are records which mention Minoan and Aegean peddlers as long ago as 3000 B.C. There were retail stores in ancient Greece and Rome. Then, in Europe during the Middle Ages, public markets became the most common means of distributing and trading goods. It was natural in the days of slow transportation to provide some central place where merchants and customers could meet for barter or the exchange or money for merchandise. For those who were too far away to frequent the marketplace, fairs were held on certain specified dates when farmers, peddlers, and craftsmen would converge from miles around in order to exhibit their wares. Stalls were set up by butchers, tinsmiths, weavers, basket makers, potters, and a host of other tradesmen. As crowds gathered, jugglers and acrobats performed their acts, and the market fair soon took on the festive air of a circus. When entertainment began to lure customers from the merchandise,

fairs became less important as markets, yet the custom persisted, and to this day, county fairs in the United States serve as outlets for farm produce and merchandise as well as for a variety of entertainments.

In Colonial America, itinerant peddlers were important distributors of merchandise. Before the development of good roads and modern transport, inland communities were comparatively isolated. As a result, peddlers did a thriving business, bringing all sorts of American and foreign-made goods to the outlying farmhouses and frontier settlements. Some were general vendors, selling pins, needles, hardware, books, combs, cotton goods, and pottery. Some specialized. There were tin merchants, clock peddlers, and vendors of cloth, thread, and fabrics. In addition, local merchants were served by wholesale peddlers.

THE GENERAL STORE

Meanwhile, frontier trading posts, which were originally established for exchanging trinkets for furs from the Indians (See *Furs*), began to stock more and more types of trade goods. It was inevitable, too, that communities should grow up around these fortified trading posts, and that the needs of farmers should be met by stocking various articles of clothing, household goods, farm implements, feed, fertilizer, rifles, and gunpowder. Thus the general store, or country store, came into being. In these early retail stores, prices were often determined by on-the-spot bargaining. Prior to the nineteenth century a large proportion of American retail business was done on the barter system.

DEPARTMENT STORES

While the general store became the primary outlet for merchandise in rural communities, the department store was strictly an urban development. It is generally believed that A. T. Stewart originated the department store concept. The owner of a New York City dry goods store, which he opened in 1823, Stewart established a much larger store on Broadway in 1848. There he offered both dry goods and apparel in a number of separate departments.

Another of the early department stores, also a New York firm, was R. H. Macy and Co., now one of the world's largest stores. Founded in 1858, it operated book, china, and silverware departments. Lord and Taylor, which was started in 1826, specialized chiefly in soft goods but at a later date added furniture and shoe departments. Interestingly, and perhaps naturally enough, most of America's great department stores began as specialty shops and gradually added departments. In Philadelphia, John Wanamaker established a men's clothing store in 1861, but it was not until 1877 that other lines were added. Similarly, Boston's Jordan Marsh Co. opened as a dry goods store in 1851 and established other departments in the 1880's.

A modern department store is a highly organized, efficient industrial unit with four main operational divisions: merchandise, operations, publicity, and accounting. Working under the general manager, the merchandise manager has the responsibility of selection and movement of merchandise; a store manager must maintain efficient service to the public; the publicity director's job is to get people into the store through newspaper, radio, and TV publicity and by good advertising in these media (See *Advertising*); and the comptroller handles finances.

In recent years, lack of trained salesclerks brought increasing emphasis upon another important executive department in large stores. Expert personnel managers are now in great demand to direct programs of improving the quality and efficiency of sales personnel.

SUPERMARKETS

The most important recent development in marketing has been the growth of the supermarket and the community shopping center. Most shopping centers are built and operated by real estate syndicates and are frequently organized as separate corporations. It is customary for a shopkeeper to rent his store in one of these centers, paying a graduated rental based on his volume of business. Unlike the old-time grocery store, the supermarket (usually the chief unit in a shopping center) is a form of department store, with food items predominating. However, the departmentalizing is arranged in self-service racks. Customers pick out the items they want, put them in wheeled carts provided by the store, and pay a "checker" at the exit when they have completed their purchases. Most supermarkets today carry many types of merchandise in addition to food, including such things as cut flowers, magazines, books, drug sundries, kitchen hardware, and toys.

MAIL-ORDER FIRMS

While there are many successful mail-order businesses in the United States, the two giants of this industry known the world over, are Sears Roebuck and Co. and Montgomery Ward and Co. It was the latter, which was first in this field, having been established in 1872. For many years thereafter, mail-order business grew rapidly, as the major firms catered particularly to people living in rural areas. But when the automobile age exploded over America (See *Automobiles*), the pace of mail-order operations slackened considerably. Although it is still big business, even Sears Roebuck and Montgomery Ward have retail stores in many major cities. These stores handle a considerable proportion of the firms' total sales.

A Sears or Montgomery Ward catalog is an amazing production of some 1,500 pages, containing several thousand illustrations, both in color and in black and white, of

A New York City block which has become famous in merchandising history, with a slogan known throughout the world.

every conceivable type of merchandise. No better cross section of American industry's products can be found, and old mail-order catalogs are highly prized by artists and researchers as illustrative source material for fashions, household appliances, and a host of other items in various periods of our history. So elaborate are these catalogs that large staffs are required, similar to the editorial staffs of publishers (See *Publishing*) to prepare copy and photographs, makeup pages, proofread and supervise printing and binding.

CHAIN STORES

Both of these leading mail-order houses operate huge chains of retail stores, but the chain store idea really originated with the Great Atlantic and Pacific Tea Company (A & P), founded in 1859. A single store was the origin of this chain as has been the case with virtually all of the important chain operations. When a successful retailer has reached his maximum volume of business in a given community, he may seek to expand by opening a store in another area. Soon he has stores in several neighborhoods of a large city. From there, it is logical for him to spread his chain into other towns and cities.

In the beginning, most chain stores featured low-priced merchandise. Woolworth's "5 and 10 cent store" was typical of that trend, a trend which has its counterpart today in the various cut-rate chains.

In spite of efforts to control pricing through Fair Trade laws requiring stores to maintain manufacturers' retail prices, a large number of cut-rate and discount stores have sprung up. Some of the larger discount chains have become big business, with annual volume amounting to more than a hundred million dollars. By making wholesale purchases in quantity and distributing merchandise through a system of many stores, the cut-rate chain is able to offer standard items at reduced prices and still make a profit.

The chain store industry was somewhat curtailed by the imposition of various taxes in many states. By increasing the rate of taxation in relation to the number of stores in an operation, state and local governments drove many large chains to reduce the number of their outlets, keeping a few large stores rather than a great many small ones.

Population shifts from metropolitan centers to the suburbs has caused an increase in the number of branches of large department stores. While these branch stores are controlled by a single company, they are not chain store operations in the usual sense. Generally speaking chain stores are a series of identical shops all carrying the same lines of merchandise. Branch stores may cater to different types of clientele; they sometimes buy independently, or they may have special departments to serve their particular localities.

CONSUMER RESEARCH

One of the most interesting aspects of modern marketing is the establishment of research departments by many reputable stores. Not only do marketing experts study consumer trends, changes of fashion and popular taste, but some of the large department stores and mail-order houses spend thousands of dollars testing merchandise. The testing laboratories of Sears Roebuck, for example, use the

Production of a mail-order house catalog is a major publishing operation. Thousands of Montgomery Ward catalogs are shown in the bindery.

Preparing Christmas decorations for a large store requires months of work by artists and display experts who start planning a year in advance.

most up-to-date instruments for checking wearing qualities, the tensile strength of metal, rubber, or fibers, and for inspecting for flaws. Particular attention is paid to the claims of manufacturers, and if elaborate claims cannot be substantiated, the store may reject the merchandise involved.

It is the philosophy of the reputable independent retailer that his store represents the consumer, not the manufacturer; the buyer rather than the seller. He is seeking the best possible merchandise at the lowest possible price, and it is his duty to his customers to protect and serve their interests at all times.

ROLE OF THE WHOLESALER

In our complex society, the business of moving goods from factories to retail outlets often requires the help of specialists who buy merchandise in bulk and redistribute it to local stores and dealers. These wholesalers, sometimes called jobbers, or middlemen, operate warehouses which serve as clearinghouses for goods from a number of manufacturers. While it may be argued that the wholesaler's share in this marketing operation contributes to increased retail prices, it is easily demonstrated that good wholesaling can actually reduce costs, or at least make practical distribution possible. For a manufacturer to pack, label, and ship thousands of small orders to individual stores would require costly clerical operations, while shipping costs of small packages to all parts of the country would be prohibitive. It is far more efficient to make bulk shipments by rail, truck, or boat to a distant city. There, the wholesaler can store large stocks of merchandise and make short, local deliveries to the stores as the need arises. Quick service is an important function of the wholesaler.

Jobbers are mostly specialists in certain types of merchandise. There are book jobbers, gift jobbers, and greeting card jobbers; wholesalers for hardware, leather goods, garments, plastic materials, and foodstuffs. Nearly every industry has its wholesalers located in important centers throughout the country.

MARKETING IS BIG BUSINESS

There are more than one and three-quarter million stores in the United States, with total retail sales amounting to about two hundred billion dollars a year. Employed by these stores are some seven and one-half million people plus thousands of part-time workers. Retailing is by all odds the greatest field for people who wish to own and operate their own businesses. Although many independent shopkeepers fail due to lack of experience and capital, retailing remains an attractive area for private enterprise. Comparatively small amounts of money are required to set up shop, the major capital expenditure being required for building an inventory. More money is needed to stock some lines than others. Photographic equipment and supplies, for example, are far more expensive items than greeting cards and stationery.

Location is an important consideration for successful retailing. A store should be accessible to a large number of people, and its merchandise should reflect the tastes and requirements of the community it serves. It would be futile to offer farm implements in a city store, or sleds in a region which never has snow! A shop owner soon learns to know his customers and to stock the items in greatest demand.

With rising labor and other costs of marketing operations, the major problem confronting American merchants is severe price competition. This, however, is a problem as old as mankind. Competition and bargaining in the marketplace is as fundamental as human nature itself. It is the basis of America's entire free enterprise system, under which the consumer is the real captain of industry, for in the long run it is he who decides what and how much will be produced and what price will be paid for manufacturers' products. The challenge to all types of merchants is, as it has always been, to find better methods of serving the consumer, at the same time reducing costs of wholesale and retail operations. Retailing costs have been estimated to be approximately one-third the selling price of most merchandise. With wholesale prices generally 50% to 60% of retail prices, a store's profit may average between 6% and 10%, a margin which has been declining in recent years.

An exciting and dynamic industry, marketing requires men and women with imagination, courage, and integrity, for it is in the marketplace that all industrial enterprise stands or falls.

Christmas time is the most active selling season for most lines of merchandise, and great stores have elaborate displays to attract customers. This scene shows a section of the crowd watching a fountain display in the Grand Court of John Wanamaker, Philadelphia, during the Christmas rush.

49 Packaging

Modern packaging employs plastics to produce colorful and attractively designed containers for a great variety of products. A few smartly styled plastic bottles of well-known products are shown above.

Before a product can be shipped from factory to market, a container must be designed. This container may be anything from a railroad tank car to an inch-high plastic squeeze bottle, or a folded cardboard box. But in times past, containers were limited to a few basic materials, which included wood, glass, pottery, woven cloth, and skins. Some of the earliest "bottles" for transporting liquids were the skins of animals. Such bags for milk and water are still used today in primitive countries. With the advance of the Industrial Revolution, manufacturers required practical shipping containers in such quantity that a separate packaging industry began to evolve.

Among the first container companies in America were glass bottle makers. In the early eighteenth century, a bottle plant was built at Salem, Mass. to provide containers for the shipment of rum and cider. (See *Glass*) Of still greater importance was the cooperage trade, since a great variety of dry products were packed in barrels. Barrelmaking is still an important segment of the packaging industry. Then, with the development of machine-made, wood-pulp paper in the middle of the nineteenth century, a whole new field of package design and engineering was opened up. (See *Paper*) In the meantime, Nicolas Appert's invention of canning in France, and the introduction of the tin canister in England were revolutionizing the packaging of foods. (See *Food Products*)

SCOPE OF U. S. PACKAGING

Not many people realize that packaging is one of the most extensive and vital activities of the modern industrial world. It is a highly diverse industry made up of producers of raw materials, converters of these materials, package machinery manufacturers, and various packaging service organizations which include design consultants, contract packagers who handle complete packaging operations for a manufacturer or distributor, and the trade associations. Many container companies specialize in certain types of packages. There are metal can companies, makers of folded boxes, manufacturers of corrugated board containers, glass bottle and jar companies. All told, the annual dollar volume in containers and packaging materials alone amounts to well over eleven billion dollars. Some idea of the size and scope of the industry may be gained from a glance at a few of its principal segments.

Aluminum foil packaging, which includes flexible foil packages, foil containers, and protective foil wraps, consumes nearly three hundred million pounds of foil each year. Some 375 U.S. companies are devoted to converted flexible packaging. They convert papers, films, and foil into bags and boxes, and their processing involves printing, laminating, and various types of coatings. Another 400 firms are engaged in the making of fiber boxes from corrugated container board. Their annual production is one of the major elements in the American economy, for it amounts to about one and three-quarter billion dollars.

Use of glass containers has been on the increase. Shipments of glass containers for food, chemicals, household and industrial materials, and a great variety of beverages total over a billion dollars annually. Research and chemical discoveries have resulted in lighter, stronger glass, with the result that glass containers are keeping pace with competitive metals and plastics. Nevertheless, metal cans

PACKAGING

still hold the lead in the container field. Third largest user of steel, the can industry comprises some two hundred twenty-five plants employing about sixty thousand workers who turn out close to two billion dollars' worth of cans per year. Approximately 2,200 different items are packaged in metal cans.

Paper bags are made from all kinds and grades of paper, as well as laminates of paper with film and foil. More than 100 companies produce grocery bags of kraft paper; merchandising or "notion and millinery" bags; and a variety of specialty bags made of glassine, impregnated papers impervious to moisture, grease, oil, and light. Many paper bags today are printed with decorative designs and advertising messages. In addition, there is a large segment of the industry devoted to the manufacture of paper sacks. These are made of heavy-duty kraft, which may be film coated, asphalt lined, wax coated, or similarly treated paper-based materials. The paper-sack industry comprises some 100 plants distributed through 29 states. They employ fourteen thousand workers and enjoy an annual sales volume in excess of three hundred million dollars.

For other industrial products, metal shipping kegs, drums, barrels and pails are made in huge quantities, consuming about a million tons of steel each year, with a dollar volume averaging two hundred fifty to three hundred million dollars.

PACKAGE ENGINEERING

One of the most fascinating of all the fields for modern design is the packaging industry. Packages and containers must be engineered for two basic purposes, function and eye appeal. Packaging experts must study products, materials, machinery, ink chemistry, transportation and

Machinery has been built to package every conceivable product. Here, bacon is inserted in packages and is automatically sealed.

A workman at Consolidated Wholesale Florists in Los Angeles uses a Bostitch arm stitcher to make up corrugated, telescope cartons for shipping flowers.

shipping problems, and a host of related subjects. Package engineering is a comparatively recent science, for it was only in the past two or three decades that manufacturers began to appreciate the role of the well-designed package in product identification and sale, In addition, the rapid advance of chemistry and plastics (which see) has opened up new concepts of package construction and design.

The large container corporations offer their clients the services of expert package engineers who not only are skilled in designing eye-catching containers to attract customers in the stores, but consider such practical aspects as the machinery used for filling the containers, the folding or fabricating methods of making the containers themselves, economy and strength in construction, and the kind of handling large cartons will receive in transit.

New plastics have given designers some of the most intriguing design possibilities. High-density polyethylene, for example, is being used for an amazing variety of squeeze bottles, and smartly styled containers of all shapes and colors. Aerosol cans and bottles, using pressure spray systems, are used for such commodities as starch, shoe polish, insect sprays, lacquers, deodorants, and antiseptics. Frozen foods and complete dinners are packed in paper-plastic or aluminum dishes, ready to be popped into the oven as they come from the store. Use of plastic foams to protect fragile goods in transit is becoming prevalent, but at the same time, technical advances in tough corrugated paperboards and other materials have greatly reduced breakage.

OUTLOOK FOR THE FUTURE

Business potential for the packaging industry is directly related to the production volume of all industry. As population and the consumption of more and more products continue to increase, there can be little doubt that package designing, engineering, and manufacturing will accelerate. This is a field for imaginative and aggressive marketing experts. It offers great opportunities to creative artists who have the ability to adapt their ideas to functional design. It requires production experts with a knowledge of papers, plastics, metals, glass, wood, textiles, and laminates, and of the various printing processes. (See *Printing*) Since modern packaging is in its infancy, the industry offers wide-open opportunities for invention and innovation.

Outdoor advertising is one of the many advertising media employed in a major advertising campaign. Dozens of billboards like this one appeared in all parts of the country in a campaign launched by U.S. Steel.

50 Advertising

Making a better mousetrap does not necessarily bring the world to your door. First, the world has to know about your mousetrap; in addition, people must be persuaded that it is really a superior contraption. Now, you could stand on your front porch and shout to passersby, urging them to come and buy your mousetrap, and this would be advertising. But it would take a long time to get many people interested. For this reason, enterprising businesses and ingenious idea men have developed ways to get selling messengers into the homes of millions of people and to attract their eyes and ears in buses, along roadsides, in the daily mail, in magazines and newspapers, and on radio and TV broadcasts. The job of selling the public has become a specialized field, involving a number of services sufficiently complex that an entire industry with a total annual volume in excess of twelve billion dollars has grown up around them.

The focal point of the advertising world is a section of Manhattan known as "Madison Avenue." While it is true that a number of advertising agency offices actually are located on Madison Avenue, some of the largest agencies are on other streets. But within an area of a few city squares, with Madison Avenue running through its center, are the giant radio and television networks; dozens of "station reps" (representatives) who sell advertising time on the New York stations; an equal number of "national reps" who handle space advertising in hun-

dreds of newspapers around the country; the main advertising and sales offices of business firms, manufacturers, and magazines; and most of the country's major advertising agencies who take care of more than three billion dollars' worth of advertising each year.

Despite the fact that at least 50% of U.S. industry's advertising is handled by New York agencies, and another 25% by agencies with branch offices in New York, there are also independent ad agencies in nearly every city in the country.

HOW DID IT ALL START?

One of the earliest forms of advertising was the painted or carved sign, usually associated with a small shop, an inn, or a merchant's place of business. Signs have been unearthed in the ruins of Pompeii; probably there were signs in use in earlier civilizations. Shortly after Gutenberg's development of printing from movable type, handbills were printed and distributed on the streets. (See *Printing*)

Early newspapers in Colonial America carried paid announcements of ship sailings, and occasionally there were advertisements for local shops and inns. But as no records of circulation figures were available, there was consequently no way to establish standard rates for space in the publications. In 1841, Volney P. Palmer established an agency in Philadelphia for the purpose of representing newspapers who wished to sell advertising space. For his services, he charged 25% of the space rates. His business prospered, and by 1849 he had set up offices in New York, Philadelphia, Boston, and Baltimore. His success attracted many imitators, some of whom were unscrupulous operators who added exorbitant commissions for themselves without telling their clients the amount of the publishers' space rates. In the 1880's, it was common practice for ad agents to pocket as much as 40% in commissions. Today, the standard agency commission is 15%. The founder of *Printer's Ink* magazine (one of the major trade publications for the advertising industry), George P. Rowell, helped put a stop to shady practices by publishing the first accurate list of 5,411 U.S. newspapers. This was in 1869.

Meanwhile, a number of important agencies were being formed. Carlton and Smith, later to be taken over by J. Walter Thompson Co., was founded in 1864. Four years later, N. W. Ayer & Son entered the field in Philadelphia. It was Ayer who, in 1875, revolutionized the industry by offering to act as the advertisers', rather than as the publishers' agent, and he offered his clients an open contract, providing all the facts concerning the rates charged by publishers for their space. Another important milestone in the development of present-day practices was the agreement by the American Newpaper Publishers Association to pay commissions to any recognized advertising agencies, but never to allow any discounts in direct dealings with advertisers. This system was further solidified when Curtis Publishing Co. made a similar agreement with J. Walter Thompson Co.

FUNCTIONS OF A MODERN AGENCY

Some time in the 1880's, agencies began to help their advertisers to plan effective ads; they soon became involved in the business of writing copy, preparing or buying artwork and photographs. As printing improved, with the advent of the screened halftone and full-color reproduction of pictures (See *Printing*), agencies began to hire expert printing production men who could supervise the buying of art and engravings, and the printing of brochures, posters, and various types of advertising literature.

In an ad agency's art department, draftsmen and layout men and women prepare sketches, buy drawings and photographs, and make up the ads as they will appear in magazines and newspapers.

Now a modern advertising agency has departments for market research, art and design, copy preparation, package design (See *Packaging*), printing production. It has specialists in each type of advertising media, including newspapers, magazines, radio, television, outdoor advertising, premium promotions, direct mail, point-of-sale display, and a variety of specialties such as match covers, brochures, and even skywriting!

If we visit one of the top-ranking agencies in New York, we find that it occupies several floors in one of the latest chrome-and-glass skyscrapers somewhere in the area from 40th to 52nd Streets and from Fifth to Lexington Avenues. The reception rooms on each floor are simply but expensively furnished, the receptionists are bright and smartly dressed young women, and the entire atmosphere is one of good taste and highly paid efficiency.

On a tour through the various departments we see dozens of offices, some large, some small. Most of these are occupied by account executives—men who work with specific "accounts," or clients—and their secretaries. An art department is staffed with a large number of draftsmen, layout men and women, and a few art directors whose job is to prepare "visuals," or comprehensive sketches of ads as they will appear in magazines; they buy drawings and photographs from free-lance artists, photographers, and various kinds of art services; and they may make dummy packages, sketches for posters, car cards, labels and so on. Each artist has his own drawing table, instruments, brushes, and paints, just as if he were working in his own private studio. In the larger agencies, some artists have separate offices. If they are among the topflight designers, they will work only on the ad campaigns for the biggest advertisers, such as Ford, General Motors, Colgate, Lever Brothers, Du Pont, General Mills, or other national accounts. Sometimes a dozen or more sketches and rough layouts will be made for a full page ad that is scheduled to appear in one of the national magazines. These are submitted to the client, usually through the ad manager of the advertising firm, who will okay one layout or ask for additional sketches.

At the same time, the copy department has been busy writing the slogans and the selling copy to be included in the ad. Often a slogan, or catch line, is the key to an entire advertising campaign. Such famous lines as "Ask the Man Who Owns One" (Packard automobiles), "I'd Walk a Mile for a Camel" (cigarettes), and "It Floats . . . 99⁴⁴⁄₁₀₀% Pure" (Ivory soap) have made advertising and merchandising history. A well-chosen phrase of three or four words can sell more of a manufacturer's product than a thousand words of dreary prose.

Good copywriters are highly paid experts who must constantly produce selling ideas as well as concise, hard-hitting copy. Frequently the heads of agencies create the copy and slogans for important clients. What they look for is sometimes referred to as a unique selling proposition, or USP. This is another way of saying that the advertising idea man must find something special about a company or its product that can be featured in advertising in a way that will induce the public to buy. Sometimes, as in the case of products such as soaps which are all pretty much alike, it is difficult to hit upon a fresh idea. Skillful admen study the products and services of their clients, dissect them, as if they were specimens in a biology class, and often find some overlooked quality or attribute on which they can build an entire advertising campaign.

PLANNING CAMPAIGNS

When a new product is about to be launched, the advertising agency is called upon to map out an assault on the buying public—a process that is not unlike drafting the detailed plans for a military campaign. In this case, the generals are the agency executives and top management of the firm whose product is to be advertised. A full campaign may be allotted a budget in six figures. It will include space in one or more national magazines, newspaper ads, radio and television spots, car cards, and store displays. With a new product, the package must be designed. Publicity experts will determine newsworthy points to be emphasized, and news releases will be prepared for editors of magazines and newspapers. If a product is sufficiently important or unusual, it will merit considerable publicity. This free advertising can be worth thousands of dollars to the client, but it requires skillful copy preparation, since editors will reject obvious commercial "plugs" unless they are either highly entertaining, filled with interesting facts or are genuinely important items of news.

After the various departments of the agency have gone to work on their parts of the campaign, sketches, copy, package designs, suggested formats for TV commercials, and publicity releases will be submitted to the account executive. When he feels he has all the elements of a good campaign, he will arrange for a meeting with the client, usually at the client's offices. Such meetings may be all-day affairs, where agency and company executives will examine artwork, photographs, slogans, and the agency's proposed schedule of ads, and they will either reject or approve the plans. Usually a great many changes are made in the plans; possibly new sketches will be required and new plans drawn up before a final okay is given.

ADVERTISING MEDIA AND RATES

The various outlets for advertising messages are known as media. In the United States they include about 1,800 daily newspapers (about 30% of annual advertising expenditures), direct mail advertising (18% of volume), 450 television stations (14% of volume), 3,500 radio stations (6% of volume), 600 to 700 popular magazines (7.7%), 350,000 billboards (1.5%), and millions of car cards in trains, trolley cars, subways and buses.

Costs of advertising in various media vary considerably. In the case of newspapers and magazines, rates are generally based on two factors: the size and the quality of their circulation. (See *Publishing*). Magazines like the *Post* and *Life,* with circulations in the millions, command higher rates than those with limited distribution. Proportionately, however, the rates in some specialized publications, designed to reach a certain group or class of people, may be higher than the rates set by daily news-

On the set a television commercial is set up and rehearsed. TV advertising today takes a major share of advertisers' dollars.

papers or magazines that are sold to the general public. From the advertiser's point of view, he may feel that he will achieve more sales for his advertising dollar in a magazine that specializes in a market he is trying to reach than in one that goes to millions of people who would never buy his product in any case. A manufacturer of model railroad equipment, for example, would want to advertise in hobby magazines and publications devoted to model railroading.

Another advertising medium which can pinpoint a selected audience is direct mail. This type of advertising is the fastest-growing and, now, the second largest advertising medium in the country. Direct mail advertisers invest more than two billion dollars annually in preparation and distribution of their sales literature, which produces twenty billion dollars in sales of goods and services each year. More than a quarter million businessmen use this medium, and for many of the smaller ones it may be their only form of advertising. It differs from other media in that it is an extension of personal selling which follows the buyer into his own home.

The rates for using color in advertising are higher than for black and white. There are also special rates for using unusual printing colors, such as silver or gold. In recent years, color has begun to appear in daily newspaper ads. Known as R O P (run of paper) color it has been greatly improved technically since the 1950's, though newspaper production men are still trying to solve problems of ink and register peculiar to their high-speed printing on soft, groundwood newsprint paper.

Another modern trend is regional advertising in national magazines. Under this plan, an advertiser, whose product is sold in only one region of the country, is able to buy space in a regional issue of such magazines as *Look* or *TV Guide,* at much less cost than he would have to pay for his ad to appear in all editions. (See *Publishing*)

Radio and TV rates also vary in accordance with the estimated sizes of audiences reached by different stations and by specific programs. Highest rates are for "prime time," meaning the time of day when it is known that a maximum number of viewers or listeners are tuned in. (See *Radio and Television*)

To guide advertisers and advertising agencies there are published lists of media and rates. The most important of these is *Standard Rate and Data,* published periodically and containing full information about publications, their latest circulations (including paid and unpaid circulation), advertising rates, page sizes, type of readership, and so on. Standard Rate and Data Service, Inc. also publishes similar information about radio and television stations and shows. The Audit Bureau of Circulations receives and tabulates sworn statements from reputable newspaper and magazine publishers, keeping this information as accurate and as up-to-date as possible at all times. Other statistical services used by the advertising industry are Gallup Audience Research Institute, Inc., Advertising Research Foundation, and Alfred Politz Research, Inc. Audience studies by specialized firms and by nonprofit industry organizations are being conducted constantly and are of vital importance to advertisers in their attempts to reach maximum audiences at the best possible price.

DOES ADVERTISING PAY?

The greatest area of controversy in this highly controversial industry surrounds the question of whether advertising is worth its cost. No one can deny that *without* advertising many products sold nationally would never have been successful. Yet it is difficult, sometimes impossible, to determine the effectiveness of a specific ad or TV commercial. One of the best and most direct methods of checking results is the use of coupon advertising in newspapers and magazines. Sometimes two differently designed ads for the same product will appear in the same issue of a newspaper. As each one carries a coupon, identified by a key or code number, it is easy to tabulate the number of coupons clipped and mailed from each ad. In this way, the advertiser and the agency can gain some idea of what type of ad will be most effective. This device is often used in a local newspaper, and after a number of such tests have been tried, a national ad will be made up using those features which drew the best results in the local paper.

Keyed coupons are used to test media, as well as the advertising copy and layout. Even television commercials can be tested by asking viewers to write for booklets or premiums, addressing their inquiries to coded box numbers.

A FASCINATING BUT DANGEROUS GAME

Advertising today is a major industry, and agency business is vast and growing. Among the leading agencies are several whose annual billings exceed one hundred million dollars. These include N. W. Ayer and Son; Ted Bates; Benton and Bowles; Foote, Cone and Belding; Grant Advertising; and Leo Burnett. With billings over two hundred million dollars a year are Young and Rubicam; Batten, Barton, Durstine and Osborn (BBDO); McCann-Erickson; and the largest of all, J. Walter Thompson.

Most agencies grow around personal relationships between a brilliant advertising man and his clients. Few large agencies are corporations, and many operate without any written contracts with the advertisers. Consequently, advertising is a highly precarious and volatile industry which depends on personalities, ideas, and sudden changes in trends and fashion.

Million-dollar clients can be and frequently are lost by ad agencies through mistakes in judgment, changes of personnel, and the mere whims of top executives who may wish a change of viewpoint. The typical account executive works under a constant tension and fear of losing his account. At the same time, the challenge and stimulation of advertising work, with its large monetary rewards, attract adventurous and imaginative men and women who work at their jobs long hours, often into the night, yet would never dream of going into any other field.

Advertising is becoming the primary means of selling manufactured products. More than 50% of grocery items and 25% of drugs and toiletries are bought in supermarkets where there are no sales clerks and where only the power of advertising and package display can influence the buying public. In many fields, the relative importance of the personal salesman has diminished while effective advertising does the job. No longer do automobile dealers canvass neighborhoods for prospects as they did in the past. They merely wait for customers, who have seen their ads, to come into the showrooms. Electrical and household appliances are largely presold through advertising; the majority of purchasers know the make of washer, toaster, or refrigerator they want before they walk into the store.

In advertising, we see the culmination of the great American industrial drama. After the metal ores are dug from the ground, the timber is cut, the chemicals are processed, the oil is tapped, the electricity to operate the mills is generated by the great power companies. Machines in thousands of factories fabricate the millions of products consumed daily by Americans. Trucks, trains, and airplanes distribute these goods to markets across the land; then the public must be informed of all this great bounty that is offered to them. There are ads in poor taste, ads that mislead, and ads that are just plain silly, yet the vast majority of American advertising is factual, informative, and colorful. It represents, in all its avenues, the dynamic story of American industry, and it reveals a land of more abundance in more things than can be claimed by any other nation in the world.

As a moral and social force, advertising has rarely been fully appreciated or understood. At its worst, it can cause people to spend money foolishly; it can lead a nation into bad habits. At its best it can dignify mankind, can raise living standards, and can create public confidence and faith in the products of industry. An educated and discerning American public cannot long be duped by dishonest claims or false advertising, however, and in the long run tasteful, honest advertising seeks its own high level. The charlatans of Madison Avenue—and there are a few—don't last long. As in every other field of endeavor, so in advertising, "the truth will out." And in the American free economy, only the good can survive.

Index